VOLUME 2 MASTERWORKS OF SCIENCE

MASTERWORKS OF
SCIENCE

VOLUME 2

GALILEO: DIALOGUES CONCERNING TWO
 NEW SCIENCES

DALTON: THE ATOMIC THEORY

FARADAY: EXPERIMENTAL RESEARCHES
 IN ELECTRICITY

MENDELEYEV: THE PERIODIC LAW

CURIE: RADIOACTIVITY

EDITED BY JOHN WARREN KNEDLER, JR.

McGraw-Hill Book Company

New York • St. Louis • San Francisco • London • Düsseldorf

Kuala Lumpur • Mexico • Montreal • Panama • São Paulo

Sydney • Toronto • Johannesburg • New Delhi • Singapore

Masterworks of Science, Volume II

Copyright 1947 by Copeland & Lamm, Inc. All rights reserved. Printed in the United States of America. No part of this publication may be reproduced, stored in a retrieval system, or transmitted, in any form or by any means, electronic, mechanical, photocopying, recording, or otherwise, without the prior written permission of the publisher.

First McGraw-Hill Paperback Edition, 1973

07-040814-9

1 2 3 4 5 6 7 8 9   MU   MU   7 9 8 7 6 5 4 3

CONTENTS

VOLUME 2 MASTERWORKS OF SCIENCE

DIALOGUES CONCERNING TWO NEW SCIENCES

by

GALILEO

CONTENTS

Dialogues Concerning Two New Sciences

GALILEO GALILEI

1564-1642

Vincenzio galilei, a poor nobleman of Florence, early recognized the talents of his son Galileo. An able musician and a good mathematician, he sent the boy, born in Pisa in 1564, first to study Greek, Latin, and logic at the monastery of Vallombrosa, near Florence, and, in 1581, to the University of Pisa to study medicine. The boy had already shown aptitude in music and in painting, and a small talent in literature—eventually visible in an inconsiderable comedy, in a few minor poems, in some critical remarks on Ariosto, and in a voluminous and eloquent correspondence. Vincenzio had, however, decided on medicine as his son's profession. He had, indeed, allowed the boy training in the recognized arts; but he had kept him wholly from any study in mathematics.

Quite by accident, Galileo overheard at the university a lecture on geometry. His interest flared so high that he persuaded his father to let him have mathematical instruction. From this time on, though he stayed at the university until he was twenty-one, he read medicine no more. Instead he devoted himself to mathematics and mechanics, and continued the study of these sciences for the remainder of a long, fruitful life. In 1585, apparently for want of funds, Vincenzio withdrew his son from the University of Pisa. The young man returned to Florence and secured an appointment as lecturer in mathematics at the Academy there.

Already, during his years in Pisa, Galileo had made the first of those observations in mechanics which were to bring him fame. He had watched the swaying of a lamp suspended on a long chain in the Cathedral of Pisa sharply enough to discover that whatever the range of the oscillations, they were executed in the same time. He conducted some verifying experiments, discovered the isochronism of the pendulum, and, perhaps because he had somewhat studied medicine, applied the newly discovered principle to the timing of the human pulse. In 1586 he published an account of a hydrostatic balance which he had invented, and his name began to be widely known in Italy. Two years later he wrote a treatise on the center of gravity in solids. As a result, he was recalled to Pisa as a professor of mathematics in the university. The young medical matriculant of seven years before had wholly shifted his ground. Yet old Vincenzio was not denied matter for pride in his son.

Once more in Pisa, Galileo made the observations in mechanics which, confirmed according to his usual method by experiments, led him to the discovery that bodies of differing masses fall with equal acceleration from rest, and to the discovery that the path of a projectile is a parabola. That he demonstrated his discoveries by dropping and tossing objects from the top of the Leaning Tower of Pisa is an often repeated story which has no foundation in fact. It is a fiction of his later biographers, supported by imaginative illustrators of "great moments in the history of science." But if not in the Leaning Tower, at least in Pisa, he made these discoveries, fundamental to the whole theory of dynamics.

Galileo's discovery about velocity and acceleration in free fall contradicted the views his contemporaries held, views for which they thought they had the authority of Aristotle. They attacked Galileo, pooh-poohed his theories, and provoked him to sarcastic replies. Thus he entered into the first of the controversies which enlivened his public life. He also earned such unpopularity that he had to resign his university appointment and return to Florence. He lived in that city quietly for a year, and was then called to Padua to become professor of mathematics in the university there. He continued to live in Padua for the next twenty years. Even when, in 1610, he left Padua permanently, he retained his professorship in the university, for it had been granted for life. The stipend from this appointment, together with the income from some sinecures which came to him as the rewards of increasing age and fame, enabled him to continue his studies, his theorizing, his experiments—and his controversies—without recourse to any activity of which the end would have been merely economic independence.

In 1609, during a visit to Venice, Galileo heard a rumor that a telescope had been invented by a lens maker in the Low Countries. He returned to Padua, busied himself with experiment, and in a few days hastened to Venice to present to the Doge the first telescope known to Venice. It magnified three diameters. Galileo patiently learned the technique of grinding and polishing lenses; he experimented with arrangements of lenses. Eventually he constructed an instrument which magnified thirty-three diameters. Meantime he had begun a series of astronomical observations with his telescopes. He observed the mountains of the moon, the satellites of Jupiter, sun spots, the constituent stars of the Milky Way. He manufactured telescopes in sufficient numbers to supply a great part of Europe, and so firmly was his name attached to the device that to this day the telescope he used—of which the modern opera glass is a type—though he was not its real inventor, is called the Galilean telescope.

The astronomical observations which Galileo made contributed a great deal to the stock of information of astronomers. Most particularly, it provided evidence for the validity of the Copernican theories—as against the Ptolemaic—explaining the motion of heavenly bodies. Galileo had accepted the Copernican ideas as early as 1597, but a fear of ridicule had restrained him from a public avowal of his opinion. In 1613, after he had demonstrated his telescope to an acclaiming public in Rome, he published *Letters on the Solar Spots* in which he argued for the Copernican views. His great reputation provoked ecclesiastical authorities to examine this work, and they found that the new views ran counter to conventional interpretation of Biblical texts. Immediately a controversy of large dimensions arose. Galileo threw himself into it avidly. He lectured and demonstrated and wrote. He sought out Biblical texts to support his position. The consequence was that in 1616 the theologians of the Holy Office decided that the Copernican theories were heretical, and Pope Paul V admonished Galileo not "to hold, teach, or defend" the condemned doctrine. He was, in short, advised to avoid theology and to restrict himself to physical reasoning; and he promised to heed the advice.

Galileo retired once more to Florence, to seven years of studious quiet. Then he published a work on comets, dedicated to Urban VIII, the new pope. The intellectual atmosphere seemed less suffocating than some years earlier. Meantime he had become ever more convinced of the truth of the Copernican theories. He now, in the freer air, reweighed all the arguments, discussed them with friends, and finally, in 1630, completed *Dialogo dei due massimi sistemi del mondo* (Dialogue Concerning the Two Chief Systems of the World), a work which really demolished the Ptolemaic doctrine and established that of Copernicus. When he published the work in 1632, Europe applauded. But the Inquisition at Rome had not forgotten that Galileo had promised sixteen years before not to "hold, teach, or defend" the forbidden doctrine. Sale of the book was banned; Galileo was cited to Rome for trial.

Eventually he did stand trial in Rome, recanted, and was condemned to recite the seven penitential psalms once a week for three years.

There is a tale that Galileo, rising from the kneeling position in which, before the trial officers, he had agreed that the earth stands stationary while the sun moves round it, stamped on the earth and muttered, "It does move, anyway." The story is pure fiction. But whatever the words he muttered, if he muttered any, it is reasonable to believe that he privately held to his published ideas. For his intellectual vigor had not declined. He had yet eight years to live, and even after he had become blind in 1637, he continued his speculations on physical subjects. Indeed, he was dictating to his pupils, Torricelli and Viviani, his latest ideas on impact when he was seized by the slow fever of which, in 1642, he died.

The later years of Galileo's life were notable not for new discoveries, but for the composition and publication of his *Dialoghi delle nuove scienze* (Dialogues Concerning New Sciences). In these he recounted the bulk of his experimental and theoretical work, and literally laid the foundations for the science of mechanics. Though some isolated notions had been grasped by his predecessors, Galileo first clearly understood and presented the idea of force as a mechanical agent. He further showed how a combination of experiment with calculation, the perpetual comparison of results, the translation of the concrete into the abstract, provide a method for investigating natural laws. Of such laws he stated many, and his work implies the knowledge and understanding of others. The science of mechanics rests upon the three Laws of Motion which Newton, not many years after Galileo's death, enunciated in their final form. Galileo never stated these Laws; yet his work suggests that he was aware of the principles they codify. In the *Dialogues,* his last work, he explored the territory which Newton was later to survey and measure. And these *Dialogues,* better than any notes on Galileo, illustrate his methods and reveal his discoveries.

(In the *Dialogues,* Galileo presents his own arguments as the words of Salviati. He also refers occasionally to himself as "Author" or as "Academician.")

DIALOGUES CONCERNING TWO NEW SCIENCES

FIRST DAY

Interlocutors: Salviati, Sagredo and Simplicio

SALVIATI. The constant activity which you Venetians display in your famous arsenal suggests to the studious mind a large field for investigation, especially that part of the work which involves mechanics; for in this department all types of instruments and machines are constantly being constructed by many artisans, among whom there must be some who, partly by inherited experience and partly by their own observations, have become highly expert and clever in explanation.

SAGREDO. You are quite right. Indeed, I myself, being curious by nature, frequently visit this place for the mere pleasure of observing the work of those who, on account of their superiority over other artisans, we call "first rank men." Conference with them has often helped me in the investigation of certain effects including not only those which are striking, but also those which are recondite and almost incredible. At times also I have been put to confusion and driven to despair of ever explaining something for which I could not account, but which my senses told me to be true. And notwithstanding the fact that what the old man told us a little while ago is proverbial and commonly accepted, yet it seemed to me altogether false, like many another saying which is current among the ignorant; for I think they introduce these expressions in order to give the appearance of knowing something about matters which they do not understand.

SALVIATI. You refer, perhaps, to that last remark of his when we asked the reason why they employed stocks, scaffolding and bracing of larger dimensions for launching a big vessel than they do for a small one; and he answered that they did this in order to avoid the danger of the ship parting under its own heavy weight, a danger to which small boats are not subject?

SAGREDO. Yes, that is what I mean; and I refer especially to his last assertion which I have always regarded as a false, though current, opinion; namely, that in speaking of these and other similar machines one cannot argue from the small to the large, because many devices which succeed on a small scale do not work on a large scale. Now, since mechanics has its foundation in geometry, where mere size cuts no figure, I do not see that the properties of circles, triangles, cylinders, cones and other solid figures will change with their size. If, therefore, a large machine be constructed in such a way that its parts bear to one another the same ratio as in a smaller one, and if the smaller is sufficiently strong for the purpose for which it was designed, I do not see why the larger also should not be able to withstand any severe and destructive tests to which it may be subjected.

SALVIATI. The common opinion is here absolutely wrong. Indeed, it is so far wrong that precisely the opposite is true, namely, that many machines can be constructed even more perfectly on a large scale than on a small; thus, for instance, a clock which indicates and strikes the hour can be made more accurate on a large scale than on a small. There are some intelligent people who maintain this same opinion, but on more reasonable grounds, when they cut loose from geometry and argue that the better performance of the large machine is owing to the imperfections and variations of the material. Here I trust you will not charge me with arrogance if I say that imperfections in the material, even those which are great enough to invalidate the clearest mathematical proof, are not sufficient to explain the deviations observed between machines in the concrete and in the abstract. Yet I shall say it and will affirm that, even if the imperfections did not exist and matter were absolutely perfect, unalterable and free from all accidental variations, still the mere fact that it is matter makes the larger machine, built of the same material and in the same proportion as the smaller, correspond with exactness to the smaller in every respect except that it will not be so strong or so resistant against violent treatment; the larger the machine, the greater its weakness. Since I assume matter to be unchangeable and always the same, it is clear that we are no less able to treat this constant and invariable property in a rigid manner than if it belonged to simple and pure mathematics. Therefore, Sagredo, you would do well to change the opinion which you, and perhaps also many other students of mechanics, have entertained concerning the ability of machines and structures to resist external disturbances, thinking that when they are built of the same material and maintain the same ratio between parts, they are able equally, or rather proportionally, to resist or yield to such external disturbances and blows. For we can demonstrate by geometry that the large machine is not proportionately stronger than the small. Finally, we may say that, for every machine and structure, whether artificial or natural, there is set a necessary limit beyond which neither art nor nature can pass; it is here understood, of course, that the material is the same and the proportion preserved.

SAGREDO. My brain already reels. My mind, like a cloud momentarily illuminated by a lightning flash, is for an instant filled with an unusual light, which now beckons to me and which now suddenly mingles and obscures strange, crude ideas. From what you have said it appears to me impossible to build two similar structures of the same material, but of different sizes and have them proportionately strong; and if this were so, it would not be possible to find two single poles made of the same wood which shall be alike in strength and resistance but unlike in size.

SALVIATI. So it is, Sagredo. And to make sure that we understand each other, I say that if we take a wooden rod of a certain length and size, fitted, say, into a wall at right angles, i. e., parallel to the horizon, it may be reduced to such a length that it will just support itself; so that if a hair's breadth be added to its length it will break under its own weight and will be the only rod of the kind in the world. Thus if, for instance, its length be a hundred times its breadth, you will not be able to find another rod whose length is also a hundred times its breadth and which, like the former, is just able to sustain its own weight and no more: all the larger ones will break while all the shorter ones will be strong enough to support something more than their own weight. And this which I have said about the ability to support itself must be understood to apply also to other tests; so that if a piece of scantling will carry the weight of ten similar to itself, a beam having the same proportions will not be able to support ten similar beams.

Please observe, gentlemen, how facts which at first seem improbable will, even on scant explanation, drop the cloak which has hidden them and stand forth in naked and simple beauty. Who does not know that a horse falling from a height of three or four cubits will break his bones, while a dog falling from the same height or a cat from a height of eight or ten cubits will suffer no injury? Equally harmless would be the fall of a grasshopper from a tower or the fall of an ant from the distance of the moon. Do not children fall with impunity from heights which would cost their elders a broken leg or perhaps a fractured skull? And just as smaller animals are proportionately stronger and more robust than the larger, so also smaller plants are able to stand up better than larger. I am certain you both know that an oak two hundred cubits high would not be able to sustain its own branches if they were distributed as in a tree of ordinary size; and that nature cannot produce a horse as large as twenty ordinary horses or a giant ten times taller than an ordinary man unless by miracle or by greatly altering the proportions of his limbs and especially of his bones, which would have to be considerably enlarged over the ordinary. Likewise the current belief that, in the case of artificial machines the very large and the small are equally feasible and lasting is a manifest error. Thus, for example, a small obelisk or column or other solid figure can certainly be laid down or set up without danger of breaking, while the very large ones will go to pieces under the slightest provocation, and that purely on account of their own weight. And here I must relate a circumstance which is worthy of your attention as indeed are all events which happen contrary to expectation, especially when a precautionary measure turns out to be a cause of disaster. A large marble column was laid out so that its two ends rested each upon a piece of beam; a little later it occurred to a mechanic that, in order to be doubly sure of its not breaking in the middle by its own weight, it would be wise to lay a third support midway; this seemed to all an excellent idea; but the sequel showed that it was quite the opposite, for not many months passed before the column was found cracked and broken exactly above the new middle support.

SIMPLICIO. A very remarkable and thoroughly unexpected accident, especially if caused by placing that new support in the middle.

SALVIATI. Surely this is the explanation, and the moment the cause is known our surprise vanishes; for when the two pieces of the column were placed on level ground it was observed that one of the end beams had, after a long while, become decayed and sunken, but that the middle one remained hard and strong, thus causing one half of the column to project in the air without any support. Under these circumstances the body therefore behaved differently from what it would have done if supported only upon the first beams; because no matter how much they might have sunken the column would have gone with them. This is an accident which could not possibly have happened to a small column, even though made of the same stone and having a length corresponding to its thickness, i. e., preserving the ratio between thickness and length found in the large pillar.

SAGREDO. I am quite convinced of the facts of the case, but I do not understand why the strength and resistance are not multiplied in the same proportion as the material; and I am the more puzzled because, on the contrary, I have noticed in other cases that the strength and resistance against breaking increase in a larger ratio than the amount of material. Thus, for instance, if two nails be driven into a wall, the one which is twice as big as the other will support not only twice as much weight as the other, but three or four times as much.

SALVIATI. Indeed you will not be far wrong if you say eight times as much; nor does this phenomenon contradict the other even though in appearance they seem so different.

SAGREDO. Will you not then, Salviati, remove these difficulties and clear away these obscurities if possible: for I imagine that this problem of resistance opens up a field of beautiful and useful ideas; and if you are pleased to make this the subject of today's discourse you will place Simplicio and me under many obligations.

SALVIATI. I am at your service if only I can call to mind what I learned from our Academician [Galileo] who had thought much upon this subject and according to his custom had demonstrated everything by geometrical methods so that one might fairly call this a new science. For, although some of his conclusions had been reached by others, first of all by Aristotle, these are not the most beautiful and, what is more important, they had not been proven in a rigid manner from fundamental principles. Now, since I wish to convince you by demonstrative reasoning rather than to persuade you by mere probabilities, I shall suppose that you are familiar with present-day mechanics so far as it is needed in our discussion. First of all it is necessary to consider what happens when a piece of wood or any other solid which coheres firmly is broken; for this is the fundamental fact, involving the first and simple principle which we must take for granted as well known.

To grasp this more clearly, imagine a cylinder or prism, AB, made of wood or other solid coherent material. Fasten the upper end, A, so that the cylinder hangs vertically. To the lower end, B, attach the weight C.

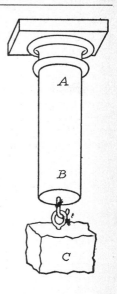

It is clear that however great they may be, the tenacity and coherence between the parts of this solid, so long as they are not infinite, can be overcome by the pull of the weight C, a weight which can be increased indefinitely until finally the solid breaks like a rope. And as in the case of the rope whose strength we know to be derived from a multitude of hemp threads which compose it, so in the case of the wood, we observe its fibres and filaments run lengthwise and render it much stronger than a hemp rope of the same thickness. But in the case of a stone or metallic cylinder where the coherence seems to be still greater the cement which holds the parts together must be something other than filaments and fibres; and yet even this can be broken by a strong pull.

SIMPLICIO. If this matter be as you say I can well understand that the fibres of the wood, being as long as the piece of wood itself, render it strong and resistant against large forces tending to break it. But how can one make a rope one hundred cubits long out of hempen fibres which are not more than two or three cubits long, and still give it so much strength? Besides, I should be glad to hear your opinion as to the manner in which the parts of metal, stone, and other materials not showing a filamentous structure are put together; for, if I mistake not, they exhibit even greater tenacity.

SALVIATI. To solve the problems which you raise it will be necessary to make a digression into subjects which have little bearing upon our present purpose.

SAGREDO. But if, by digressions, we can reach new truth, what harm is there in making one now, so that we may not lose this knowledge, remembering that such an opportunity, once omitted, may not return; remembering also that we are not tied down to a fixed and brief method but that we meet solely for our own entertainment? Indeed, who knows but that we may thus frequently discover something more interesting and beautiful than the solution originally sought? I beg of you, therefore, to grant the request of Simplicio, which is also mine; for I am no less curious and desirous than he to learn what is the binding material which holds together the parts of solids so that they can scarcely be separated. This information is also needed to understand the coherence of the parts of fibres themselves of which some solids are built up.

SALVIATI. I am at your service, since you desire it. The first question is, How are fibres, each not more than two or three cubits in length, so tightly bound together in the case of a rope one hundred cubits long that great force is required to break it?

Now tell me, Simplicio, can you not hold a hempen fibre so tightly between your fingers that I, pulling by the other end, would break it before drawing it away from you? Certainly you can. And now when the fibres of hemp are held not only at the ends, but are grasped by the surrounding medium throughout their entire length is it not manifestly more difficult to tear them loose from what holds them than to break them? But in the case of the rope the very act of twisting causes the threads to bind one another in such a way that when the rope is stretched with a great force the fibres break rather than separate from each other.

At the point where a rope parts the fibres are, as everyone knows, very short, nothing like a cubit long, as they would be if the parting of the rope occurred, not by the breaking of the filaments, but by their slipping one over the other.

SAGREDO. In confirmation of this it may be remarked that ropes sometimes break not by a lengthwise pull but by excessive twisting. This, it seems to me, is a conclusive argument because the threads bind one another so tightly that the compressing fibres do not permit those which are compressed to lengthen the spirals even that little bit by which it is necessary for them to lengthen in order to surround the rope which, on twisting, grows shorter and thicker.

SALVIATI. You are quite right. Now see how one fact suggests another. The thread held between the fingers does not yield to one who wishes to draw it away even when pulled with considerable force, but resists because it is held back by a double compression, seeing that the upper finger presses against the lower as hard as the lower against the upper. Now, if we could retain only one of these pressures there is no doubt that only half the original resistance would remain; but since we are not able, by lifting, say, the upper finger, to remove one of these pressures without also removing the other, it becomes necessary to preserve one of them by means of a new device which causes the thread to press itself against the finger or against some other solid body upon which it rests; and thus it is brought about that the very force which pulls it in order to snatch it away compresses it more and more as the pull increases. This is accomplished by wrapping the thread around the solid in the manner of a spiral; and will be better understood by means of a figure. Let AB and CD be two cylinders between which is stretched the thread EF: and for the sake of greater clearness we will imagine it to be a small cord. If these

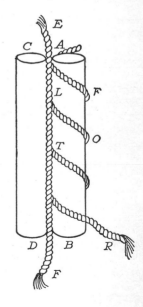

two cylinders be pressed strongly together, the cord EF, when drawn by the end F, will undoubtedly stand a considerable pull before it slips between the two compressing solids. But if we remove one of these cylinders the cord, though remaining in contact with the other, will not thereby be prevented from slipping freely. On the other hand, if one holds the cord loosely against the top of the cylinder A, winds it in the spiral form AFLOTR, and then pulls it by the end R, it is evident that the cord will begin to bind the cylinder; the greater the number of spirals the more tightly will the cord be pressed against the cylinder by any given pull. Thus as the number of turns increases, the line of contact becomes longer and in consequence more resistant; so that the cord slips and yields to the tractive force with increasing difficulty.

Is it not clear that this is precisely the kind of resistance which one meets in the case of a thick hemp rope where the fibres form thousands and thousands of similar spirals? And, indeed, the binding effect of these turns is so great that a few short rushes woven together into a few interlacing spirals form one of the strongest of ropes which I believe they call pack rope.

SAGREDO. What you say has cleared up two points which I did not previously understand. One fact is how two, or at most three, turns of a rope around the axle of a windlass cannot only hold it fast, but can also prevent it from slipping when pulled by the immense force of the weight which it sustains; and moreover how, by turning the windlass, this same axle, by mere friction of the rope around it, can wind up and lift huge stones while a mere boy is able to handle the slack of the rope. The other fact has to do with a simple but clever device, invented by a young kinsman of mine, for the purpose of descending from a window by means of a rope without lacerating the palms of his hands, as had happened to him shortly before and greatly to his discomfort. A small sketch will make this clear. He took a wooden cylinder, AB, about as thick as a walking stick and about one span long: on this he cut a spiral channel of about one turn and a half, and large enough to just receive the rope which he wished to use. Having introduced the rope at the end A and led it out again at the end B, he enclosed both the cylinder and the rope in a case of wood or tin, hinged along the side so that it could be easily opened and closed. After he had fastened the rope to a firm support above, he could, on grasping and squeezing the case with both hands, hang by his arms. The pressure on the rope, lying between the case and the cylinder, was such that he could, at will, either grasp the case more tightly and hold himself from slipping, or slacken his hold and descend as slowly as he wished.

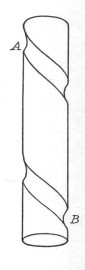

SALVIATI. A truly ingenious device! I feel, however, that for a complete explanation other considerations might well enter; yet I must not now digress upon this particular topic since you are waiting to hear what I think about the breaking strength of other materials which, unlike ropes and most woods, do not show a filamentous structure. The coherence of these bodies is, in my estimation, produced by other causes which may be grouped under two heads. One is that much-talked-of repugnance which nature exhibits towards a vacuum; but this horror of a vacuum not being sufficient, it is necessary to introduce another cause in the form of a gluey or viscous substance which binds firmly together the component parts of the body.

First I shall speak of the vacuum, demonstrating by definite experiment the quality and quantity of its force. If you take two highly polished and smooth plates of marble, metal, or glass and place them face to face, one will slide over the other with the greatest ease, showing conclusively that there is nothing of a viscous nature between them. But when you attempt to separate them and keep them at a constant distance apart, you find the plates exhibit such a repugnance to separation that the upper one will carry the lower one with it and keep it lifted indefinitely, even when the latter is big and heavy.

This experiment shows the aversion of nature for empty space, even during the brief moment required for the outside air to rush in and fill up the region between the two plates. It is also observed that if two plates are not thoroughly polished, their contact is imperfect so that when you attempt to separate them slowly the only resistance offered is that of weight; if, however, the pull be sudden, then the lower plate rises, but quickly falls back, having followed the upper plate only for that very short interval of time required for the expansion of the small amount of air remaining between the plates, in consequence of their not fitting, and for the entrance of the surrounding air. This resistance which is exhibited between the two plates is doubtless likewise present between the parts of a solid, and enters, at least in part, as a concomitant cause of their coherence.

SAGREDO. Allow me to interrupt you for a moment, please; for I want to speak of something which just occurs to me, namely, when I see how the lower plate follows the upper one and how rapidly it is lifted, I feel sure that, contrary to the opinion of many philosophers, including perhaps even Aristotle himself, motion in a vacuum is not instantaneous. If this were so the two plates mentioned above would separate without any resistance whatever, seeing that the same instant of time would suffice for their separation and for the surrounding medium to rush in and fill the vacuum between them. The fact that the lower plate follows the upper one allows us to infer, not only that motion in a vacuum is not instantaneous, but also that, between the two plates, a vacuum really exists, at least for a very short time, sufficient to allow the surrounding medium to rush in and fill the vacuum; for if there were no vacuum there would be no need of any motion in the medium. One must admit then that a vacuum is sometimes produced by violent motion or contrary to the laws of nature (although in my opinion nothing occurs contrary to nature except the impossible, and that never occurs).

But here another difficulty arises. While experiment convinces me of the correctness of this conclusion, my mind is not entirely satisfied as to the cause to which this effect is to be attributed. For the separation of the plates precedes the formation of the vacuum which is produced as a consequence of this separation; and since it appears to me that, in the order of nature, the cause must precede the effect, even though it appears to follow in point of time, and since every positive effect must have a positive cause, I do not see how the adhesion of two plates and their resistance to separation—actual facts—can be referred to a vacuum as cause when this vacuum is yet to follow. According to the infallible maxim of the Philosopher, the non-existent can produce no effect.

SIMPLICIO. Seeing that you accept this axiom of Aristotle, I hardly think you will reject another excellent and reliable maxim of his, namely, Nature undertakes only that which happens without resistance; and in this saying, it appears to me, you will find the solution of your difficulty. Since nature abhors a vacuum, she prevents that from which a vacuum would follow as a necessary consequence. Thus it happens that nature prevents the separation of the two plates.

SAGREDO. Now admitting that what Simplicio says is an adequate solution of my difficulty, it seems to me, if I may be allowed to resume my former argument, that this very resistance to a vacuum ought to be sufficient to hold together the parts either of stone or of metal or the parts of any other solid which is knit together more strongly and which is more resistant to separation. If for one effect there be only one cause, or if, more being assigned, they can be reduced to one, then why is not this vacuum which really exists a sufficient cause for all kinds of resistance?

SALVIATI. I do not wish just now to enter this discussion as to whether the vacuum alone is sufficient to hold together the separate parts of a solid body; but I assure you that the vacuum which acts as a sufficient cause in the case of the two plates is not alone sufficient to bind together the parts of a solid cylinder of marble or metal which, when pulled violently, separates and divides. And now if I find a method of distinguishing this well known resistance, depending upon the vacuum, from every other kind which might increase the coherence, and if I show you that the aforesaid resistance alone is not nearly sufficient for such an effect, will you not grant that we are bound to introduce another cause? Help him, Simplicio, since he does not know what reply to make.

SIMPLICIO. Surely, Sagredo's hesitation must be owing to another reason, for there can be no doubt concerning a conclusion which is at once so clear and logical.

SAGREDO. You have guessed rightly, Simplicio. I was wondering whether, if a million of gold each year from Spain were not sufficient to pay the army, it might not be necessary to make provision other than small coin for the pay of the soldiers.

But go ahead, Salviati; assume that I admit your conclusion and show us your method of separating the action of the vacuum from other causes; and by measuring it show us how it is not sufficient to produce the effect in question.

SALVIATI. Your good angel assist you. I will tell you how to separate the force of the vacuum from the others, and afterwards how to measure it. For this purpose let us consider a continuous substance whose parts lack all resistance to separation except that derived from a vacuum, such as is the case with water, a fact fully demonstrated by our Academician in one of his treatises. Whenever a cylinder of water is subjected to a pull and offers a resistance to the separation of its parts this can be attributed to no other cause than the resistance of the vacuum. In order to try such

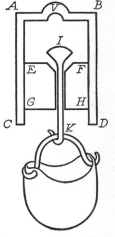

an experiment I have invented a device which I can better explain by means of a sketch than by mere words. Let CABD represent the cross section of a cylinder either of metal or, preferably, of glass, hollow inside and accurately turned. Into this is introduced a perfectly fitting cylinder of wood, represented in cross section by EGHF, and capable of up-and-down motion. Through the middle of this cylinder is bored a hole to receive an iron wire, carrying a hook at the end K, while the upper end of the wire, I, is provided with a conical head. The wooden cylinder is countersunk at the top so as to receive, with a perfect fit, the conical head I of the wire, IK, when pulled down by the end K.

Now insert the wooden cylinder EH in the hollow cylinder AD, so as not to touch the upper end of the latter but to leave free a space of two or three fingerbreadths; this space is to be filled with water by holding the vessel with the mouth CD upwards, pushing down on the stopper EH, and at the same time keeping the conical head of the wire, I, away from the hollow portion of the wooden cylinder. The air is thus allowed to escape alongside the iron wire (which does not make a close fit) as soon as one presses down on the wooden stopper. The air having been allowed to escape and the iron wire having been drawn back so that it fits snugly against the conical depression in the wood, invert the vessel, bringing it mouth downwards, and hang on the hook K a vessel which can be filled with sand or any heavy material in quantity sufficient to finally separate the upper surface of the stopper, EF, from the lower surface of the water to which it was attached only by the resistance of the vacuum. Next weigh the stopper and wire together with the attached vessel and its contents; we shall then have the force of the vacuum. If one attaches to a cylinder of marble or glass a weight which, together with the weight of the marble or glass itself, is just equal to the sum of the weights before mentioned, and if breaking occurs we shall then be justified in saying that the vacuum alone holds the parts of the marble and glass together; but if this weight does not suffice and if breaking occurs only after adding, say, four times this weight, we shall then be compelled to say that the vacuum furnishes only one fifth of the total resistance.

SIMPLICIO. No one can doubt the cleverness of the device; yet it presents many difficulties which make me doubt its reliability. For who will assure us that the air does not creep in between the glass and stopper even if it is well packed with tow or other yielding material? I question also whether oiling with wax or turpentine will suffice to make the cone, I, fit snugly on its seat. Besides, may not the parts of the water expand and dilate? Why may not the air or exhalations or some other more subtile substances penetrate the pores of the wood, or even of the glass itself?

SALVIATI. With great skill indeed has Simplicio laid before us the difficulties; and he has even partly suggested how to prevent the air from penetrating the wood or passing between the wood and the glass. But now let me point out that, as our experience increases, we shall learn whether or not these alleged difficulties really exist. For if, as is the case with air, water is by nature expansible, although only under severe treatment, we shall see the stopper descend; and if we put a small excavation in the upper part of the glass vessel, such as indicated by V, then the air or any other tenuous and gaseous substance, which might penetrate the pores of glass or wood, would pass through the water and collect in this receptacle V. But if these things do not happen we may rest assured that our experiment has been performed with proper caution; and we shall discover that water does not dilate and that glass does not allow any material, however tenuous, to penetrate it.

SAGREDO. Thanks to this discussion, I have learned the cause of a certain effect which I have long wondered at and despaired of understanding. I once saw a cistern which had been provided with a pump under the mistaken impression that the water might thus be drawn with less effort or in greater quantity than by means of the ordinary bucket. The stock of the pump carried its sucker and valve in the upper part so that the water was lifted by attraction and not by a push as is the case with pumps in which the sucker is placed lower down. This pump worked perfectly so long as the water in the cistern stood above a certain level; but below this level the pump failed to work. When I first noticed this phenomenon I thought the machine was out of order; but the workman whom I called in to repair it told me the defect was not in the pump but in the water which had fallen too low to be raised through such a height; and he added that it was not possible, either by a pump or by any other machine working on the principle of attraction, to lift water a hair's breadth above eighteen cubits; whether the pump be large or small this is the extreme limit of the lift. Up to this time I had been so thoughtless that, although I knew a rope, or rod of wood, or of iron, if sufficiently long, would break by its own weight when held by the upper end, it never occurred to me that the same thing would happen, only much more easily, to a column of water. And really is not that thing which is attracted in the pump a column of water attached at the upper end and stretched more and more until finally a point is reached where it breaks, like a rope, on account of its excessive weight?

SALVIATI. That is precisely the way it works; this fixed elevation of eighteen cubits is true for any quantity of water whatever, be the pump large or small or even as fine as a straw. We may therefore say that, on weighing the water contained in a tube eighteen cubits long, no matter what the diameter, we shall obtain the value of the resistance of the vacuum in a cylinder of any solid material having a bore of this same diameter. And having gone so far, let us see how easy it is to find to what length cylinders of metal, stone, wood, glass, etc., of any diameter can be elongated without breaking by their own weight.

Take for instance a copper wire of any length and thickness; fix the upper end and to the other end attach a greater and greater load until finally the wire breaks; let the maximum load be, say, fifty pounds. Then it is clear that if fifty pounds of copper, in addition to the weight of the wire itself which may be, say, $\frac{1}{8}$ ounce, is drawn out into wire of this same size we shall have the greatest length of this kind of wire which can sustain its own weight. Suppose the wire which breaks to be one cubit in length and $\frac{1}{8}$ ounce in weight; then since it supports 50 lbs. in addition to its own weight, i. e., 4800 eighths-of-an-ounce, it follows that all copper wires, independent of size, can sustain themselves up to a length of 4801 cubits and no more. Since then a copper rod can sustain its own weight up to a length of 4801 cubits it follows that that part of the breaking strength which depends upon the vacuum, comparing it with the remaining factors of resistance, is equal to the weight of a rod of water, eighteen cubits long and as thick as the copper rod. If, for example, copper is nine times as heavy as water, the breaking strength of any copper rod, in so far as it depends upon the vacuum, is equal to the weight of two cubits of this same rod. By a similar method one can find the maximum length of wire or rod of any material which will just sustain its own weight, and can at the same time discover the part which the vacuum plays in its breaking strength.

SAGREDO. It still remains for you to tell us upon what depends the resistance to breaking, other than that of the vacuum; what is the gluey or viscous substance which cements together the parts of the solid? For I cannot imagine a glue that will not burn up in a highly heated furnace in two or three months, or certainly within ten or a hundred. For if gold, silver and glass are kept for a long while in the molten state and are removed from the furnace, their parts, on cooling, immediately reunite and bind themselves together as before. Not only so, but whatever difficulty arises with respect to the cementation of the parts of the glass arises also with regard to the parts of the glue; in other words, what is that which holds these parts together so firmly?

SALVIATI. A little while ago, I expressed the hope that your good angel might assist you. I now find myself in the same straits. Experiment leaves no doubt that the reason why two plates cannot be separated, except with violent effort, is that they are held together by the resistance of the vacuum; and the same can be said of two large pieces of a marble or bronze column. This being so, I do not see why this same cause may not explain the coherence of smaller parts and indeed of the very smallest particles of these materials. Now, since each effect must have one true and sufficient cause and since I find no other cement, am I not justified in trying to discover whether the vacuum is not a sufficient cause?

SIMPLICIO. But seeing that you have already proved that the resistance which the large vacuum offers to the separation of two large parts of a solid is really very small in comparison with that cohesive force which binds together the most minute parts, why do you hesitate to regard this latter as something very different from the former?

SALVIATI. Sagredo has already answered this question when he re-marked that each individual soldier was being paid from coin collected by a general tax of pennies and farthings, while even a million of gold would not suffice to pay the entire army. And who knows but that there may be other extremely minute vacua which affect the smallest particles so that that which binds together the contiguous parts is throughout of the same mintage?

In reply to the question raised by Simplicio, one may say that although each particular vacuum is exceedingly minute and therefore easily overcome, yet their number is so extraordinarily great that their com-bined resistance is, so to speak, multiplied almost without limit. The nature and the amount of force which results from adding together an immense number of small forces is clearly illustrated by the fact that a weight of millions of pounds, suspended by great cables, is overcome and lifted, when the south wind carries innumerable atoms of water, sus-pended in thin mist, which moving through the air penetrate between the fibres of the tense ropes in spite of the tremendous force of the hang-ing weight. When these particles enter the narrow pores they swell the ropes, thereby shorten them, and perforce lift the heavy mass.

SAGREDO. There can be no doubt that any resistance, so long as it is not infinite, may be overcome by a multitude of minute forces. Thus a vast number of ants might carry ashore a ship laden with grain. And since experience shows us daily that one ant can easily carry one grain, it is clear that the number of grains in the ship is not infinite, but falls below a certain limit. If you take another number four or six times as great, and if you set to work a corresponding number of ants they will carry the grain ashore and the boat also. It is true that this will call for a prodigious number of ants, but in my opinion this is precisely the case with the vacua which bind together the least particles of a metal.

SALVIATI. But even if this demanded an infinite number would you still think it impossible?

SAGREDO. Not if the mass of metal were infinite.

SAGREDO. The phenomenon of light is one which I have many times remarked with astonishment. I have, for instance, seen lead melted instantly by means of a concave mirror only three hands in diameter. Hence I think that if the mirror were very large, well polished and of a parabolic figure, it would just as readily and quickly melt any other metal, seeing that the small mirror, which was not well polished and had only a spherical shape, was able so energetically to melt lead and burn every combustible substance. Such effects as these render credible to me the marvels accomplished by the mirrors of Archimedes.

SALVIATI. Speaking of the effects produced by the mirrors of Archimedes, it was his own books (which I had already read and studied with infinite astonishment) that rendered credible to me all the miracles described by various writers. And if any doubt had remained the book which Father Buonaventura Cavalieri has recently published on the subject of the burning glass and which I have read with admiration would have removed the last difficulty.

SAGREDO. I also have seen this treatise and have read it with pleasure and astonishment; and knowing the author I was confirmed in the opinion which I had already formed of him that he was destined to become one of the leading mathematicians of our age. But now, with regard to the surprising effect of solar rays in melting metals, must we believe that such a furious action is devoid of motion or that it is accompanied by the most rapid of motions?

SALVIATI. We observe that other combustions and resolutions are accompanied by motion, and that, the most rapid; note the action of lightning and of powder as used in mines and petards; note also how the charcoal flame, mixed as it is with heavy and impure vapors, increases its power to liquefy metals whenever quickened by a pair of bellows. Hence I do not understand how the action of light, although very pure, can be devoid of motion and that of the swiftest type.

SAGREDO. But of what kind and how great must we consider this speed of light to be? Is it instantaneous or momentary or does it like other motions require time? Can we not decide this by experiment?

SIMPLICIO. Everyday experience shows that the propagation of light is instantaneous; for when we see a piece of artillery fired, at great distance, the flash reaches our eyes without lapse of time; but the sound reaches the ear only after a noticeable interval.

SAGREDO. Well, Simplicio, the only thing I am able to infer from this familiar bit of experience is that sound, in reaching our ear, travels more slowly than light; it does not inform me whether the coming of the light is instantaneous or whether, although extremely rapid, it still occupies time. An observation of this kind tells us nothing more than one in which it is claimed that "As soon as the sun reaches the horizon its light reaches our eyes"; but who will assure me that these rays had not reached this limit earlier than they reached our vision?

SALVIATI. The small conclusiveness of these and other similar observations once led me to devise a method by which one might accurately ascertain whether illumination, i. e., the propagation of light, is really instantaneous. The fact that the speed of sound is as high as it is, assures us that the motion of light cannot fail to be extraordinarily swift. The experiment which I devised was as follows:

Let each of two persons take a light contained in a lantern, or other receptacle, such that by the interposition of the hand, the one can shut off or admit the light to the vision of the other. Next let them stand opposite each other at a distance of a few cubits and practice until they acquire such skill in uncovering and occulting their lights that the instant one sees the light of his companion he will uncover his own. After a few trials the response will be so prompt that without sensible error the uncovering of one light is immediately followed by the uncovering of the other, so that as soon as one exposes his light he will instantly see that of the other. Having acquired skill at this short distance let the two experimenters, equipped as before, take up positions separated by a distance of two or three miles and let them perform the same experiment at night, noting carefully whether the exposures and occultations occur in the same manner as at short distances; if they do, we may safely conclude that the propagation of light is instantaneous; but if time is required at a distance of three miles which, considering the going of one light and the coming of the other, really amounts to six, then the delay ought to be easily observable. If the experiment is to be made at still greater distances, say eight or ten miles, telescopes may be employed, each observer adjusting one for himself at the place where he is to make the experiment at night; then although the lights are not large and are therefore invisible to the naked eye at so great a distance, they can readily be covered and uncovered since by aid of the telescopes, once adjusted and fixed, they will become easily visible.

SAGREDO. This experiment strikes me as a clever and reliable invention. But tell us what you conclude from the results.

SALVIATI. In fact I have tried the experiment only at a short distance, less than a mile, from which I have not been able to ascertain with certainty whether the appearance of the opposite light was instantaneous or not; but if not instantaneous it is extraordinarily rapid—I should call it momentary; and for the present I should compare it to motion which we see in the lightning flash between clouds eight or ten miles distant from us. We see the beginning of this light—I might say its head and source—located at a particular place among the clouds; but it immediately spreads to the surrounding ones, which seems to be an argument that at least some time is required for propagation; for if the illumination were instantaneous and not gradual, we should not be able to distinguish its origin—its center, so to speak—from its outlying portions.

SAGREDO. I quite agree with the peripatetic philosophers in denying the penetrability of matter. As to the vacua I should like to hear a thorough discussion of Aristotle's demonstration in which he opposes them, and what you, Salviati, have to say in reply. I beg of you, Simplicio, that you give us the precise proof of the Philosopher and that you, Salviati, give us the reply.

SIMPLICIO. So far as I remember, Aristotle inveighs against the ancient view that a vacuum is a necessary prerequisite for motion and that the latter could not occur without the former. In opposition to this view Aristotle shows that it is precisely the phenomenon of motion, as we shall see, which renders untenable the idea of a vacuum. His method is to divide the argument into two parts. He first supposes bodies of different weight to move in the same medium; then supposes, one and the same body to move in different media. In the first case, he supposes bodies of different weight to move in one and the same medium with different speeds which stand to one another in the same ratio as the weights; so that, for example, a body which is ten times as heavy as another will move ten times as rapidly as the other. In the second case he assumes that the speeds of one and the same body moving in different media are in inverse ratio to the densities of these media; thus, for instance, if the density of water were ten times that of air, the speed in air would be ten times greater than in water. From this second supposition, he shows that, since the tenuity of a vacuum differs infinitely from that of any medium filled with matter however rare, any body which moves in a plenum through a certain space in a certain time ought to move through a vacuum instantaneously; but instantaneous motion is an impossibility; it is therefore impossible that a vacuum should be produced by motion.

SALVIATI. The argument is, as you see, *ad hominem,* that is, it is directed against those who thought the vacuum a prerequisite for motion. Now if I admit the argument to be conclusive and concede also that motion cannot take place in a vacuum, the assumption of a vacuum considered absolutely and not with reference to motion, is not thereby invalidated. But to tell you what the ancients might possibly have replied and in order to better understand just how conclusive Aristotle's demonstration is, we may, in my opinion, deny both of his assumptions. And as to the first, I greatly doubt that Aristotle ever tested by experiment whether it be true that two stones, one weighing ten times as much as the other, if allowed to fall, at the same instant, from a height of, say, 100 cubits, would so differ in speed that when the heavier had reached the ground, the other would not have fallen more than 10 cubits.

SIMPLICIO. His language would seem to indicate that he had tried the experiment, because he says: *We see the heavier;* now the word *see* shows that he had made the experiment.

SAGREDO. But I, Simplicio, who have made the test can assure you that a cannon ball weighing one or two hundred pounds, or even more, will not reach the ground by as much as a span ahead of a musket ball weighing only half a pound, provided both are dropped from a height of 200 cubits.

SALVIATI. But, even without further experiment, it is possible to prove clearly, by means of a short and conclusive argument, that a heavier body does not move more rapidly than a lighter one provided both bodies are of the same material and in short such as those mentioned by Aristotle. But tell me, Simplicio, whether you admit that each falling body acquires a definite speed fixed by nature, a velocity which cannot be increased or diminished except by the use of force or resistance.

Simplicio. There can be no doubt but that one and the same body moving in a single medium has a fixed velocity which is determined by nature and which cannot be increased except by the addition of momentum or diminished except by some resistance which retards it.

Salviati. If then we take two bodies whose natural speeds are different, it is clear that on uniting the two, the more rapid one will be partly retarded by the slower, and the slower will be somewhat hastened by the swifter. Do you not agree with me in this opinion?

Simplicio. You are unquestionably right.

Salviati. But if this is true, and if a large stone moves with a speed of, say, eight while a smaller moves with a speed of four, then when they are united, the system will move with a speed less than eight; but the two stones when tied together make a stone larger than that which before moved with a speed of eight. Hence the heavier body moves with less speed than the lighter; an effect which is contrary to your supposition. Thus you see how, from your assumption that the heavier body moves more rapidly than the lighter one. I infer that the heavier body moves more slowly.

Simplicio. I am all at sea because it appears to me that the smaller stone when added to the larger increases its weight and by adding weight I do not see how it can fail to increase its speed or, at least, not to diminish it.

Salviati. Here again you are in error, Simplicio, because it is not true that the smaller stone adds weight to the larger.

Simplicio. This is, indeed, quite beyond my comprehension.

Salviati. It will not be beyond you when I have once shown you the mistake under which you are laboring. Note that it is necessary to distinguish between heavy bodies in motion and the same bodies at rest. A large stone placed in a balance not only acquires additional weight by having another stone placed upon it, but even by the addition of a handful of hemp its weight is augmented six to ten ounces according to the quantity of hemp. But if you tie the hemp to the stone and allow them to fall freely from some height, do you believe that the hemp will press down upon the stone and thus accelerate its motion or do you think the motion will be retarded by a partial upward pressure? One always feels the pressure upon his shoulders when he prevents the motion of a load resting upon him; but if one descends just as rapidly as the load would fall how can it gravitate or press upon him? Do you not see that this would be the same as trying to strike a man with a lance when he is running away from you with a speed which is equal to, or even greater, than that with which you are following him? You must therefore conclude that, during free and natural fall, the small stone does not press upon the larger and consequently does not increase its weight as it does when at rest.

SIMPLICIO. But what if we should place the larger stone upon the smaller?

SALVIATI. Its weight would be increased if the larger stone moved more rapidly; but we have already concluded that when the small stone moves more slowly it retards to some extent the speed of the larger, so that the combination of the two, which is a heavier body than the larger of the two stones, would move less rapidly, a conclusion which is contrary to your hypothesis. We infer therefore that large and small bodies move with the same speed provided they are of the same specific gravity.

SIMPLICIO. Your discussion is really admirable; yet I do not find it easy to believe that a bird shot falls as swiftly as a cannon ball.

SALVIATI. Why not say a grain of sand as rapidly as a grindstone? But, Simplicio, I trust you will not follow the example of many others who divert the discussion from its main intent and fasten upon some statement of mine which lacks a hairsbreadth of the truth and, under this hair, hide the fault of another which is as big as a ship's cable. Aristotle says that "an iron ball of one hundred pounds falling from a height of one hundred cubits reaches the ground before a one-pound ball has fallen a single cubit." I say that they arrive at the same time. You find, on making the experiment, that the larger outstrips the smaller by two finger-breadths, that is, when the larger has reached the ground, the other is short of it by two fingerbreadths; now you would not hide behind these two fingers the ninety-nine cubits of Aristotle, nor would you mention my small error and at the same time pass over in silence his very large one. Aristotle declares that bodies of different weights, in the same medium, travel (in so far as their motion depends upon gravity) with speeds which are proportional to their weights; this he illustrates by use of bodies in which it is possible to perceive the pure and unadulterated effect of gravity, eliminating other considerations, for example, figure, as being of small importance, influences which are greatly dependent upon the medium which modifies the single effect of gravity alone. Thus we observe that gold, the densest of all substances, when beaten out into a very thin leaf, goes floating through the air; the same thing happens with stone when ground into a very fine powder. But if you wish to maintain the general proposition you will have to show that the same ratio of speeds is preserved in the case of all heavy bodies, and that a stone of twenty pounds moves ten times as rapidly as one of two; but I claim that this is false and that, if they fall from a height of fifty or a hundred cubits, they will reach the earth at the same moment.

SIMPLICIO. Perhaps the result would be different if the fall took place not from a few cubits but from some thousands of cubits.

SALVIATI. If this were what Aristotle meant you would burden him with another error which would amount to a falsehood; because, since there is no such sheer height available on earth, it is clear that Aristotle could not have made the experiment; yet he wishes to give us the impression of his having performed it when he speaks of such an effect as one which we see.

SIMPLICIO. In fact, Aristotle does not employ this principle, but uses the other one which is not, I believe, subject to these same difficulties.

SALVIATI. But the one is as false as the other; and I am surprised that you yourself do not see the fallacy and that you do not perceive that if it were true that, in media of different densities and different resistances, such as water and air, one and the same body moved in air more rapidly than in water, in proportion as the density of water is greater than that of air, then it would follow that any body which falls through air ought also to fall through water. But this conclusion is false inasmuch as many bodies which descend in air not only do not descend in water, but actually rise.

SIMPLICIO. I do not understand the necessity of your inference; and in addition I will say that Aristotle discusses only those bodies which fall in both media, not those which fall in air but rise in water.

SALVIATI. The arguments which you advance for the Philosopher are such as he himself would have certainly avoided so as not to aggravate his first mistake. But tell me now whether the density of the water, or whatever it may be that retards the motion, bears a definite ratio to the density of air which is less retardative; and if so fix a value for it at your pleasure.

SIMPLICIO. Such a ratio does exist; let us assume it to be ten; then, for a body which falls in both these media, the speed in water will be ten times slower than in air.

SALVIATI. I shall now take one of those bodies which fall in air but not in water, say a wooden ball, and I shall ask you to assign to it any speed you please for its descent through air.

SIMPLICIO. Let us suppose it moves with a speed of twenty.

SALVIATI. Very well. Then it is clear that this speed bears to some smaller speed the same ratio as the density of water bears to that of air; and the value of this smaller speed is two. So that really if we follow exactly the assumption of Aristotle we ought to infer that the wooden ball which falls in air, a substance ten times less-resisting than water, with a speed of twenty would fall in water with a speed of two, instead of coming to the surface from the bottom as it does; unless perhaps you wish to reply, which I do not believe you will, that the rising of the wood through the water is the same as its falling with a speed of two. But since the wooden ball does not go to the bottom, I think you will agree with me that we can find a ball of another material, not wood, which does fall in water with a speed of two.

SIMPLICIO. Undoubtedly we can; but it must be of a substance considerably heavier than wood.

SALVIATI. That is it exactly. But if this second ball falls in water with a speed of two, what will be its speed of descent in air? If you hold to the rule of Aristotle you must reply that it will move at the rate of twenty; but twenty is the speed which you yourself have already assigned to the wooden ball; hence this and the other heavier ball will each move through air with the same speed. But now how does the Philosopher harmonize this result with his other, namely, that bodies of different weight move through the same medium with different speeds—speeds which are proportional to their weights? But without going into the matter more deeply, how have these common and obvious properties escaped your notice? Have you not observed that two bodies which fall in water, one with a speed a hundred times as great as that of the other, will fall in air with speeds so nearly equal that one will not surpass the other by as much as one hundredth part? Thus, for example, an egg made of marble will descend in water one hundred times more rapidly than a hen's egg, while in air falling from a height of twenty cubits the one will fall short of the other by less than four fingerbreadths. In short, a heavy body which sinks through ten cubits of water in three hours will traverse ten cubits of air in one or two pulse beats; and if the heavy body be a ball of lead it will easily traverse the ten cubits of water in less than double the time required for ten cubits of air. And here, I am sure, Simplicio, you find no ground for difference or objection. We conclude, therefore, that the argument does not bear against the existence of a vacuum; but if it did, it would only do away with vacua of considerable size which neither I nor, in my opinion, the ancients ever believed to exist in nature, although they might possibly be produced by force as may be gathered from various experiments whose description would here occupy too much time.

SAGREDO. Seeing that Simplicio is silent, I will take the opportunity of saying something. Since you have clearly demonstrated that bodies of different weights do not move in one and the same medium with velocities proportional to their weights, but that they all move with the same speed, understanding of course that they are of the same substance or at least of the same specific gravity; certainly not of different specific gravities, for I hardly think you would have us believe a ball of cork moves with the same speed as one of lead; and again since you have clearly demonstrated that one and the same body moving through differently resisting media does not acquire speeds which are inversely proportional to the resistances, I am curious to learn what are the ratios actually observed in these cases.

SALVIATI. These are interesting questions and I have thought much concerning them. I will give you the method of approach and the result which I finally reached. Having once established the falsity of the proposition that one and the same body moving through differently resisting media acquires speeds which are inversely proportional to the resistances of these media, and having also disproved the statement that in the same medium bodies of different weight acquire velocities proportional to their weights (understanding that this applies also to bodies which differ merely in specific gravity), I then began to combine these two facts and to consider what would happen if bodies of different weight were placed in media of different resistances; and I found that the differences in speed were greater in those media which were more resistant, that is, less yield-ing. This difference was such that two bodies which differed scarcely at all in their speed through air would, in water, fall the one with a speed ten times as great as that of the other. Further, there are bodies which will fall rapidly in air, whereas if placed in water not only will not sink but will remain at rest or will even rise to the top: for it is possible to find some kinds of wood, such as knots and roots, which remain at rest in water but fall rapidly in air.

SAGREDO. I have often tried with the utmost patience to add grains of sand to a ball of wax until it should acquire the same specific gravity as water and would therefore remain at rest in this medium. But with all my care I was never able to accomplish this. Indeed, I do not know whether there is any solid substance whose specific gravity is, by nature, so nearly equal to that of water that if placed anywhere in water it will remain at rest.

SALVIATI. In this, as in a thousand other operations, men are surpassed by animals. In this problem of yours one may learn much from the fish which are very skillful in maintaining their equilibrium not only in one kind of water, but also in waters which are notably different either by their own nature or by some accidental muddiness or through salinity, each of which produces a marked change. So perfectly indeed can fish keep their equilibrium that they are able to remain motionless in any position. This they accomplish, I believe, by means of an apparatus espe-cially provided by nature, namely, a bladder located in the body and com-municating with the mouth by means of a narrow tube through which they are able, at will, to expel a portion of the air contained in the bladder: by rising to the surface they can take in more air; thus they make them-selves heavier or lighter than water at will and maintain equilibrium.

SAGREDO. By means of another device I was able to deceive some friends to whom I had boasted that I could make up a ball of wax that would be in equilibrium in water. In the bottom of a vessel I placed some salt water and upon this some fresh water; then I showed them that the ball stopped in the middle of the water, and that, when pushed to the bottom or lifted to the top, it would not remain in either of these places but would return to the middle.

SALVIATI. This experiment is not without usefulness. For when phy-sicians are testing the various qualities of waters, especially their specific gravities, they employ a ball of this kind so adjusted that, in certain water, it will neither rise nor fall. Then in testing another water, differing ever so slightly in specific gravity, the ball will sink if this water be lighter and rise if it be heavier. And so exact is this experiment that the addition of two grains of salt to six pounds of water is sufficient to make the ball rise to the surface from the bottom to which it had fallen. To illustrate the precision of this experiment and also to clearly demonstrate the non-resistance of water to division, I wish to add that this notable difference in specific gravity can be produced not only by solution of some heavier substance, but also by merely heating or cooling; and so sensitive is water to this process that by simply adding four drops of another water which is slightly warmer or cooler than the six pounds one can cause the ball to sink or rise; it will sink when the warm water is poured in and will rise upon the addition of cold water. Now you can see how mistaken are those philosophers who ascribe to water viscosity or some other coherence of parts which offers resistance to separation of parts and to penetration.

SAGREDO. With regard to this question I have found many convincing arguments in a treatise by our Academician; but there is one great difficulty of which I have not been able to rid myself, namely, if there be no tenacity or coherence between the particles of water how is it possible for those large drops of water to stand out in relief upon cabbage leaves without scattering or spreading out?

SALVIATI. Although those who are in possession of the truth are able to solve all objections raised, I would not arrogate to myself such power; nevertheless my inability should not be allowed to becloud the truth. To begin with let me confess that I do not understand how these large globules of water stand out and hold themselves up, although I know for a certainty that it is not owing to any internal tenacity acting between the particles of water; whence it must follow that the cause of this effect is external. Beside the experiments already shown to prove that the cause is not internal, I can offer another which is very convincing. If the particles of water which sustain themselves in a heap, while surrounded by air, did so in virtue of an internal cause then they would sustain themselves much more easily when surrounded by a medium in which they exhibit less tendency to fall than they do in air; such a medium would be any fluid heavier than air, as, for instance, wine: and therefore if some wine be poured about such a drop of water, the wine might rise until the drop was entirely covered, without the particles of water, held together by this internal coherence, ever parting company. But this is not the fact; for as soon as the wine touches the water, the latter without waiting to be covered scatters and spreads out underneath the wine if it be red. The cause of this effect is therefore external and is possibly to be found in the surrounding air. Indeed there appears to be a considerable antagonism between air and water as I have observed in the following experiment. Having taken a glass globe which had a mouth of about the same diameter as a straw, I filled it with water and turned it mouth downwards; nevertheless, the water, although quite heavy and prone to descend, and the air, which is very light and disposed to rise through the water, refused, the one to descend and the other to ascend through the opening, but both remained stubborn and defiant. On the other hand, as soon as I apply to this opening a glass of red wine, which is almost inappreciably lighter than water, red streaks are immediately observed to ascend slowly through the water while the water with equal slowness descends through the wine without mixing, until finally the globe is completely filled with wine and the water has all gone down into the vessel below. What then can we say except that there exists, between water and air, a certain incompatibility which I do not understand, but perhaps . . .

SIMPLICIO. I feel almost like laughing at the great antipathy which Salviati exhibits against the use of the word antipathy; and yet it is excellently adapted to explain the difficulty.

SALVIATI. All right, if it please Simplicio, let this word antipathy be the solution of our difficulty. Returning from this digression, let us again take up our problem. We have already seen that the difference of speed between bodies of different specific gravities is most marked in those media which are the most resistant: thus, in a medium of quicksilver, gold not merely sinks to the bottom more rapidly than lead but it is the only substance that will descend at all; all other metals and stones rise to the surface and float. On the other hand the variation of speed in air between balls of gold, lead, copper, porphyry, and other heavy materials is so slight that in a fall of 100 cubits a ball of gold would surely not outstrip one of copper by as much as four fingers. Having observed this I came to the conclusion that in a medium totally devoid of resistance all bodies would fall with the same speed.

SIMPLICIO. This is a remarkable statement, Salviati. But I shall never believe that even in a vacuum, if motion in such a place were possible, a lock of wool and a bit of lead can fall with the same velocity.

SALVIATI. A little more slowly, Simplicio. Your difficulty is not so recondite nor am I so imprudent as to warrant you in believing that I have not already considered this matter and found the proper solution. Hence for my justification and for your enlightenment hear what I have to say. Our problem is to find out what happens to bodies of different weight moving in a medium devoid of resistance, so that the only difference in speed is that which arises from inequality of weight. Since no medium except one entirely free from air and other bodies, be it ever so tenuous and yielding, can furnish our senses with the evidence we are looking for, and since such a medium is not available, we shall observe what happens in the rarest and least resistant media as compared with what happens in denser and more resistant media. Because if we find as a fact that the variation of speed among bodies of different specific gravities is less and less according as the medium becomes more and more yielding, and if finally in a medium of extreme tenuity, though not a perfect vacuum, we find that, in spite of great diversity of specific gravity, the difference in speed is very small and almost inappreciable, then we are justified in believing it highly probable that in a vacuum all bodies would fall with the same speed. Let us, in view of this, consider what takes place in air, where for the sake of a definite figure and light material imagine an inflated bladder. The air in this bladder when surrounded by air will weigh little or nothing, since it can be only slightly compressed; its weight then is small being merely that of the skin which does not amount to the thousandth part of a mass of lead having the same size as the inflated bladder. Now, Simplicio, if we allow these two bodies to fall from a height of four or six cubits, by what distance do you imagine the lead will anticipate the bladder? You may be sure that the lead will not travel three times, or even twice, as swiftly as the bladder, although you would have made it move a thousand times as rapidly.

SIMPLICIO. It may be as you say during the first four or six cubits of the fall; but after the motion has continued a long while, I believe that the lead will have left the bladder behind not only six out of twelve parts of the distance but even eight or ten.

SALVIATI. I quite agree with you and doubt not that, in very long distances, the lead might cover one hundred miles while the bladder was traversing one; but, my dear Simplicio, this phenomenon which you adduce against my proposition is precisely the one which confirms it. Let me once more explain that the variation of speed observed in bodies of different specific gravities is not caused by the difference of specific gravity but depends upon external circumstances and, in particular, upon the resistance of the medium, so that if this is removed all bodies would fall with the same velocity; and this result I deduce mainly from the fact which you have just admitted and which is very true, namely, that, in the case of bodies which differ widely in weight, their velocities differ more and more as the spaces traversed increase, something which would not occur if the effect depended upon differences of specific gravity. For since these specific gravities remain constant, the ratio between the distances traversed ought to remain constant whereas the fact is that this ratio keeps on increasing as the motion continues. Thus a very heavy body in a fall of one cubit will not anticipate a very light one by so much as the tenth part of this space; but in a fall of twelve cubits the heavy body would outstrip the other by one-third, and in a fall of one hundred cubits by 90/100, etc.

SIMPLICIO. Very well: but, following your own line of argument, if differences of weight in bodies of different specific gravities cannot produce a change in the ratio of their speeds, on the ground that their specific gravities do not change, how is it possible for the medium, which also we suppose to remain constant, to bring about any change in the ratio of these velocities?

SALVIATI. This objection with which you oppose my statement is clever; and I must meet it. I begin by saying that a heavy body has an inherent tendency to move with a constantly and uniformly accelerated motion toward the common center of gravity, that is, toward the center of our earth, so that during equal intervals of time it receives equal increments of momentum and velocity. This, you must understand, holds whenever all external and accidental hindrances have been removed; but of these there is one which we can never remove, namely, the medium which must be penetrated and thrust aside by the falling body. This quiet, yielding, fluid medium opposes motion through it with a resistance which is proportional to the rapidity with which the medium must give way to the passage of the body; which body, as I have said, is by nature continuously accelerated so that it meets with more and more resistance in the medium and hence a diminution in its rate of gain of speed until finally the speed reaches such a point and the resistance of the medium becomes so great that, balancing each other, they prevent any further acceleration and reduce the motion of the body to one which is uniform and which will thereafter maintain a constant value. There is, therefore, an increase in the resistance of the medium, not on account of any change in its essential properties, but on account of the change in rapidity with which it must yield and give way laterally to the passage of the falling body which is being constantly accelerated.

Now seeing how great is the resistance which the air offers to the slight momentum of the bladder and how small that which it offers to the large weight of the lead, I am convinced that, if the medium were entirely removed, the advantage received by the bladder would be so great and that coming to the lead so small that their speeds would be equalized. Assuming this principle, that all falling bodies acquire equal speeds in a medium which, on account of a vacuum or something else, offers no resistance to the speed of the motion, we shall be able accordingly to determine the ratios of the speeds of both similar and dissimilar bodies moving either through one and the same medium or through different space-filling, and therefore resistant, media. This result we may obtain by observing how much the weight of the medium detracts from the weight of the moving body, which weight is the means employed by the falling body to open a path for itself and to push aside the parts of the medium, something which does not happen in a vacuum where, therefore, no difference [of speed] is to be expected from a difference of specific gravity. And since it is known that the effect of the medium is to diminish the weight of the body by the weight of the medium displaced, we may accomplish our purpose by diminishing in just this proportion the speeds of the falling bodies, which in a non-resisting medium we have assumed to be equal.

Thus, for example, imagine lead to be ten thousand times as heavy as air while ebony is only one thousand times as heavy. Here we have two substances whose speeds of fall in a medium devoid of resistance are equal: but, when air is the medium, it will subtract from the speed of the lead one part in ten thousand, and from the speed of the ebony one part in one thousand, i. e. ten parts in ten thousand. While therefore lead and ebony would fall from any given height in the same interval of time, provided the retarding effect of the air were removed, the lead will, in air, lose in speed one part in ten thousand; and the ebony, ten parts in ten thousand. In other words, if the elevation from which the bodies start be divided into ten thousand parts, the lead will reach the ground leaving the ebony behind by as much as ten, or at least nine, of these parts. Is it not clear then that a leaden ball allowed to fall from a tower two hundred cubits high will outstrip an ebony ball by less than four inches? Now ebony weighs a thousand times as much as air but this inflated bladder only four times as much; therefore air diminishes the inherent and natural speed of ebony by one part in a thousand; while that of the bladder which, if free from hindrance, would be the same, experiences a diminution in air amounting to one part in four. So that when the ebony ball, falling from the tower, has reached the earth, the bladder will have traversed only three-quarters of this distance. Lead is twelve times as heavy as water; but ivory is only twice as heavy. The speeds of these two substances which, when entirely unhindered, are equal will be diminished in water, that of lead by one part in twelve, that of ivory by half. Accordingly when the lead has fallen through eleven cubits of water the ivory will have fallen through only six. Employing this principle we shall, I believe, find a much closer agreement of experiment with our computation than with that of Aristotle.

In a similar manner we may find the ratio of the speeds of one and the same body in different fluid media, not by comparing the different resistances of the media, but by considering the excess of the specific gravity of the body above those of the media. Thus, for example, tin is one thousand times heavier than air and ten times heavier than water; hence, if we divide its unhindered speed into 1000 parts, air will rob it of one of these parts so that it will fall with a speed of 999, while in water its speed will be 900, seeing that water diminishes its weight by one part in ten while air by only one part in a thousand.

Again take a solid a little heavier than water, such as oak, a ball of which will weigh let us say 1000 drachms; suppose an equal volume of water to weigh 950, and an equal volume of air, 2; then it is clear that if the unhindered speed of the ball is 1000, its speed in air will be 998, but in water only 50, seeing that the water removes 950 of the 1000 parts which the body weighs, leaving only 50.

Such a solid would therefore move almost twenty times as fast in air as in water, since its specific gravity exceeds that of water by one part in twenty. And here we must consider the fact that only those substances which have a specific gravity greater than water can fall through it—substances which must, therefore, be hundreds of times heavier than air; hence when we try to obtain the ratio of the speed in air to that in water, we may, without appreciable error, assume that air does not, to any considerable extent, diminish the free weight and consequently the unhindered speed of such substances. Having thus easily found the excess of the weight of these substances over that of water, we can say that their speed in air is to their speed in water as their free weight is to the excess of this weight over that of water. For example, a ball of ivory weighs 20 ounces; an equal volume of water weighs 17 ounces; hence the speed of ivory in air bears to its speed in water the approximate ratio of 20:3.

SAGREDO. I have made a great step forward in this truly interesting subject upon which I have long labored in vain. In order to put these theories into practice we need only discover a method of determining the specific gravity of air with reference to water and hence with reference to other heavy substances.

SIMPLICIO. But if we find that air has levity instead of gravity what then shall we say of the foregoing discussion which, in other respects, is very clever?

SALVIATI. I should say that it was empty, vain, and trifling. But can you doubt that air has weight when you have the clear testimony of Aristotle affirming that all the elements have weight including air, and excepting only fire? As evidence of this he cites the fact that a leather bottle weighs more when inflated than when collapsed.

SIMPLICIO. I am inclined to believe that the increase of weight observed in the inflated leather bottle or bladder arises, not from the gravity of the air, but from the many thick vapors mingled with it in these lower regions. To this I would attribute the increase of weight in the leather bottle.

SALVIATI. I would not have you say this, and much less attribute it to Aristotle; because, if speaking of the elements, he wished to persuade me by experiment that air has weight and were to say to me: "Take a leather bottle, fill it with heavy vapors and observe how its weight increases," I would reply that the bottle would weigh still more if filled with bran; and would then add that this merely proves that bran and thick vapors are heavy, but in regard to air I should still remain in the same doubt as before. However, the experiment of Aristotle is good and the proposition is true. But I cannot say as much of a certain other consideration, taken at face value; this consideration was offered by a philosopher whose name slips me; but I know I have read his argument which is that air exhibits greater gravity than levity, because it carries heavy bodies downward more easily than it does light ones upward.

SAGREDO. Fine indeed! So according to this theory air is much heavier than water, since all heavy bodies are carried downward more easily through air than through water, and all light bodies buoyed up more easily through water than through air; further there is an infinite number of heavy bodies which fall through air but ascend in water and there is an infinite number of substances which rise in water and fall in air. But, Simplicio, the question as to whether the weight of the leather bottle is owing to thick vapors or to pure air does not affect our problem which is to discover how bodies move through this vapor-laden atmosphere of ours. Returning now to the question which interests me more, I should like, for the sake of more complete and thorough knowledge of this matter, not only to be strengthened in my belief that air has weight but also to learn, if possible, how great its specific gravity is. Therefore, Salviati, if you can satisfy my curiosity on this point pray do so.

SALVIATI. The experiment with the inflated leather bottle of Aristotle proves conclusively that air possesses positive gravity and not, as some have believed, levity, a property possessed possibly by no substance whatever; for if air did possess this quality of absolute and positive levity, it should on compression exhibit greater levity and, hence, a greater tendency to rise; but experiment shows precisely the opposite.

As to the other question, namely, how to determine the specific gravity of air, I have employed the following method. I took a rather large glass bottle with a narrow neck and attached to it a leather cover, binding it tightly about the neck of the bottle: in the top of this cover I inserted and firmly fastened the valve of a leather bottle, through which

I forced into the glass bottle, by means of a syringe, a large quantity of air. And since air is easily condensed one can pump into the bottle two or three times its own volume of air. After this I took an accurate balance and weighed this bottle of compressed air with the utmost precision, adjusting the weight with fine sand. I next opened the valve and allowed the compressed air to escape; then replaced the flask upon the balance and found it perceptibly lighter: from the sand which had been used as a counterweight I now removed and laid aside as much as was necessary to again secure balance. Under these conditions there can be no doubt but that the weight of the sand thus laid aside represents the weight of the air which had been forced into the flask and had afterwards escaped. But after all this experiment tells me merely that the weight of the compressed air is the same as that of the sand removed from the balance; when however it comes to knowing certainly and definitely the weight of air as compared with that of water or any other heavy substance this I cannot hope to do without first measuring the volume of compressed air; for this measurement I have devised the two following methods.

According to the first method one takes a bottle with a narrow neck similar to the previous one; over the mouth of this bottle is slipped a leather tube which is bound tightly about the neck of the flask; the other end of this tube embraces the valve attached to the first flask and is tightly bound about it. This second flask is provided with a hole in the bottom through which an iron rod can be placed so as to open, at will, the valve above mentioned and thus permit the surplus air of the first to escape after it has once been weighed: but this second bottle must be filled with water. Having prepared everything in the manner above described, open the valve with the rod; the air will rush into the flask containing the water and will drive it through the hole at the bottom, it being clear that the volume of water thus displaced is equal to the volume of air escaped from the other vessel. Having set aside this displaced water, weigh the vessel from which the air has escaped (which is supposed to have been weighed previously while containing the compressed air), and remove the surplus of sand as described above; it is then manifest that the weight of this sand is precisely the weight of a volume of air equal to the volume of water displaced and set aside; this water we can weigh and find how many times its weight contains the weight of the removed sand, thus determining definitely how many times heavier water is than air; and we shall find, contrary to the opinion of Aristotle, that this is not 10 times, but, as our experiment shows, more nearly 400 times.

The second method is more expeditious and can be carried out with a single vessel fitted up as the first was. Here no air is added to that which the vessel naturally contains but water is forced into it without allowing any air to escape; the water thus introduced necessarily compresses the air. Having forced into the vessel as much water as possible, filling it, say, three-fourths full, which does not require any extraordinary effort, place it upon the balance and weigh it accurately; next hold the vessel mouth up, open the valve, and allow the air to escape; the volume of the air thus escaping is precisely equal to the volume of water contained in the flask. Again weigh the vessel which will have diminished in weight on account of the escaped air; this loss in weight represents the weight of a volume of air equal to the volume of water contained in the vessel.

SIMPLICIO. No one can deny the cleverness and ingenuity of your devices; but while they appear to give complete intellectual satisfaction they confuse me in another direction. For since it is undoubtedly true that the elements when in their proper places have neither weight nor levity, I cannot understand how it is possible for that portion of air, which appeared to weigh, say, 4 drachms of sand, should really have such a weight in air as the sand which counterbalances it. It seems to me, therefore, that the experiment should be carried out, not in air, but in a medium in which the air could exhibit its property of weight if such it really has.

SALVIATI. The objection of Simplicio is certainly to the point and must therefore either be unanswerable or demand an equally clear solution. It is perfectly evident that that air which, under compression, weighed as much as the sand, loses this weight when once allowed to escape into its own element, while, indeed, the sand retains its weight. Hence for this experiment it becomes necessary to select a place where air as well as sand can gravitate; because, as has been often remarked, the medium diminishes the weight of any substance immersed in it by an amount equal to the weight of the displaced medium; so that air in air loses all its weight. If therefore this experiment is to be made with accuracy it should be performed in a vacuum where every heavy body exhibits its momentum without the slightest diminution. If then, Simplicio, we were to weigh a portion of air in a vacuum would you then be satisfied and assured of the fact?

SIMPLICIO. Yes truly: but this is to wish or ask the impossible.

SALVIATI. Your obligation will then be very great if, for your sake, I accomplish the impossible. But I do not want to sell you something which I have already given you; for in the previous experiment we weighed the air in vacuum and not in air or other medium. The fact that any fluid medium diminishes the weight of the mass immersed in it is due, Simplicio, to the resistance which this medium offers to its being opened up, driven aside, and finally lifted up. The evidence for this is seen in the readiness with which the fluid rushes to fill up any space formerly occupied by the mass; if the medium were not affected by such an immersion then it would not react against the immersed body. Tell me now, when you have a flask, in air, filled with its natural amount of air and then proceed to pump into the vessel more air, does this extra charge in any way separate or divide or change the circumambient air? Does the vessel perhaps expand so that the surrounding medium is displaced in order to give more room? Certainly not. Therefore one is able to say that this extra charge of air is not immersed in the surrounding medium for it occupies no space in it, but is, as it were, in a vacuum.

Indeed, it is really in a vacuum; for it diffuses into the vacuities which are not completely filled by the original and uncondensed air. In fact I do not see any difference between the enclosed and the surrounding media: for the surrounding medium does not press upon the enclosed medium and, *vice versa,* the enclosed medium exerts no pressure against the surrounding one; this same relationship exists in the case of any matter in a vacuum, as well as in the case of the extra charge of air compressed into the flask. The weight of this condensed air is therefore the same as that which it would have set free in a vacuum. It is true of course that the weight of the sand used as a counterpoise would be a little greater *in vacuo* than in free air. We must, then, say that the air is slightly lighter than the sand required to counterbalance it, that is to say, by an amount equal to the weight *in vacuo* of a volume of air equal to the volume of the sand.

SIMPLICIO. The previous experiments, in my opinion, left something to be desired: but now I am fully satisfied.

SALVIATI. The facts set forth by me up to this point and, in particular, the one which shows that difference of weight, even when very great, is without effect in changing the speed of falling bodies, so that as far as weight is concerned they all fall with equal speed: this idea is, I say, so new, and at first glance so remote from fact, that if we do not have the means of making it just as clear as sunlight, it had better not be mentioned; but having once allowed it to pass my lips I must neglect no experiment or argument to establish it.

SAGREDO. Not only this but also many other of your views are so far removed from the commonly accepted opinions and doctrines that if you were to publish them you would stir up a large number of antagonists; for human nature is such that men do not look with favor upon discoveries—either of truth or fallacy—in their own field, when made by others than themselves. They call him an innovator of doctrine, an unpleasant title, by which they hope to cut those knots which they cannot untie, and by subterranean mines they seek to destroy structures which patient artisans have built with customary tools. But as for ourselves who have no such thoughts, the experiments and arguments which you have thus far adduced are fully satisfactory; however if you have any experiments which are more direct or any arguments which are more convincing we will hear them with pleasure.

SALVIATI. The experiment made to ascertain whether two bodies, differing greatly in weight, will fall from a given height with the same speed offers some difficulty; because, if the height is considerable, the retarding effect of the medium, which must be penetrated and thrust aside by the falling body, will be greater in the case of the small momentum of the very light body than in the case of the great force of the heavy body; so that, in a long distance, the light body will be left behind; if the height be small, one may well doubt whether there is any difference; and if there be a difference it will be inappreciable.

It occurred to me therefore to repeat many times the fall through a small height in such a way that I might accumulate all those small intervals of time that elapse between the arrival of the heavy and light bodies respectively at their common terminus, so that this sum makes an interval of time which is not only observable, but easily observable. In order to employ the slowest speeds possible and thus reduce the change which the resisting medium produces upon the simple effect of gravity it occurred to me to allow the bodies to fall along a plane slightly inclined to the horizontal. For in such a plane, just as well as in a vertical plane, one may discover how bodies of different weight behave: and besides this, I also wished to rid myself of the resistance which might arise from contact of the moving body with the aforesaid inclined plane. Accordingly I took two balls, one of lead and one of cork, the former more than a hundred times heavier than the latter, and suspended them by means of two equal fine threads, each four or five cubits long. Pulling each ball aside from the perpendicular, I let them go at the same instant, and they, falling along the circumferences of circles having these equal strings for semi-diameters, passed beyond the perpendicular and returned along the same path. This free vibration repeated a hundred times showed clearly that the heavy body maintains so nearly the period of the light body that neither in a hundred swings nor even in a thousand will the former anticipate the latter by as much as a single moment, so perfectly do they keep step. We can also observe the effect of the medium which, by the resistance which it offers to motion, diminishes the vibration of the cork more than that of the lead, but without altering the frequency of either; even when the arc traversed by the cork did not exceed five or six degrees while that of the lead was fifty or sixty, the swings were performed in equal times.

SIMPLICIO. If this be so, why is not the speed of the lead greater than that of the cork, seeing that the former traverses sixty degrees in the same interval in which the latter covers scarcely six?

SALVIATI. But what would you say, Simplicio, if both covered their paths in the same time when the cork, drawn aside through thirty degrees, traverses an arc of sixty, while the lead pulled aside only two degrees traverses an arc of four? Would not then the cork be proportionately swifter? And yet such is the experimental fact. But observe this: having pulled aside the pendulum of lead, say through an arc of fifty degrees, and set it free, it swings beyond the perpendicular almost fifty degrees, thus describing an arc of nearly one hundred degrees; on the return swing it describes a little smaller arc; and after a large number of such vibrations it finally comes to rest. Each vibration, whether of ninety, fifty, twenty, ten, or four degrees, occupies the same time: accordingly the speed of the moving body keeps on diminishing since in equal intervals of time it traverses arcs which grow smaller and smaller.

Precisely the same things happen with the pendulum of cork, suspended by a string of equal length, except that a smaller number of vibrations is required to bring it to rest, since on account of its lightness it is less able to overcome the resistance of the air; nevertheless the vibrations, whether large or small, are all performed in time-intervals which are not only equal among themselves, but also equal to the period of the lead pendulum. Hence it is true that, if while the lead is traversing an arc of fifty degrees the cork covers one of only ten, the cork moves more slowly than the lead; but on the other hand it is also true that the cork may cover an arc of fifty while the lead passes over one of only ten or six; thus, at different times, we have now the cork, now the lead, moving more rapidly. But if these same bodies traverse equal arcs in equal times we may rest assured that their speeds are equal.

SIMPLICIO. I hesitate to admit the conclusiveness of this argument because of the confusion which arises from your making both bodies move now rapidly, now slowly and now very slowly, which leaves me in doubt as to whether their velocities are always equal.

SAGREDO. Allow me, if you please, Salviati, to say just a few words. Now tell me, Simplicio, whether you admit that one can say with certainty that the speeds of the cork and the lead are equal whenever both, starting from rest at the same moment and descending the same slopes, always traverse equal spaces in equal times?

SIMPLICIO. This can neither be doubted nor gainsaid.

SAGREDO. Now it happens, in the case of the pendulums, that each of them traverses now an arc of sixty degrees, now one of fifty, or thirty or ten or eight or four or two, etc.; and when they both swing through an arc of sixty degrees they do so in equal intervals of time; the same thing happens when the arc is fifty degrees or thirty or ten or any other number; and therefore we conclude that the speed of the lead in an arc of sixty degrees is equal to the speed of the cork when the latter also swings through an arc of sixty degrees; in the case of a fifty-degree arc these speeds are also equal to each other; so also in the case of other arcs. But this is not saying that the speed which occurs in an arc of sixty is the same as that which occurs in an arc of fifty; nor is the speed in an arc of fifty equal to that in one of thirty, etc.; but the smaller the arcs, the smaller the speeds; the fact observed is that one and the same moving body requires the same time for traversing a large arc of sixty degrees as for a small arc of fifty or even a very small arc of ten; all these arcs, indeed, are covered in the same interval of time. It is true therefore that the lead and the cork each diminish their speed in proportion as their arcs diminish; but this does not contradict the fact that they maintain equal speeds in equal arcs.

My reason for saying these things has been rather because I wanted to learn whether I had correctly understood Salviati, than because I thought Simplicio had any need of a clearer explanation than that given by Salviati which like everything else of his is extremely lucid, so lucid, indeed, that when he solves questions which are difficult not merely in appearance, but in reality and in fact, he does so with reasons, observations and experiments which are common and familiar to everyone.

In this manner he has, as I have learned from various sources, given occasion to a highly esteemed professor for undervaluing his discoveries on the ground that they are commonplace, and established upon a mean and vulgar basis; as if it were not a most admirable and praiseworthy feature of demonstrative science that it springs from and grows out of principles well-known, understood and conceded by all.

But let us continue with this light diet; and if Simplicio is satisfied to understand and admit that the gravity inherent in various falling bodies has nothing to do with the difference of speed observed among them, and that all bodies, in so far as their speeds depend upon it, would move with the same velocity, pray tell us, Salviati, how you explain the appreciable and evident inequality of motion; please reply also to the objection urged by Simplicio—an objection in which I concur—namely, that a cannon ball falls more rapidly than a bird shot. From my point of view, one might expect the difference of speed to be small in the case of bodies of the same substance moving through any single medium, whereas the larger ones will descend, during a single pulse beat, a distance which the smaller ones will not traverse in an hour, or in four, or even in twenty hours; as for instance in the case of stones and fine sand and especially that very fine sand which produces muddy water and which in many hours will not fall through as much as two cubits, a distance which stones not much larger will traverse in a single pulse beat.

SALVIATI. The action of the medium in producing a greater retardation upon those bodies which have a less specific gravity has already been explained by showing that they experience a diminution of weight. But to explain how one and the same medium produces such different retardations in bodies which are made of the same material and have the same shape, but differ only in size, requires a discussion more clever than that by which one explains how a more expanded shape or an opposing motion of the medium retards the speed of the moving body. The solution of the present problem lies, I think, in the roughness and porosity which are generally and almost necessarily found in the surfaces of solid bodies. When the body is in motion these rough places strike the air or other ambient medium. The evidence for this is found in the humming which accompanies the rapid motion of a body through air, even when that body is as round as possible. One hears not only humming, but also hissing and whistling, whenever there is any appreciable cavity or elevation upon the body. We observe also that a round solid body rotating in a lathe produces a current of air. But what more do we need? When a top spins on the ground at its greatest speed do we not hear a distinct buzzing of high pitch? This sibilant note diminishes in pitch as the speed of rotation slackens, which is evidence that these small rugosities on the surface meet resistance in the air. There can be no doubt, therefore, that in the motion of falling bodies these rugosities strike the surrounding fluid and retard the speed; and this they do so much the more in proportion as the surface is larger, which is the case of small bodies as compared with greater.

SIMPLICIO. Stop a moment please, I am getting confused. For although I understand and admit that friction of the medium upon the surface of the body retards its motion and that, if other things are the same, the larger surface suffers greater retardation, I do not see on what ground you say that the surface of the smaller body is larger. Besides if, as you say, the larger surface suffers greater retardation the larger solid should move more slowly, which is not the fact. But this objection can be easily met by saying that, although the larger body has a larger surface, it has also a greater weight, in comparison with which the resistance of the larger surface is no more than the resistance of the small surface in comparison with its smaller weight; so that the speed of the larger solid does not become less. I therefore see no reason for expecting any difference of speed so long as the driving weight diminishes in the same proportion as the retarding power of the surface.

SALVIATI. I shall answer all your objections at once. You will admit, of course, Simplicio, that if one takes two equal bodies, of the same material and same figure, bodies which would therefore fall with equal speeds, and if he diminishes the weight of one of them in the same proportion as its surface (maintaining the similarity of shape) he would not thereby diminish the speed of this body.

SIMPLICIO. This inference seems to be in harmony with your theory which states that the weight of a body has no effect in either accelerating or retarding its motion.

SALVIATI. I quite agree with you in this opinion from which it appears to follow that, if the weight of a body is diminished in greater proportion than its surface, the motion is retarded to a certain extent; and this retardation is greater and greater in proportion as the diminution of weight exceeds that of the surface.

SIMPLICIO. This I admit without hesitation.

SALVIATI. Now you must know, Simplicio, that it is not possible to diminish the surface of a solid body in the same ratio as the weight, and at the same time maintain similarity of figure. For since it is clear that in the case of a diminishing solid the weight grows less in proportion to the volume, and since the volume always diminishes more rapidly than the surface, when the same shape is maintained, the weight must therefore diminish more rapidly than the surface. But geometry teaches us that, in the case of similar solids, the ratio of two volumes is greater than the ratio of their surfaces; which, for the sake of better understanding, I shall illustrate by a particular case.

Take, for example, a cube two inches on a side so that each face has an area of four square inches and the total area, i. e., the sum of the six faces, amounts to twenty-four square inches; now imagine this cube to be sawed through three times so as to divide it into eight smaller cubes, each one inch on the side, each face one inch square, and the total surface of each cube six square inches instead of twenty-four as in the case of the larger cube. It is evident therefore that the surface of the little cube is only one-fourth that of the larger, namely, the ratio of six to twenty-four; but the volume of the solid cube itself is only one-eighth; the volume, and hence also the weight, diminishes therefore much more rapidly than the surface. If we again divide the little cube into eight others we shall have, for the total surface of one of these, one and one-half square inches, which is one-sixteenth of the surface of the original cube; but its volume is only one-sixty-fourth part. Thus, by two divisions, you see that the volume is diminished four times as much as the surface. And, if the subdivision be continued until the original solid be reduced to a fine powder, we shall find that the weight of one of these smallest particles has diminished hundreds and hundreds of times as much as its surface. And this which I have illustrated in the case of cubes holds also in the case of all similar solids. Observe then how much greater the resistance, arising from contact of the surface of the moving body with the medium, in the case of small bodies than in the case of large; and when one considers that the rugosities on the very small surfaces of fine dust particles are perhaps no smaller than those on the surfaces of larger solids which have been carefully polished, he will see how important it is that the medium should be very fluid and offer no resistance to being thrust aside, easily yielding to a small force. You see, therefore, Simplicio, that I was not mistaken when, not long ago, I said that the surface of a small solid is comparatively greater than that of a large one.

SIMPLICIO. I am quite convinced; and, believe me, if I were again beginning my studies, I should follow the advice of Plato and start with mathematics, a science which proceeds very cautiously and admits nothing as established until it has been rigidly demonstrated.

SAGREDO. This discussion has afforded me great pleasure. And now although there are still some details, in connection with the subject under discussion, concerning which I might ask questions yet, if we keep making one digression after another, it will be long before we reach the main topic which has to do with the variety of properties found in the resistance which solid bodies offer to fracture; and, therefore, if you please, let us return to the subject which we originally proposed to discuss.

SALVIATI. Very well; but the questions which we have already considered are so numerous and so varied, and have taken up so much time, that there is not much of this day left to spend upon our main topic which abounds in geometrical demonstrations calling for careful consideration. May I, therefore, suggest that we postpone the meeting until tomorrow, not only for the reason just mentioned but also in order that I may bring with me some papers in which I have set down in an orderly way the theorems and propositions dealing with the various phases of this subject, matters which, from memory alone, I could not present in the proper order.

SAGREDO. I fully concur in your opinion and all the more willingly because this will leave time today to take up some of my difficulties with the subject which we have just been discussing. One question is whether we are to consider the resistance of the medium as sufficient to destroy the acceleration of a body of very heavy material, very large volume, and spherical figure. I say *spherical* in order to select a volume which is contained within a minimum surface and therefore less subject to retardation.

Another question deals with the vibrations of pendulums which may be regarded from several viewpoints; the first is whether all vibrations, large, medium, and small, are performed in exactly and precisely equal times: another is to find the ratio of the times of vibration of pendulums supported by threads of unequal length.

SALVIATI. These are interesting questions: but I fear that here, as in the case of all other facts, if we take up for discussion any one of them, it will carry in its wake so many other facts and curious consequences that time will not remain today for the discussion of all.

SAGREDO. If these are as full of interest as the foregoing, I would gladly spend as many days as there remain hours between now and nightfall; and I dare say that Simplicio would not be wearied by these discussions.

SIMPLICIO. Certainly not; especially when the questions pertain to natural science and have not been treated by other philosophers.

SALVIATI. Now taking up the first question, I can assert without hesitation that there is no sphere so large, or composed of material so dense, but that the resistance of the medium, although very slight, would check its acceleration and would, in time, reduce its motion to uniformity; a statement which is strongly supported by experiment. For if a falling body, as time goes on, were to acquire a speed as great as you please, no such speed, impressed by external forces, can be so great but that the body will first acquire it and then, owing to the resisting medium, lose it. Thus, for instance, if a cannon ball, having fallen a distance of four cubits through the air and having acquired a speed of, say, ten units were to strike the surface of the water, and if the resistance of the water were not able to check the momentum of the shot, it would either increase in speed or maintain a uniform motion until the bottom were reached: but such is not the observed fact; on the contrary, the water when only a few cubits deep hinders and diminishes the motion in such a way that the shot delivers to the bed of the river or lake a very slight impulse. Clearly then if a short fall through the water is sufficient to deprive a cannon ball of its speed, this speed cannot be regained by a fall of even a thousand cubits. How could a body acquire, in a fall of a thousand cubits, that which it loses in a fall of four? But what more is needed? Do we not observe that the enormous momentum, delivered to a shot by a cannon, is so deadened by passing through a few cubits of water that the ball, so far from injuring the ship, barely strikes it? Even the air, although a very yielding medium, can also diminish the speed of a falling body, as may be easily understood from similar experiments. For if a gun be fired downwards from the top of a very high tower the shot will make a smaller impression upon the ground than if the gun had been fired from an elevation of only four or six cubits; this is clear evidence that the momentum of the ball, fired from the top of the tower, diminishes continually from the instant it leaves the barrel until it reaches the ground.

Therefore a fall from ever so great an altitude will not suffice to give to a body that momentum which it has once lost through the resistance of the air, no matter how it was originally acquired. In like manner, the destructive effect produced upon a wall by a shot fired from a gun at a distance of twenty cubits cannot be duplicated by the fall of the same shot from any altitude however great. My opinion is, therefore, that under the circumstances which occur in nature, the acceleration of any body falling from rest reaches an end and that the resistance of the medium finally reduces its speed to a constant value which is thereafter maintained.

SAGREDO. These experiments are in my opinion much to the purpose; the only question is whether an opponent might not make bold to deny the fact in the case of bodies which are very large and heavy or to assert that a cannon ball, falling from the distance of the moon or from the upper regions of the atmosphere, would deliver a heavier blow than if just leaving the muzzle of the gun.

SALVIATI. No doubt many objections may be raised not all of which can be refuted by experiment: however in this particular case the following consideration must be taken into account, namely, that it is very likely that a heavy body falling from a height will, on reaching the ground, have acquired just as much momentum as was necessary to carry it to that height; as may be clearly seen in the case of a rather heavy pendulum which, when pulled aside fifty or sixty degrees from the vertical, will acquire precisely that speed and force which are sufficient to carry it to an equal elevation save only that small portion which it loses through friction on the air. In order to place a cannon ball at such a height as might suffice to give it just that momentum which the powder imparted to it on leaving the gun we need only fire it vertically upwards from the same gun; and we can then observe whether on falling back it delivers a blow equal to that of the gun fired at close range; in my opinion it would be much weaker. The resistance of the air would, therefore, I think, prevent the muzzle velocity from being equalled by a natural fall from rest at any height whatsoever.

We come now to the other questions, relating to pendulums, a subject which may appear to many exceedingly arid, especially to those philosophers who are continually occupied with the more profound questions of nature. Nevertheless, the problem is one which I do not scorn. I am encouraged by the example of Aristotle whom I admire especially because he did not fail to discuss every subject which he thought in any degree worthy of consideration.

Impelled by your queries I may give you some of my ideas concerning certain problems in music, a splendid subject, upon which so many eminent men have written: among these is Aristotle himself who has discussed numerous interesting acoustical questions. Accordingly, if on the basis of some easy and tangible experiments, I shall explain some striking phenomena in the domain of sound, I trust my explanations will meet your approval.

SAGREDO. I shall receive them not only gratefully but eagerly. For, although I take pleasure in every kind of musical instrument and have paid considerable attention to harmony, I have never been able to fully understand why some combinations of tones are more pleasing than others, or why certain combinations not only fail to please but are even highly offensive. Then there is the old problem of two stretched strings in unison; when one of them is sounded, the other begins to vibrate and to emit its note; nor do I understand the different ratios of harmony and some other details.

SALVIATI. Let us see whether we cannot derive from the pendulum a satisfactory solution of all these difficulties. And first, as to the question whether one and the same pendulum really performs its vibrations, large, medium, and small, all in exactly the same time, I shall rely upon what I have already heard from our Academician. He has clearly shown that the time of descent is the same along all chords, whatever the arcs which subtend them, as well along an arc of 180° (i. e., the whole diameter) as along one of 100°, 60°, 10°, 2°, ½°, or 4'. It is understood, of course, that these arcs all terminate at the lowest point of the circle, where it touches the horizontal plane.

If now we consider descent along arcs instead of their chords then, provided these do not exceed 90°, experiment shows that they are all traversed in equal times; but these times are greater for the chord than for the arc, an effect which is all the more remarkable because at first glance one would think just the opposite to be true. For since the terminal points of the two motions are the same and since the straight line included between these two points is the shortest distance between them, it would seem reasonable that motion along this line should be executed in the shortest time; but this is not the case, for the shortest time—and therefore the most rapid motion—is that employed along the arc of which this straight line is the chord.

As to the times of vibration of bodies suspended by threads of different lengths, they bear to each other the same proportion as the square roots of the lengths of the thread; or one might say the lengths are to each other as the squares of the times; so that if one wishes to make the vibration time of one pendulum twice that of another, he must make its suspension four times as long. In like manner, if one pendulum has a suspension nine times as long as another, this second pendulum will execute three vibrations during each one of the first; from which it follows that the lengths of the suspending cords bear to each other the [inverse] ratio of the squares of the number of vibrations performed in the same time.

SAGREDO. Then, if I understand you correctly, I can easily measure the length of a string whose upper end is attached at any height whatever even if this end were invisible and I could see only the lower extremity. For if I attach to the lower end of this string a rather heavy weight and give it a to-and-fro motion, and if I ask a friend to count a number of its vibrations, while I, during the same time-interval, count the number of vibrations of a pendulum which is exactly one cubit in length, then knowing the number of vibrations which each pendulum makes in the given interval of time one can determine the length of the string. Suppose, for example, that my friend counts 20 vibrations of the long cord during the same time in which I count 240 of my string which is one cubit in length; taking the squares of the two numbers, 20 and 240, namely 400 and 57600, then, I say, the long string contains 57600 units of such length that my pendulum will contain 400 of them; and since the length of my string is one cubit, I shall divide 57600 by 400 and thus obtain 144. Accordingly I shall call the length of the string 144 cubits.

SALVIATI. Nor will you miss it by as much as a handsbreadth, especially if you observe a large number of vibrations.

SAGREDO. You give me frequent occasion to admire the wealth and profusion of nature when, from such common and even trivial phenomena, you derive facts which are not only striking and new but which are often far removed from what we would have imagined. Thousands of times I have observed vibrations especially in churches where lamps, suspended by long cords, had been inadvertently set into motion; but the most which I could infer from these observations was that the view of those who think that such vibrations are maintained by the medium is highly improbable: for, in that case, the air must needs have considerable judgment and little else to do but kill time by pushing to and fro a pendent weight with perfect regularity. But I never dreamed of learning that one and the same body, when suspended from a string a hundred cubits long and pulled aside through an arc of 90° or even 1° or ½°, would employ the same time in passing through the least as through the largest of these arcs; and, indeed, it still strikes me as somewhat unlikely. Now I am waiting to hear how these same simple phenomena can furnish solutions for those acoustical problems—solutions which will be at least partly satisfactory.

SALVIATI. First of all one must observe that each pendulum has its own time of vibration so definite and determinate that it is not possible to make it move with any other period than that which nature has given it. For let any one take in his hand the cord to which the weight is attached and try, as much as he pleases, to increase or diminish the frequency of its vibrations; it will be time wasted. On the other hand, one can confer motion upon even a heavy pendulum which is at rest by simply blowing against it; by repeating these blasts with a frequency which is the same as that of the pendulum one can impart considerable motion. Suppose that by the first puff we have displaced the pendulum from the vertical by, say, half an inch; then if, after the pendulum has returned and is about to begin the second vibration, we add a second puff, we shall impart additional motion; and so on with other blasts provided they are applied at the right instant, and not when the pendulum is coming toward us since in this case the blast would impede rather than aid the motion. Continuing thus with many impulses we impart to the pendulum such momentum that a greater impulse than that of a single blast will be needed to stop it.

SAGREDO. Even as a boy, I observed that one man alone by giving these impulses at the right instant was able to ring a bell so large that when four, or even six, men seized the rope and tried to stop it they were lifted from the ground, all of them together being unable to counterbalance the momentum which a single man, by properly timed pulls, had given it.

SALVIATI. Your illustration makes my meaning clear and is quite as well fitted, as what I have just said, to explain the wonderful phenomenon of the strings of the cittern or of the spinet, namely, the fact that a vibrating string will set another string in motion and cause it to sound not only when the latter is in unison but even when it differs from the former by an octave or a fifth. A string which has been struck begins to vibrate and continues the motion as long as one hears the sound; these vibrations cause the immediately surrounding air to vibrate and quiver; then these ripples in the air expand far into space and strike not only all the strings of the same instrument but even those of neighboring instruments. Since that string which is tuned to unison with the one plucked is capable of vibrating with the same frequency, it acquires, at the first impulse, a slight oscillation; after receiving two, three, twenty, or more impulses, delivered at proper intervals, it finally accumulates a vibratory motion equal to that of the plucked string, as is clearly shown by equality of amplitude in their vibrations. This undulation expands through the air and sets into vibration not only strings, but also any other body which happens to have the same period as that of the plucked string. Accordingly if we attach to the side of an instrument small pieces of bristle or other flexible bodies, we shall observe that, when a spinet is sounded, only those pieces respond that have the same period as the string which has been struck; the remaining pieces do not vibrate in response to this string, nor do the former pieces respond to any other tone.

If one bows the bass string on a viola rather smartly and brings near it a goblet of fine, thin glass having the same tone as that of the string, this goblet will vibrate and audibly resound. That the undulations of the medium are widely dispersed about the sounding body is evinced by the fact that a glass of water may be made to emit a tone merely by the friction of the finger tip upon the rim of the glass; for in this water is produced a series of regular waves. The same phenomenon is observed to better advantage by fixing the base of the goblet upon the bottom of a rather large vessel of water filled nearly to the edge of the goblet; for if, as before, we sound the glass by friction of the finger, we shall see ripples spreading with the utmost regularity and with high speed to large distances about the glass. I have often remarked, in thus sounding a rather large glass nearly full of water, that at first the waves are spaced with great uniformity, and when, as sometimes happens, the tone of the glass jumps an octave higher I have noted that at this moment each of the aforesaid waves divides into two; a phenomenon which shows clearly that the ratio involved in the octave is two.

SAGREDO. More than once have I observed this same thing, much to my delight and also to my profit. For a long time I have been perplexed about these different harmonies since the explanations hitherto given by those learned in music impress me as not sufficiently conclusive. They tell us that the diapason, i. e., the octave, involves the ratio of two, that the diapente which we call the fifth involves a ratio of 3:2, etc.; because if the open string of a monochord be sounded and afterwards a bridge be placed in the middle and the half length be sounded one hears the octave; and if the bridge be placed at 1/3 the length of the string, then on plucking first the open string and afterwards 2/3 of its length the fifth is given; for this reason they say that the octave depends upon the ratio of two to one and the fifth upon the ratio of three to two. This explanation does not impress me as sufficient to establish 2 and 3/2 as the natural ratios of the octave and the fifth; and my reason for thinking so is as follows. There are three different ways in which the tone of a string may be sharpened, namely, by shortening it, by stretching it, and by making it thinner. If the tension and size of the string remain constant one obtains the octave by shortening it to one-half, i. e., by sounding first the open string and then one-half of it; but if length and size remain constant and one attempts to produce the octave by stretching he will find that it does not suffice to double the stretching weight; it must be quadrupled; so that, if the fundamental note is produced by a weight of one pound, four will be required to bring out the octave.

And finally if the length and tension remain constant, while one changes the size of the string he will find that in order to produce the octave the size must be reduced to ¼ that which gave the fundamental. And what I have said concerning the octave, namely, that its ratio as derived from the tension and size of the string is the square of that derived from the length, applies equally well to all other musical intervals.

Thus if one wishes to produce a fifth by changing the length he finds that the ratio of the lengths must be sesquialteral, in other words he sounds first the open string, then two-thirds of it; but if he wishes to produce this same result by stretching or thinning the string then it becomes necessary to square the ratio 3/2 that is by taking 9/4; accordingly, if the fundamental requires a weight of 4 pounds, the higher note will be produced not by 6, but by 9 pounds; the same is true in regard to size, the string which gives the fundamental is larger than that which yields the fifth in the ratio of 9 to 4.

In view of these facts, I see no reason why those wise philosophers should adopt 2 rather than 4 as the ratio of the octave, or why in the case of the fifth they should employ the sesquialteral ratio, 3/2, rather than that of 9/4. Since it is impossible to count the vibrations of a sounding string on account of its high frequency, I should still have been in doubt as to whether a string, emitting the upper octave, made twice as many vibrations in the same time as one giving the fundamental, had it not been for the following fact, namely, that at the instant when the tone jumps to the octave, the waves which constantly accompany the vibrating glass divide up into smaller ones which are precisely half as long as the former.

SALVIATI. This is a beautiful experiment enabling us to distinguish individually the waves which are produced by the vibrations of a sonorous body, which spread through the air, bringing to the tympanum of the ear a stimulus which the mind translates into sound. But since these waves in the water last only so long as the friction of the finger continues and are, even then, not constant but are always forming and disappearing, would it not be a fine thing if one had the ability to produce waves which would persist for a long while, even months and years, so as to easily measure and count them?

SAGREDO. Such an invention would, I assure you, command my admiration.

SALVIATI. The device is one which I hit upon by accident; my part consists merely in the observation of it and in the appreciation of its value as a confirmation of something to which I had given profound consideration; and yet the device is, in itself, rather common. As I was scraping a brass plate with a sharp iron chisel in order to remove some spots from it and was running the chisel rather rapidly over it, I once or twice, during many strokes, heard the plate emit a rather strong and clear whistling sound; on looking at the plate more carefully, I noticed a long row of fine streaks parallel and equidistant from one another. Scraping with the chisel over and over again, I noticed that it was only when the plate emitted this hissing noise that any marks were left upon it; when the scraping was not accompanied by this sibilant note there was not the least trace of such marks. Repeating the trick several times and making the stroke, now with greater now with less speed, the whistling followed with a pitch which was correspondingly higher and lower. I noted also that the marks made when the tones were higher were closer together; but when the tones were deeper, they were farther apart. I also observed that when, during a single stroke, the speed increased toward the end the sound became sharper and the streaks grew closer together, but always in such a way as to remain sharply defined and equidistant. Besides whenever the stroke was accompanied by hissing I felt the chisel tremble in my grasp and a sort of shiver run through my hand. In short we see and hear in the case of the chisel precisely that which is seen and heard in the case of a whisper followed by a loud voice; for, when the breath is emitted without the production of a tone, one does not feel either in the throat or mouth any motion to speak of in comparison with that which is felt in the larynx and upper part of the throat when the voice is used, especially when the tones employed are low and strong.

At times I have also observed among the strings of the spinet two which were in unison with two of the tones produced by the aforesaid scraping; and among those which differed most in pitch I found two which were separated by an interval of a perfect fifth. Upon measuring the distance between the markings produced by the two scrapings it was found that the space which contained 45 of one contained 30 of the other, which is precisely the ratio assigned to the fifth.

But now before proceeding any farther I want to call your attention to the fact that, of the three methods for sharpening a tone, the one which you refer to as the fineness of the string should be attributed to its weight.

So long as the material of the string is unchanged, the size and weight vary in the same ratio. Thus in the case of gut strings, we obtain the octave by making one string 4 times as large as the other; so also in the case of brass one wire must have 4 times the size of the other; but if now we wish to obtain the octave of a gut string, by use of brass wire, we must make it, not four times as large, but four times as heavy as the gut string: as regards size therefore the metal string is not four times as big but four times as heavy. The wire may therefore be even thinner than the gut notwithstanding the fact that the latter gives the higher note. Hence if two spinets are strung, one with gold wire the other with brass, and if the corresponding strings each have the same length, diameter, and tension it follows that the instrument strung with gold will have a pitch about one-fifth lower than the other because gold has a density almost twice that of brass. And here it is to be noted that it is the weight rather than the size of a moving body which offers resistance to change of motion contrary to what one might at first glance think. For it seems reasonable to believe that a body which is large and light should suffer greater retardation of motion in thrusting aside the medium than would one which is thin and heavy; yet here exactly the opposite is true.

Returning now to the original subject of discussion, I assert that the ratio of a musical interval is not immediately determined either by the length, size, or tension of the strings but rather by the ratio of their frequencies, that is, by the number of pulses of air waves which strike the tympanum of the ear, causing it also to vibrate with the same frequency. This fact established, we may possibly explain why certain pairs of notes, differing in pitch, produce a pleasing sensation, others a less pleasant effect, and still others a disagreeable sensation. Such an explanation would be tantamount to an explanation of the more or less perfect consonances and of dissonances. The unpleasant sensation produced by the latter arises, I think, from the discordant vibrations of two different tones which strike the ear out of time. Especially harsh is the dissonance between notes whose frequencies are incommensurable; such a case occurs when one has two strings in unison and sounds one of them open, together with a part of the other which bears the same ratio to its whole length as the side of a square bears to the diagonal; this yields a dissonance similar to the augmented fourth or diminished fifth.

Agreeable consonances are pairs of tones which strike the ear with a certain regularity; this regularity consists in the fact that the pulses delivered by the two tones, in the same interval of time, shall be commensurable in number, so as not to keep the eardrum in perpetual torment, bending in two different directions in order to yield to the ever-discordant impulses.

The first and most pleasing consonance is, therefore, the octave since, for every pulse given to the tympanum by the lower string, the sharp string delivers two; accordingly at every other vibration of the upper string both pulses are delivered simultaneously so that one-half the entire number of pulses are delivered in unison. But when two strings are in unison their vibrations always coincide and the effect is that of a single string; hence we do not refer to it as consonance. The fifth is also a pleasing interval since for every two vibrations of the lower string the upper one gives three, so that considering the entire number of pulses from the upper string one-third of them will strike in unison, i. e., between each pair of concordant vibrations there intervene two single vibrations; and when the interval is a fourth, three single vibrations intervene. In case the interval is a second where the ratio is 9/8 it is only every ninth vibration of the upper string which reaches the ear simultaneously with one of the lower; all the others are discordant and produce a harsh effect upon the recipient ear which interprets them as dissonances.

SIMPLICIO. Won't you be good enough to explain this argument a little more clearly?

SALVIATI. Let AB denote the length of a wave emitted by the lower string and CD that of a higher string which is emitting the octave of AB; divide AB in the middle at E. If the two strings begin their motions at A

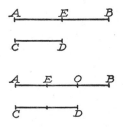

and C, it is clear that when the sharp vibration has reached the end D, the other vibration will have travelled only as far as E, which, not being a terminal point, will emit no pulse; but there is a blow delivered at D. Accordingly when the one wave comes back from D to C, the other passes on from E to B; hence the two pulses from B and C strike the drum of the ear simultaneously. Seeing that these vibrations are repeated again and again in the same manner, we conclude that each alternate pulse from CD falls in unison with one from AB. But each of the pulsations at the terminal points, A and B, is constantly accompanied by one which leaves always from C or always from D. This is clear because if we suppose the waves to reach A and C at the same instant, then, while one wave travels from A to B, the other will proceed from C to D and back to C, so that waves strike at C and B simultaneously; during the passage of the wave from B back to A the disturbance at C goes to D and again returns to C, so that once more the pulses at A and C are simultaneous.

Next let the vibrations AB and CD be separated by an interval of a fifth, that is, by a ratio of 3/2; choose the points E and O such that they will divide the wave length of the lower string into three equal parts and imagine the vibrations to start at the same instant from each of the terminals A and C. It is evident that when the pulse has been delivered at the terminal D, the wave in AB has travelled only as far as O; the drum of the ear receives, therefore, only the pulse from D. Then during the return of the one vibration from D to C, the other will pass from O to B and then back to O, producing an isolated pulse at B—a pulse which is out of time but one which must be taken into consideration.

Now since we have assumed that the first pulsations started from the terminals A and C at the same instant, it follows that the second pulsation, isolated at D, occurred after an interval of time equal to that required for passage from C to D or, what is the same thing, from A to O; but the next pulsation, the one at B, is separated from the preceding by only half this interval, namely, the time required for passage from O to B. Next while the one vibration travels from O to A, the other travels from C to D, the result of which is that two pulsations occur simultaneously at A and D. Cycles of this kind follow one after another, i. e., one solitary pulse of the lower string interposed between two solitary pulses of the upper string. Let us now imagine time to be divided into very small equal intervals; then if we assume that, during the first two of these intervals, the disturbances which occurred simultaneously at A and C have travelled as far as O and D and have produced a pulse at D; and if we assume that during the third and fourth intervals one disturbance returns from D to C, producing a pulse at C, while the other, passing on from O to B and back to O, produces a pulse at B; and if finally, during the fifth and sixth intervals, the disturbances travel from O and C to A and D, producing a pulse at each of the latter two, then the sequence in which the pulses strike the ear will be such that, if we begin to count time from any instant where two pulses are simultaneous, the eardrum will, after the lapse of two of the said intervals, receive a solitary pulse; at the end of the third interval, another solitary pulse; so also at the end of the fourth interval; and two intervals later, i. e., at the end of the sixth interval, will be heard two pulses in unison. Here ends the cycle—the anomaly, so to speak—which repeats itself over and over again.

SAGREDO. I can no longer remain silent; for I must express to you the great pleasure I have in hearing such a complete explanation of phenomena with regard to which I have so long been in darkness. Now I understand why unison does not differ from a single tone; I understand why the octave is the principal harmony, but so like unison as often to be mistaken for it and also why it occurs with the other harmonies. It resembles unison because the pulsations of strings in unison always occur simultaneously, and those of the lower string of the octave are always accompanied by those of the upper string; and among the latter is interposed a solitary pulse at equal intervals and in such a manner as to produce no disturbance; the result is that such a harmony is rather too much softened and lacks fire. But the fifth is characterized by its displaced beats and by the interposition of two solitary beats of the upper string and one solitary beat of the lower string between each pair of simultaneous pulses; these three solitary pulses are separated by intervals of time equal to half the interval which separates each pair of simultaneous beats from the solitary beats of the upper string. Thus the effect of the fifth is to produce a tickling of the eardrum such that its softness is modified with sprightliness, giving at the same moment the impression of a gentle kiss and of a bite.

Salviati. Seeing that you have derived so much pleasure from these novelties, I must show you a method by which the eye may enjoy the same game as the ear. Suspend three balls of lead, or other heavy material, by means of strings of different length such that while the longest makes two vibrations the shortest will make four and the medium three; this will take place when the longest string measures 16, either in handbreadths or in any other unit, the medium 9 and the shortest 4, all measured in the same unit.

Now pull all these pendulums aside from the perpendicular and release them at the same instant; you will see a curious interplay of the threads passing each other in various manners but such that at the completion of every fourth vibration of the longest pendulum, all three will arrive simultaneously at the same terminus, whence they start over again to repeat the same cycle. This combination of vibrations, when produced on strings, is precisely that which yields the interval of the octave and the intermediate fifth. If we employ the same disposition of apparatus but change the lengths of the threads, always however in such a way that their vibrations correspond to those of agreeable musical intervals, we shall see a different crossing of these threads but always such that, after a definite interval of time and after a definite number of vibrations, all the threads, whether three or four, will reach the same terminus at the same instant, and then begin a repetition of the cycle.

If however the vibrations of two or more strings are incommensurable so that they never complete a definite number of vibrations at the same instant, or if commensurable they return only after a long interval of time and after a large number of vibrations, then the eye is confused by the disorderly succession of crossed threads. In like manner the ear is pained by an irregular sequence of air waves which strike the tympanum without any fixed order.

But, gentlemen, whither have we drifted during these many hours lured on by various problems and unexpected digressions? The day is already ended and we have scarcely touched the subject proposed for discussion. Indeed we have deviated so far that I remember only with difficulty our early introduction and the little progress made in the way of hypotheses and principles for use in later demonstrations.

Sagredo. Let us then adjourn for today in order that our minds may find refreshment in sleep and that we may return tomorrow, if so please you, and resume the discussion of the main question.

Salviati. I shall not fail to be here tomorrow at the same hour, hoping not only to render you service but also to enjoy your company.

END OF FIRST DAY

SECOND DAY

SAGREDO. While Simplicio and I were awaiting your arrival we were trying to recall that last consideration which you advanced as a principle and basis for the results you intended to obtain; this consideration dealt with the resistance which all solids offer to fracture and depended upon a certain cement which held the parts glued together so that they would yield and separate only under considerable pull. Later we tried to find the explanation of this coherence, seeking it mainly in the vacuum; this was the occasion of our many digressions which occupied the entire day and led us far afield from the original question which, as I have already stated, was the consideration of the resistance that solids offer to fracture.

SALVIATI. I remember it all very well. Resuming the thread of our discourse, whatever the nature of this resistance which solids offer to large tractive forces there can at least be no doubt of its existence; and though this resistance is very great in the case of a direct pull, it is found, as a rule, to be less in the case of bending forces. Thus, for example, a rod of steel or of glass will sustain a longitudinal pull of a thousand pounds while a weight of fifty pounds would be quite sufficient to break it if the rod were fastened at right angles into a vertical wall. It is this second type of resistance which we must consider, seeking to discover in what proportion it is found in prisms and cylinders of the same material, whether alike or unlike in shape, length, and thickness. In this discussion I shall take for granted the well-known mechanical principle which has been shown to govern the behavior of a bar, which we call a lever, namely, that the force bears to the resistance the inverse ratio of the distances which separate the fulcrum from the force and resistance respectively.

SIMPLICIO. This was demonstrated first of all by Aristotle, in his *Mechanics*.

SALVIATI. Yes, I am willing to concede him priority in point of time; but as regards rigor of demonstration the first place must be given to Archimedes. This principle established, I desire, before passing to any other subject, to call your attention to the fact that these forces, resistances, moments, figures, etc., may be considered either in the abstract, dissociated from matter, or in the concrete, associated with matter. Hence the properties which belong to figures that are merely geometrical and non-material must be modified when we fill these figures with matter and therefore give them weight. Take, for example, the lever BA which, resting upon the support E, is used to lift a heavy stone D. The principle just demonstrated makes it clear that a force applied at the extremity B will just suffice to equilibrate the resistance offered by the heavy body D provided this force bears to the force at D the same ratio as the distance AC bears to the distance CB; and this is true so long as we consider only the moments of the single force at B and of the resistance at D, treating the lever as an immaterial body devoid of weight. But if we take into account the weight of the lever itself—an instrument which may be made either of wood or of iron—it is manifest that, when this weight has been added to the force at B, the ratio will be changed and must therefore be expressed in different terms. Hence before going further let us agree to distinguish between these two points of view; when we consider an instrument in the abstract, i. e., apart from the weight of its own material, we shall speak of

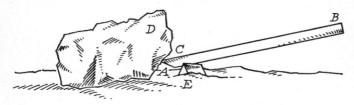

"taking it in an absolute sense"; but if we fill one of these simple and absolute figures with matter and thus give it weight, we shall refer to such a material figure as a "moment" or "compound force."

Let us now return to our original subject; then, if what has hitherto been said is clear, it will be easily understood that,

Proposition I

A prism or solid cylinder of glass, steel, wood or other breakable material which is capable of sustaining a very heavy weight when applied longitudinally is, as previously remarked, easily broken by the transverse application of a weight which may be much smaller in proportion as the length of the cylinder exceeds its thickness.

Let us imagine a solid prism ABCD fastened into a wall at the end AB, and supporting a weight E at the other end; understand also that the wall is vertical and that the prism or cylinder is fastened at right angles to the wall. It is clear that, if the cylinder breaks, fracture will occur at the point B where the edge of the mortise acts as a fulcrum for the lever BC, to which the force is applied; the thickness of the solid BA is the other arm of the lever along which is located the resistance. This resistance opposes the separation of the part BD, lying outside the wall, from that portion lying inside. From the preceding, it follows that the magnitude of the force applied at C bears to the magnitude of the resistance, found in the thickness of the prism, i. e., in the attachment of the base BA to its contiguous parts, the same ratio which the length CB bears to half the length BA; if now we define absolute resistance to fracture as that offered to a longitudinal pull (in which case the stretching force acts in the same direction as that through which the body is moved), then it follows that the absolute resistance of the prism BD is to the breaking load placed at the end of the lever BC in the same ratio as the length BC is to the half of AB in the case of a prism, or the semi-diameter in the case of a cylinder. This is our first proposition. Observe that in what has here been said the weight of the solid BD itself has been left out of consideration, or rather, the prism has been assumed to be devoid of weight. But if the weight of the prism is to be taken account of in conjunction with the weight E, we must add to the weight E one half that of the prism BD: so that if, for example, the latter weighs two pounds and the weight E is ten pounds we must treat the weight E as if it were eleven pounds.

SIMPLICIO. Why not twelve?

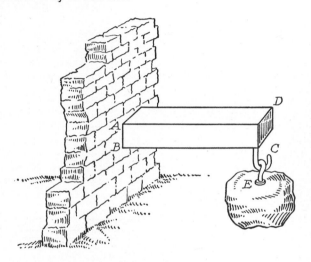

SALVIATI. The weight E, my dear Simplicio, hanging at the extreme end C, acts upon the lever BC with its full moment of ten pounds: so also would the solid BD if suspended at the same point exert its full moment of two pounds; but, as you know, this solid is uniformly distributed throughout its entire length, BC, so that the parts which lie near the end B are less effective than those more remote.

Accordingly if we strike a balance between the two, the weight of the entire prism may be considered as concentrated at its center of gravity which lies midway of the lever BC. But a weight hung at the extremity C exerts a moment twice as great as it would if suspended from the middle: therefore if we consider the moments of both as located at the end C we must add to the weight E one-half that of the prism.

SIMPLICIO. I understand perfectly; and moreover, if I mistake not, the force of the two weights BD and E, thus disposed, would exert the same moment as would the entire weight BD together with twice the weight E suspended at the middle of the lever BC.

SALVIATI. Precisely so, and a fact worth remembering. Now we can readily understand

Proposition II

How and in what proportion a rod, or rather a prism, whose width is greater than its thickness offers more resistance to fracture when the force is applied in the direction of its breadth than in the direction of its thickness.

For the sake of clearness, take a ruler *ad* whose width is *ac* and whose thickness, *cb,* is much less than its width. The question now is why will the ruler, if stood on edge, as in the first figure, withstand a great weight T, while, when laid flat, as in the second figure, it will not support the weight X which is less than T. The answer is evident when we remember that in the one case the fulcrum is at the line *bc,* and in the other case at *ca,* while the distance at which the force is applied is the same in both cases, namely, the length *bd:* but in the first case the distance of the resistance from the fulcrum—half the line *ca*—is greater than in the other case where it is only half of *bc.* Therefore the weight T is greater than X in the same ratio as half the width *ca* is greater than half the thickness *bc,* since the former acts as a lever arm for *ca,* and the latter for *cb,* against

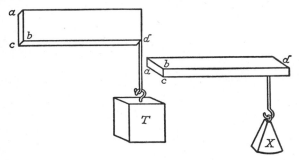

the same resistance, namely, the strength of all the fibres in the cross-section *ab.* We conclude, therefore, that any given ruler, or prism, whose width exceeds its thickness, will offer greater resistance to fracture when standing on edge than when lying flat, and this in the ratio of the width to the thickness.

Proposition III

Considering now the case of a prism or cylinder growing longer in a horizontal direction, we must find out in what ratio the moment of its own weight increases in comparison with its resistance to fracture. This moment I find increases in proportion to the square of the length. In order to prove this let AD be a prism or cylinder lying horizontal with its end A firmly fixed in a wall. Let the length of the prism be increased by the addition of the portion BE. It is clear that merely changing the length of the lever from AB to AC will, if we disregard its weight, increase the moment of the force [at the end] tending to produce fracture at A in the ratio of CA to BA. But, besides this, the weight of the solid portion BE, added to the weight of the solid AB, increases the moment of the total weight in the ratio of the weight of the prism AE to that of the prism AB, which is the same as the ratio of the length AC to AB.

It follows, therefore, that, when the length and weight are simultaneously increased in any given proportion, the moment, which is the product of these two, is increased in a ratio which is the square of the preceding proportion. The conclusion is then that the bending moments due to the weight of prisms and cylinder⌐ which have the same thickness but

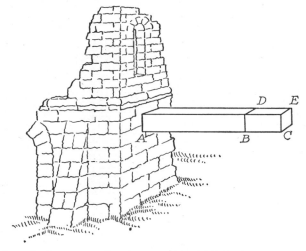

different lengths bear to each other a ratio which is the square of the ratio of their lengths, or, what is the same thing, the ratio of the squares of their lengths.

SIMPLICIO. Before proceeding further I should like to have one of my difficulties removed. Up to this point you have not taken into consideration a certain other kind of resistance which, it appears to me, diminishes as the solid grows longer, and this is quite as true in the case of bending as in pulling; it is precisely thus that in the case of a rope we observe that a very long one is less able to support a large weight than a short one. Whence, I believe, a short rod of wood or iron will support a greater weight than if it were long, provided the force be always applied longitudinally and not transversely, and provided also that we take into account the weight of the rope itself which increases with its length.

SALVIATI. I fear, Simplicio, if I correctly catch your meaning, that in this particular you are making the same mistake as many others; that is if you mean to say that a long rope, one of perhaps 40 cubits, cannot hold up so great a weight as a shorter length, say one or two cubits, of the same rope.

SIMPLICIO. That is what I meant, and as far as I see the proposition is highly probable.

SALVIATI. On the contrary, I consider it not merely improbable but false; and I think I can easily convince you of your error. Let AB represent the rope, fastened at the upper end A: at the lower end attach a weight C whose force is just sufficient to break the rope. Now, Simplicio, point out the exact place where you think the break ought to occur.

SIMPLICIO. Let us say D.

SALVIATI. And why at D?

SIMPLICIO. Because at this point the rope is not strong enough to support, say, 100 pounds, made up of the portion of the rope DB and the stone C.

SALVIATI. Accordingly whenever the rope is stretched with the weight of 100 pounds at D it will break there.

SIMPLICIO. I think so.

SALVIATI. But tell me, if instead of attaching the weight at the end of the rope, B, one fastens it at a point nearer D, say, at E: or if, instead of fixing the upper end of the rope at A, one fastens it at some point F, just above D, will not the rope, at the point D, be subject to the same pull of 100 pounds?

SIMPLICIO. It would, provided you include with the stone C the portion of rope EB.

SALVIATI. Let us therefore suppose that the rope is stretched at the point D with a weight of 100 pounds, then according to your own admission it will break; but FE is only a small portion of AB; how can you therefore maintain that the long rope is weaker than the short one? Give up then this erroneous view which you share with many very intelligent people, and let us proceed.

Proposition IV

Among heavy prisms and cylinders of similar figure, there is one and only one which under the stress of its own weight lies just on the limit between breaking and not breaking: so that every larger one is unable to carry the load of its own weight and breaks; while every smaller one is able to withstand some additional force tending to break it.

Let AB be a heavy prism, the longest possible that will just sustain its own weight, so that if it be lengthened the least bit it will break. Then, I say, this prism is unique among all similar prisms—infinite in number—in occupying that boundary line between breaking and not breaking; so that every larger one will break under its own weight, and every smaller one will not break, but will be able to withstand some force in addition to its own weight.

Let the prism CE be similar to, but larger than, AB: then, I say, it will not remain intact but will break under its own weight. Lay off the portion CD, equal in length to AB. And since the resistance [bending strength] of CD is to that of AB as the cube of the thickness of CD is to the cube of the thickness of AB, that is, as the prism CE is to the similar prism AB, it follows that the weight of CE is the utmost load which a prism of the length CD can sustain; but the length of CE is greater; therefore the prism CE will break. Now take another prism FG which is smaller than AB. Let FH equal AB, then it can be shown in a similar manner that the resistance [bending strength] of FG is to that of AB as the prism FG is to the prism AB provided the distance AB that is FH is equal to the distance FG; but AB is greater than FG, and therefore the

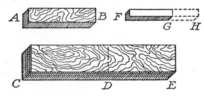

moment of the prism FG applied at G is not sufficient to break the prism FG.

SAGREDO. The demonstration is short and clear; while the proposition which, at first glance, appeared improbable is now seen to be both true and inevitable. In order therefore to bring this prism into that limiting condition which separates breaking from not breaking, it would be necessary to change the ratio between thickness and length either by increasing the thickness or by diminishing the length.

From what has already been demonstrated, you can plainly see the impossibility of increasing the size of structures to vast dimensions either in art or in nature; likewise the impossibility of building ships, palaces, or temples of enormous size in such a way that their oars, yards, beams, iron bolts, and, in short, all their other parts will hold together; nor can nature produce trees of extraordinary size because the branches would break down under their own weight; so also it would be impossible to build up the bony structures of men, horses, or other animals so as to hold together and perform their normal functions if these animals were to be increased enormously in height; for this increase in height can be accomplished only by employing a material which is harder and stronger than usual, or by enlarging the size of the bones, thus changing their shape until the form and appearance of the animals suggest a monstrosity. This is perhaps what our wise Poet [Ariosto] had in mind, when he says, in describing a huge giant:

> Impossible it is to reckon his height
> So beyond measure is his size.

To illustrate briefly, I have sketched a bone whose natural length has been increased three times and whose thickness has been multiplied until, for a correspondingly large animal, it would perform the same function which the small bone performs for its small animal. From the figures here shown you can see how out of proportion the enlarged bone appears. Clearly then if one wishes to maintain in a great giant the same proportion of limb as that found in an ordinary man he must either find a harder and stronger material for making the bones, or he must admit a diminution of strength in comparison with men of medium stature; for if his height be increased inordinately he will fall and be crushed under his own weight. Whereas, if the size of a body be diminished, the strength of that body is not diminished in the same proportion; indeed the smaller the body the greater its relative strength. Thus a small dog could prob-

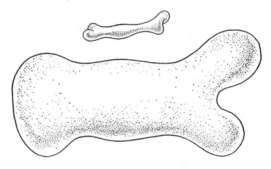

ably carry on his back two or three dogs of his own size; but I believe that a horse could not carry even one of his own size.

SIMPLICIO. This may be so; but I am led to doubt it on account of the enormous size reached by certain fish, such as the whale which, I understand, is ten times as large as an elephant; yet they all support themselves.

SALVIATI. Your question, Simplicio, suggests another principle, one which had hitherto escaped my attention and which enables giants and other animals of vast size to support themselves and to move about as well as smaller animals do. This result may be secured either by increasing the strength of the bones and other parts intended to carry not only their weight but also the superincumbent load; or, keeping the proportions of the bony structure constant, the skeleton will hold together in the same manner or even more easily, provided one diminishes, in the proper proportion, the weight of the bony material, of the flesh, and of anything else which the skeleton has to carry. It is this second principle which is employed by nature in the structure of fish, making their bones and muscles not merely light but entirely devoid of weight.

SIMPLICIO. The trend of your argument, Salviati, is evident. Since fish live in water which on account of its density or, as others would say, heaviness diminishes the weight of bodies immersed in it, you mean to say that, for this reason, the bodies of fish will be devoid of weight and will be supported without injury to their bones. But this is not all; for although the remainder of the body of the fish may be without weight, there can be no question but that their bones have weight. Take the case of a whale's rib, having the dimensions of a beam; who can deny its great weight or its tendency to go to the bottom when placed in water? One would, therefore, hardly expect these great masses to sustain themselves.

SALVIATI. A very shrewd objection! And now, in reply, tell me whether you have ever seen fish stand motionless at will under water, neither descending to the bottom nor rising to the top, without the exertion of force by swimming?

SIMPLICIO. This is a well-known phenomenon.

SALVIATI. The fact then that fish are able to remain motionless under water is a conclusive reason for thinking that the material of their bodies has the same specific gravity as that of water; accordingly, if in their make-up there are certain parts which are heavier than water there must be others which are lighter, for otherwise they would not produce equilibrium.

Hence, if the bones are heavier, it is necessary that the muscles or other constituents of the body should be lighter in order that their buoyancy may counterbalance the weight of the bones. In aquatic animals therefore circumstances are just reversed from what they are with land animals inasmuch as, in the latter, the bones sustain not only their own weight but also that of the flesh, while in the former it is the flesh which supports not only its own weight but also that of the bones. We must therefore cease to wonder why these enormously large animals inhabit the water rather than the land, that is to say, the air.

SIMPLICIO. I am convinced and I only wish to add that what we call land animals ought really to be called air animals, seeing that they live in the air, are surrounded by air, and breathe air.

SAGREDO. I have enjoyed Simplicio's discussion including both the question raised and its answer. Moreover I can easily understand that one of these giant fish, if pulled ashore, would not perhaps sustain itself for any great length of time, but would be crushed under its own mass as soon as the connections between the bones gave way.

SALVIATI. I am inclined to your opinion; and, indeed, I almost think that the same thing would happen in the case of a very big ship which floats on the sea without going to pieces under its load of merchandise and armament, but which on dry land and in air would probably fall apart. But let us proceed.

Hitherto we have considered the moments and resistances of prisms and solid cylinders fixed at one end with a weight applied at the other end; three cases were discussed, namely, that in which the applied force was the only one acting, that in which the weight of the prism itself is also taken into consideration, and that in which the weight of the prism alone is taken into consideration. Let us now consider these same prisms and cylinders when supported at both ends or at a single point placed somewhere between the ends. In the first place, I remark that a cylinder carrying only its own weight and having the maximum length, beyond which it will break, will, when supported either in the middle or at both ends, have twice the length of one which is mortised into a wall and supported only at one end. This is very evident because, if we denote the cylinder by ABC and if we assume that one-half of it, AB, is the greatest possible length capable of supporting its own weight with one end fixed at B, then, for the same reason, if the cylinder is carried on the point C, the first half will be counterbalanced by the other half BC. So also in the case of the cylinder DEF, if its length be such that it will support only one-half this length when the end D is held fixed, or the other half when the end F is fixed, then it is evident that when supports, such as H and I, are placed under the ends D and F respectively the moment of any additional force or weight placed at E will produce fracture at this point.

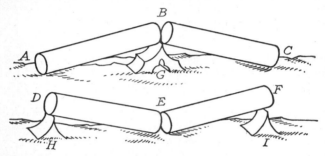

SAGREDO. What shall we say, Simplicio? Must we not confess that geometry is the most powerful of all instruments for sharpening the wit and training the mind to think correctly? Was not Plato perfectly right when he wished that his pupils should be first of all well grounded in mathematics? As for myself, I quite understood the property of the lever and how, by increasing or diminishing its length, one can increase or diminish the moment of force and of resistance; and yet, in the solution of the present problem I was not slightly, but greatly, deceived.

SIMPLICIO. Indeed I begin to understand that while logic is an excellent guide in discourse, it does not, as regards stimulation to discovery, compare with the power of sharp distinction which belongs to geometry.

SAGREDO. Logic, it appears to me, teaches us how to test the conclusiveness of any argument or demonstration already discovered and completed; but I do not believe that it teaches us to discover correct arguments and demonstrations.

END OF SECOND DAY

THIRD DAY

CHANGE OF POSITION

MY PURPOSE is to set forth a very new science dealing with a very ancient subject. There is, in nature, perhaps nothing older than motion, concerning which the books written by philosophers are neither few nor small; nevertheless I have discovered by experiment some properties of it which are worth knowing and which have not hitherto been either observed or demonstrated. Some superficial observations have been made, as, for instance, that the free motion of a heavy falling body is continuously accelerated; but to just what extent this acceleration occurs has not yet been announced; for so far as I know, no one has yet pointed out that the distances traversed, during equal intervals of time, by a body falling from rest, stand to one another in the same ratio as the odd numbers beginning with unity.

It has been observed that missiles and projectiles describe a curved path of some sort; however no one has pointed out the fact that this path is a parabola. But this and other facts, not few in number or less worth knowing, I have succeeded in proving; and what I consider more important, there have been opened up to this vast and most excellent science, of which my work is merely the beginning, ways and means by which other minds more acute than mine will explore its remote corners.

NATURALLY ACCELERATED MOTION

The properties belonging to uniform motion have been discussed; but accelerated motion remains to be considered.

And first of all it seems desirable to find and explain a definition best fitting natural phenomena. For anyone may invent an arbitrary type of motion and discuss its properties; thus, for instance, some have imagined helices and conchoids as described by certain motions which are not met with in nature, and have very commendably established the properties which these curves possess in virtue of their definitions; but we have decided to consider the phenomena of bodies falling with an acceleration such as actually occurs in nature and to make this definition of accelerated motion exhibit the essential features of observed accelerated motions. And this, at last, after repeated efforts we trust we have succeeded in doing. In this belief we are confirmed mainly by the consideration that experimental results are seen to agree with and exactly correspond with those properties which have been, one after another, demonstrated by us. Finally, in the investigation of naturally accelerated motion we were led, by hand as it were, in following the habit and custom of nature herself, in all her various other processes, to employ only those means which are most common, simple and easy.

For I think no one believes that swimming or flying can be accomplished in a manner simpler or easier than that instinctively employed by fishes and birds.

When, therefore, I observe a stone initially at rest falling from an elevated position and continually acquiring new increments of speed, why should I not believe that such increases take place in a manner which is exceedingly simple and rather obvious to everybody? If now we examine the matter carefully we find no addition or increment more simple than that which repeats itself always in the same manner. This we readily understand when we consider the intimate relationship between time and motion; for just as uniformity of motion is defined by and conceived through equal times and equal spaces (thus we call a motion uniform when equal distances are traversed during equal time-intervals), so also we may, in a similar manner, through equal time-intervals, conceive additions of speed as taking place without complication; thus we may picture to our mind a motion as uniformly and continuously accelerated when, during any equal intervals of time whatever, equal increments of speed are given to it. Thus if any equal intervals of time whatever have elapsed, counting from the time at which the moving body left its position of rest and began to descend, the amount of speed acquired during the first two time-intervals will be double that acquired during the first time-interval alone; so the amount added during three of these time-intervals will be treble; and that in four, quadruple that of the first time-interval. To put the matter more clearly, if a body were to continue its motion with the same speed which it had acquired during the first time-interval and were to retain this same uniform speed, then its motion would be twice as slow as that which it would have if its velocity had been acquired during *two* time-intervals.

And thus, it seems, we shall not be far wrong if we put the increment of speed as proportional to the increment of time; hence the definition of motion which we are about to discuss may be stated as follows: A motion is said to be uniformly accelerated when, starting from rest, it acquires, during equal time-intervals, equal increments of speed.

SAGREDO. Although I can offer no rational objection to this or indeed to any other definition, devised by any author whomsoever, since all definitions are arbitrary, I may nevertheless without offense be allowed to doubt whether such a definition as the above, established in an abstract manner, corresponds to and describes that kind of accelerated motion which we meet in nature in the case of freely falling bodies. And since the Author apparently maintains that the motion described in his definition is that of freely falling bodies, I would like to clear my mind of certain difficulties in order that I may later apply myself more earnestly to the propositions and their demonstrations.

SALVIATI. It is well that you and Simplicio raise these difficulties. They are, I imagine, the same which occurred to me when I first saw this treatise, and which were removed either by discussion with the Author himself, or by turning the matter over in my own mind.

SAGREDO. When I think of a heavy body falling from rest, that is, starting with zero speed and gaining speed in proportion to the time from the beginning of the motion; such a motion as would, for instance, in eight beats of the pulse acquire eight degrees of speed; having at the end of the fourth beat acquired four degrees; at the end of the second, two; at the end of the first, one: and since time is divisible without limit, it follows from all these considerations that if the earlier speed of a body is less than its present speed in a constant ratio, then there is no degree of speed however small (or, one may say, no degree of slowness however great) with which we may not find this body travelling after starting from infinite slowness, i. e., from rest. So that if that speed which it had at the end of the fourth beat was such that, if kept uniform, the body would traverse two miles in an hour, and if keeping the speed which it had at the end of the second beat, it would traverse one mile an hour, we must infer that, as the instant of starting is more and more nearly approached, the body moves so slowly that, if it kept on moving at this rate, it would not traverse a mile in an hour, or in a day, or in a year or in a thousand years; indeed, it would not traverse a span in an even greater time; a phenomenon which baffles the imagination, while our senses show us that a heavy falling body suddenly acquires great speed.

SALVIATI. This is one of the difficulties which I also at the beginning experienced, but which I shortly afterwards removed; and the removal was effected by the very experiment which creates the difficulty for you. You say the experiment appears to show that immediately after a heavy body starts from rest it acquires a very considerable speed: and I say that the same experiment makes clear the fact that the initial motions of a falling body, no matter how heavy, are very slow and gentle. Place a heavy body upon a yielding material, and leave it there without any pressure except that owing to its own weight; it is clear that if one lifts this body a cubit or two and allows it to fall upon the same material, it will, with this impulse, exert a new and greater pressure than that caused by its mere weight; and this effect is brought about by the [weight of the] falling body together with the velocity acquired during the fall, an effect which will be greater and greater according to the height of the fall, that is, according as the velocity of the falling body becomes greater. From the quality and intensity of the blow we are thus enabled to accurately estimate the speed of a falling body. But tell me, gentlemen, is it not true that if a block be allowed to fall upon a stake from a height of four cubits and drives it into the earth, say, four fingerbreadths, that coming from a height of two cubits it will drive the stake a much less distance, and from the height of one cubit a still less distance; and finally if the block be lifted only one fingerbreadth how much more will it accomplish than if merely laid on top of the stake without percussion? Certainly very little. If it be lifted only the thickness of a leaf, the effect will be altogether imperceptible. And since the effect of the blow depends upon the velocity of this striking body, can anyone doubt the motion is very slow and the speed more than small whenever the effect [of the blow] is imperceptible?

See now the power of truth; the same experiment which at first glance seemed to show one thing, when more carefully examined, assures us of the contrary.

But without depending upon the above experiment, which is doubtless very conclusive, it seems to me that it ought not to be difficult to establish such a fact by reasoning alone. Imagine a heavy stone held in the air at rest; the support is removed and the stone set free; then since it is heavier than the air it begins to fall, and not with uniform motion but slowly at the beginning and with a continuously accelerated motion. Now since velocity can be increased and diminished without limit, what reason is there to believe that such a moving body starting with infinite slowness, that is, from rest, immediately acquires a speed of ten degrees rather than one of four, or of two, or of one, or of a half, or of a hundredth; or, indeed, of any of the infinite number of small values [of speed]? Pray listen. I hardly think you will refuse to grant that the gain of speed of the stone falling from rest follows the same sequence as the diminution and loss of this same speed when, by some impelling force, the stone is thrown to its former elevation: but even if you do not grant this, I do not see how you can doubt that the ascending stone, diminishing in speed, must before coming to rest pass through every possible degree of slowness.

SIMPLICIO. But if the number of degrees of greater and greater slowness is limitless, they will never be all exhausted, therefore such an ascending heavy body will never reach rest, but will continue to move without limit always at a slower rate; but this is not the observed fact.

SALVIATI. This would happen, Simplicio, if the moving body were to maintain its speed for any length of time at each degree of velocity; but it merely passes each point without delaying more than an instant: and since each time-interval however small may be divided into an infinite number of instants, these will always be sufficient [in number] to correspond to the infinite degrees of diminished velocity.

That such a heavy rising body does not remain for any length of time at any given degree of velocity is evident from the following: because if, some time-interval having been assigned, the body moves with the same speed in the last as in the first instant of that time-interval, it could from this second degree of elevation be in like manner raised through an equal height, just as it was transferred from the first elevation to the second, and by the same reasoning would pass from the second to the third and would finally continue in uniform motion forever.

SALVIATI. The present does not seem to be the proper time to investigate the cause of the acceleration of natural motion concerning which various opinions have been expressed by various philosophers, some explaining it by attraction to the center, others to repulsion between the very small parts of the body, while still others attribute it to a certain stress in the surrounding medium which closes in behind the falling body and drives it from one of its positions to another. Now, all these fantasies, and others too, ought to be examined; but it is not really worth while. At present it is the purpose of our Author merely to investigate and to demonstrate some of the properties of accelerated motion (whatever the cause of this acceleration may be)—meaning thereby a motion, such that the momentum of its velocity goes on increasing after departure from rest, in simple proportionality to the time, which is the same as saying that in equal time-intervals the body receives equal increments of velocity; and if we find the properties [of accelerated motion] which will be demonstrated later are realized in freely falling and accelerated bodies, we may conclude that the assumed definition includes such a motion of falling bodies and that their speed goes on increasing as the time and the duration of the motion.

SAGREDO. So far as I see at present, the definition might have been put a little more clearly perhaps without changing the fundamental idea, namely, uniformly accelerated motion is such that its speed increases in proportion to the space traversed; so that, for example, the speed acquired by a body in falling four cubits would be double that acquired in falling two cubits and this latter speed would be double that acquired in the first cubit. Because there is no doubt but that a heavy body falling from the height of six cubits has, and strikes with, a momentum double that it had at the end of three cubits, triple that which it would have if it had fallen from two, and sextuple that which it would have had at the end of one.

SALVIATI. It is very comforting to me to have had such a companion in error; and moreover let me tell you that your proposition seems so highly probable that our Author himself admitted, when I advanced this opinion to him, that he had for some time shared the same fallacy. But what most surprised me was to see two propositions so inherently probable that they commanded the assent of everyone to whom they were presented, proven in a few simple words to be not only false, but impossible.

SIMPLICIO. I am one of those who accept the proposition, and believe that a falling body acquires force in its descent, its velocity increasing in proportion to the space, and that the momentum of the falling body is doubled when it falls from a doubled height; these propositions, it appears to me, ought to be conceded without hesitation or controversy.

SALVIATI. And yet they are as false and impossible as that motion should be completed instantaneously; and here is a very clear demonstration of it. If the velocities are in proportion to the spaces traversed, or to be traversed, then these spaces are traversed in equal intervals of time; if, therefore, the velocity with which the falling body traverses a space of eight feet were double that with which it covered the first four feet (just as the one distance is double the other) then the time-intervals required for these passages would be equal. But for one and the same body to fall eight feet and four feet in the same time is possible only in the case of instantaneous [discontinuous] motion; but observation shows us that the motion of a falling body occupies time, and less of it in covering a distance of four feet than of eight feet; therefore it is not true that its velocity increases in proportion to the space.

The falsity of the other proposition may be shown with equal clearness. For if we consider a single striking body the difference of momentum in its blows can depend only upon difference of velocity; for if the striking body falling from a double height were to deliver a blow of double momentum, it would be necessary for this body to strike with a doubled velocity; but with this doubled speed it would traverse a doubled space in the same time-interval; observation however shows that the time required for fall from the greater height is longer.

SAGREDO. You present these recondite matters with too much evidence and ease; this great facility makes them less appreciated than they would be had they been presented in a more abstruse manner. For, in my opinion, people esteem more lightly that knowledge which they acquire with so little labor than that acquired through long and obscure discussion.

SALVIATI. If those who demonstrate with brevity and clearness the fallacy of many popular beliefs were treated with contempt instead of gratitude the injury would be quite bearable; but on the other hand it is very unpleasant and annoying to see men, who claim to be peers of anyone in a certain field of study, take for granted certain conclusions which later are quickly and easily shown by another to be false. I do not describe such a feeling as one of envy, which usually degenerates into hatred and anger against those who discover such fallacies; I would call it a strong desire to maintain old errors, rather than accept newly discovered truths. This desire at times induces them to unite against these truths, although at heart believing in them, merely for the purpose of lowering the esteem in which certain others are held by the unthinking crowd. Indeed, I have heard from our Academician many such fallacies held as true but easily refutable; some of these I have in mind.

SAGREDO. You must not withhold them from us, but, at the proper time, tell us about them even though an extra session be necessary. But now, continuing the thread of our talk, it would seem that up to the present we have established the definition of uniformly accelerated motion which is expressed as follows:

A motion is said to be equally or uniformly accelerated when, starting from rest, its momentum receives equal increments in equal times.

SALVIATI. This definition established, the Author makes a single assumption, namely,

The speeds acquired by one and the same body moving down planes of different inclinations are equal when the heights of these planes are equal.

By the height of an inclined plane we mean the perpendicular let fall from the upper end of the plane upon the horizontal line drawn through the lower end of the same plane. Thus, to illustrate, let the line AB be horizontal, and let the planes CA and CD be inclined to it; then the Author calls the perpendicular CB the "height" of the planes CA and CD; he supposes that the speeds acquired by one and the same body, descending along the planes CA and CD to the terminal points A and D, are equal since the heights of these planes are the same, CB; and also it must be understood that this speed is that which would be acquired by the same body falling from C to B.

SAGREDO. Your assumption appears to me so reasonable that it ought to be conceded without question, provided of course there are no chance or outside resistances, and that the planes are hard and smooth, and that the figure of the moving body is perfectly round, so that neither plane nor moving body is rough. All resistance and opposition having been removed, my reason tells me at once that a heavy and perfectly round ball descending along the lines CA, CD, CB would reach the terminal points A, D, B, with equal momenta.

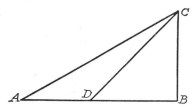

SALVIATI. Your words are very plausible; but I hope by experiment to increase the probability to an extent which shall be little short of a rigid demonstration.

Imagine this page to represent a vertical wall, with a nail driven into it; and from the nail let there be suspended a lead bullet of one or two ounces by means of a fine vertical thread, AB, say from four to six feet long. On this wall draw a horizontal line DC, at right angles to the vertical thread AB, which hangs about two fingerbreadths in front of the wall. Now bring the thread AB with the attached ball into the position AC and set it free; first it will be observed to descend along the arc CBD, to pass the point B, and to travel along the arc BD, till it almost reaches the horizontal CD, a slight shortage being caused by the resistance of the air and the string; from this we may rightly infer that the ball in its descent through the arc CB acquired a momentum on reaching B, which was just sufficient to carry it through a similar arc BD to the same height. Having repeated this experiment many times, let us now drive a nail into the wall close to the perpendicular AB, say at E or F, so that it projects out some five or six fingerbreadths in order that the thread, again carrying the bullet through the arc CB, may strike upon the nail E when the bullet reaches B, and thus compel it to traverse the arc BG, described about E as center. From this we can see what can be done by the same momentum which previously starting at the same point B carried the same body through the arc BD to the horizontal CD. Now, gentlemen, you will observe with pleasure that the ball swings to the point G in the horizontal, and you would see the same thing happen if the obstacle were placed at some lower point, say at F, about which the ball would describe the arc BI, the rise of the ball always terminating exactly on the line CD. But when the nail is placed so low that the remainder of the thread below it will not reach to the height CD (which would happen if the nail were placed nearer B than to the intersection of AB with the horizontal CD) then the thread leaps over the nail and twists itself about it.

This experiment leaves no room for doubt as to the truth of our supposition; for since the two arcs CB and DB are equal and similarly placed, the momentum acquired by the fall through the arc CB is the same as that gained by fall through the arc DB; but the momentum acquired at B, owing to fall through CB, is able to lift the same body through the arc BD; therefore, the momentum acquired in the fall BD is equal to that which lifts the same body through the same arc from B to D; so, in general, every momentum acquired by fall through an arc is equal to that which can lift the same body through the same arc. But all these momenta which cause a rise through the arcs BD, BG, and BI are

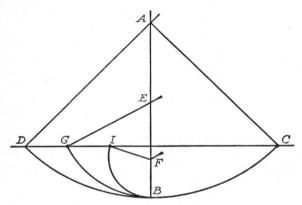

equal, since they are produced by the same momentum, gained by fall through CB, as experiment shows. Therefore all the momenta gained by fall through the arcs DB, GB, IB are equal.

SAGREDO. The argument seems to me so conclusive and the experiment so well adapted to establish the hypothesis that we may, indeed, consider it as demonstrated.

SALVIATI. I do not wish, Sagredo, that we trouble ourselves too much about this matter, since we are going to apply this principle mainly in motions which occur on plane surfaces, and not upon curved, along which acceleration varies in a manner greatly different from that which we have assumed for planes.

So that, although the above experiment shows us that the descent of the moving body through the arc CB confers upon it momentum just sufficient to carry it to the same height through any of the arcs BD, BG, BI, we are not able, by similar means, to show that the event would be identical in the case of a perfectly round ball descending along planes whose inclinations are respectively the same as the chords of these arcs. It seems likely, on the other hand, that, since these planes form angles at the point B, they will present an obstacle to the ball which has descended along the chord CB and starts to rise along the chord BD, BG, BI.

In striking these planes some of its momentum will be lost and it will not be able to rise to the height of the line CD; but this obstacle, which interferes with the experiment, once removed, it is clear that the momentum (which gains in strength with descent) will be able to carry the body to the same height. Let us then, for the present, take this as a postulate, the absolute truth of which will be established when we find that the inferences from it correspond to and agree perfectly with experiment. The Author having assumed this single principle passes next to the propositions which he clearly demonstrates; the first of these is as follows:

Theorem I, Proposition I

The time in which any space is traversed by a body starting from rest and uniformly accelerated is equal to the time in which that same space would be traversed by the same body moving at a uniform speed whose value is the mean of the highest speed and the speed just before acceleration began.

Let us represent by the line AB the time in which the space CD is traversed by a body which starts from rest at C and is uniformly accelerated; let the final and highest value of the speed gained during the interval AB be represented by the line EB drawn at right angles to AB; draw the line AE, then all lines drawn from equidistant points on AB and parallel to BE will represent the increasing values of the speed, beginning with the instant A. Let the point F bisect the line EB; draw FG parallel to BA, and GA parallel to FB, thus forming a parallelogram AGFB which will be equal in area to the triangle AEB, since the side GF bisects the side AE at the point I; for if the parallel lines in the triangle AEB are extended to GI, then the sum of all the parallels contained in the quadrilateral is equal to the sum of those contained in the triangle AEB; for those in the triangle IEF are equal to those contained in the triangle GIA, while those included in the trapezium AIFB are common. Since each and every instant of time in the time-interval AB has its corresponding point on the line AB, from which points parallels drawn in and limited by the triangle AEB represent the increasing values of the growing velocity, and since parallels contained within the rectangle represent the values of a speed which is not increasing, but constant, it appears, in like manner, that the momenta assumed by the moving body may also be represented, in the case of the accelerated

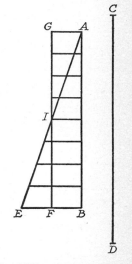

motion, by the increasing parallels of the triangle AEB, and, in the case of the uniform motion, by the parallels of the rectangle GB. For, what the momenta may lack in the first part of the accelerated motion (the deficiency of the momenta being represented by the parallels of the triangle AGI) is made up by the momenta represented by the parallels of the triangle IEF.

Hence it is clear that equal spaces will be traversed in equal times by two bodies, one of which, starting from rest, moves with a uniform acceleration, while the momentum of the other, moving with uniform speed, is one-half its maximum momentum under accelerated motion.

Q.E.D.

Theorem II, Proposition II

The spaces described by a body falling from rest with a uniformly accelerated motion are to each other as the squares of the time-intervals employed in traversing these distances.

Let the time beginning with any instant A be represented by the straight line AB in which are taken any two time-intervals AD and AE. Let HI represent the distance through which the body, starting from rest at H, falls with uniform acceleration. If HL repre-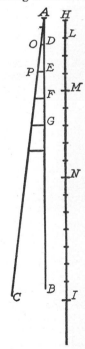sents the space traversed during the time-interval AD, and HM that covered during the interval AE, then the space MH stands to the space LH in a ratio which is the square of the ratio of the time AE to the time AD; or we may say simply that the distances HM and HL are related as the squares of AE and AD.

Draw the line AC making any angle whatever with the line AB; and from the points D and E, draw the parallel lines DO and EP; of these two lines, DO represents the greatest velocity attained during the interval AD, while EP represents the maximum velocity acquired during the interval AE. But it has just been proved that so far as distances traversed are concerned it is precisely the same whether a body falls from rest with a uniform acceleration or whether it falls during an equal time-interval with a constant speed which is one-half the maximum speed attained during the accelerated motion. It follows therefore that the distances HM and HL are the same as would be traversed, during the time-intervals AE and AD, by uniform velocities equal to one-half those represented by DO and EP respectively. If, therefore, one can show that the distances HM and HL are in the same ratio as the squares of the time-intervals AE and AD, our proposition will be proven.

It has been shown that the spaces traversed by two particles in uniform motion bear to one another a ratio which is equal to the product of the ratio of the velocities by the ratio of the times. But in this case the ratio of the velocities is the same as the ratio of the time-intervals (for the ratio of AE to AD is the same as that of ½EP to ½DO or of EP to DO). Hence the ratio of the spaces traversed is the same as the squared ratio of the time-intervals.   Q.E.D.

Evidently then the ratio of the distances is the square of the ratio of the final velocities, that is, of the lines EP and DO, since these are to each other as AE to AD.

Corollary

Hence it is clear that if we take any equal intervals of time whatever, counting from the beginning of the motion, such as AD, DE, EF, FG, in which the spaces HL, LM, MN, NI are traversed, these spaces will bear to one another the same ratio as the series of odd numbers, 1, 3, 5, 7; for this is the ratio of the differences of the squares of the lines [which represent time], differences which exceed one another by equal amounts, this excess being equal to the smallest line [viz. the one representing a single time-interval]: or we may say [that this is the ratio] of the differences of the squares of the natural numbers beginning with unity.

While, therefore, during equal intervals of time the velocities increase as the natural numbers, the increments in the distances traversed during these equal time-intervals are to one another as the odd numbers beginning with unity.

Simplicio. I am convinced that matters are as described, once having accepted the definition of uniformly accelerated motion. But as to whether this acceleration is that which one meets in nature in the case of falling bodies, I am still doubtful; and it seems to me, not only for my own sake but also for all those who think as I do, that this would be the proper moment to introduce one of those experiments—and there are many of them, I understand—which illustrate in several ways the conclusions reached.

Salviati. The request which you, as a man of science, make, is a very reasonable one; for this is the custom—and properly so—in those sciences where mathematical demonstrations are applied to natural phenomena, as is seen in the case of perspective, astronomy, mechanics, music, and others where the principles, once established by well-chosen experiments, become the foundations of the entire superstructure. I hope therefore it will not appear to be a waste of time if we discuss at considerable length this first and most fundamental question upon which hinge numerous consequences of which we have in this book only a small number, placed there by the Author, who has done so much to open a pathway hitherto closed to minds of speculative turn. So far as experiments go they have not been neglected by the Author; and often, in his company, I have attempted in the following manner to assure myself that the acceleration actually experienced by falling bodies is that above described.

A piece of wooden moulding or scantling, about 12 cubits long, half a cubit wide, and three fingerbreadths thick, was taken; on its edge was cut a channel a little more than one finger in breadth; having made this groove very straight, smooth, and polished, and having lined it with parchment, also as smooth and polished as possible, we rolled along it a hard, smooth, and very round bronze ball. Having placed this board in a sloping position, by lifting one end some one or two cubits above the other, we rolled the ball, as I was just saying, along the channel, noting, in a manner presently to be described, the time required to make the descent. We repeated this experiment more than once in order to measure the time with an accuracy such that the deviation between two observations never exceeded one-tenth of a pulse beat. Having performed this operation and having assured ourselves of its reliability, we now rolled the ball only one-quarter the length of the channel; and having measured the time of its descent, we found it precisely one-half of the former. Next we tried other distances, comparing the time for the whole length with that for the half, or with that for two-thirds, or three-fourths, or indeed for any fraction; in such experiments, repeated a full hundred times, we always found that the spaces traversed were to each other as the squares of the times, and this was true for all inclinations of the plane, i. e., of the channel, along which we rolled the ball. We also observed that the times of descent, for various inclinations of the plane, bore to one another precisely that ratio which, as we shall see later, the Author had predicted and demonstrated for them.

For the measurement of time, we employed a large vessel of water placed in an elevated position; to the bottom of this vessel was soldered a pipe of small diameter giving a thin jet of water, which we collected in a small glass during the time of each descent, whether for the whole length of the channel or for a part of its length; the water thus collected was weighed, after each descent, on a very accurate balance; the differences and ratios of these weights gave us the differences and ratios of the times, and this with such accuracy that although the operation was repeated many, many times, there was no appreciable discrepancy in the results.

SIMPLICIO. I would like to have been present at these experiments; but feeling confidence in the care with which you performed them, and in the fidelity with which you relate them, I am satisfied and accept them as true and valid.

SALVIATI. Then we can proceed without discussion.

Theorem III, Proposition III

If one and the same body, starting from rest, falls along an inclined plane and also along a vertical, each having the same height, the

times of descent will be to each other as the lengths of the inclined
plane and the vertical.

Let AC be the inclined plane and AB the perpendicular, each having
the same vertical height above the horizontal, namely, BA; then I say,
the time of descent of one and the same body along the plane AC bears
a ratio to the time of fall along the perpendicular AB, which is the same
as the ratio of the length AC to the length AB. Let DG, EI and LF be any
lines parallel to the horizontal CB; then it follows from what has preceded
that a body starting from A will acquire the same speed at the point G
as at D, since in each case the vertical fall is the same; in like manner the
speeds at I and E will be the same; so also those at L and F. And in
general the speeds at the two extremities of any parallel drawn from any
point on AB to the corresponding point on AC will be equal.

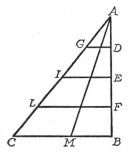

Thus the two distances AC and AB are traversed at the same speed.
But it has already been proved that if two distances are traversed by a
body moving with equal speeds, then the ratio of the times of descent
will be the ratio of the distances themselves; therefore, the time of descent
along AC is to that along AB as the length of the plane AC is to the
vertical distance AB.   Q.E.D.

SAGREDO. It seems to me that the above could have been proved clearly
and briefly on the basis of a proposition already demonstrated, namely,
that the distance traversed in the case of accelerated motion along AC or
AB is the same as that covered by a uniform speed whose value is one-
half the maximum speed, CB; the two distances AC and AB having been
traversed at the same uniform speed it is evident, from Proposition I,
that the times of descent will be to each other as the distances.

Theorem IV, Proposition IV

If from the highest or lowest point in a vertical circle there be
drawn any inclined planes meeting the circumference the times of
descent along these chords are each equal to the other.

On the horizontal line GH construct a vertical circle. From its lowest
point—the point of tangency with the horizontal—draw the diameter FA

and from the highest point, A, draw inclined planes to B and C, any points whatever on the circumference; then the times of descent along these are equal. Draw BD and CE perpendicular to the diameter; make AI a mean proportional between the heights of the planes, AE and AD; and since the rectangles FA.AE and FA.AD are respectively equal to the squares of AC and AB, while the rectangle FA.AE is to the rectangle FA.AD as AE is to AD, it follows that the square of AC is to the square of AB as the length AE is to the length AD. But since the length AE is to AD as the square of AI is to the square of AD, it follows that the squares on the lines AC and AB are to each other as the squares on the lines AI and AD, and hence also the length AC is to the length AB as AI

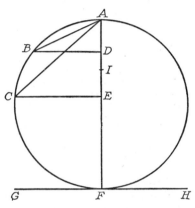

is to AD. But it has previously been demonstrated that the ratio of the time of descent along AC to that along AB is equal to the product of the two ratios AC to AB and AD to AI; but this last ratio is the same as that of AB to AC. Therefore the ratio of the time of descent along AC to that along AB is the product of the two ratios, AC to AB and AB to AC. The ratio of these times is therefore unity. Hence follows our proposition.

By use of the principles of mechanics one may obtain the same result.

Scholium

We may remark that any velocity once imparted to a moving body will be rigidly maintained as long as the external causes of acceleration or retardation are removed, a condition which is found only on horizontal planes; for in the case of planes which slope downwards there is already present a cause of acceleration, while on planes sloping upward there is retardation; from this it follows that motion along a horizontal plane is perpetual; for, if the velocity be uniform, it cannot be diminished or slackened, much less destroyed. Further, although any velocity which a body may have acquired through natural fall is permanently maintained so far as its own nature is concerned, yet it must be remembered that if, after descent along a plane inclined downwards, the body is deflected to a plane inclined upwards, there is already existing in this latter plane a cause of retardation; for in any such plane this same body is subject to a natural acceleration downwards. Accordingly we have here the superposition of two different states, namely, the velocity acquired during the preceding fall which if acting alone would carry the body at a uniform rate to infinity, and the velocity which results from a natural acceleration downwards common to all bodies. It seems altogether reasonable, therefore, if we wish to trace the future history of a body which has descended along some inclined plane and has been deflected along some plane inclined upwards, for us to assume that the maximum speed acquired during descent is permanently maintained during the ascent. In the ascent, however, there supervenes a natural inclination downwards, namely, a motion which, starting from rest, is accelerated at the usual rate. If perhaps this discussion is a little obscure, the following figure will help to make it clearer.

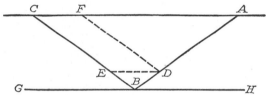

Let us suppose that the descent has been made along the downward sloping plane AB, from which the body is deflected so as to continue its motion along the upward sloping plane BC; and first let these planes be of equal length and placed so as to make equal angles with the horizontal line GH. Now it is well known that a body, starting from rest at A, and descending along AB, acquires a speed which is proportional to the time, which is a maximum at B, and which is maintained by the body so long as all causes of fresh acceleration or retardation are removed; the acceleration to which I refer is that to which the body would be subject if its motion were continued along the plane AB extended, while the retardation is that which the body would encounter if its motion were deflected along the plane BC inclined upwards; but, upon the horizontal plane GH, the body would maintain a uniform velocity equal to that which it had acquired at B after fall from A; moreover this velocity is such that, during an interval of time equal to the time of descent through AB, the body will traverse a horizontal distance equal to twice AB. Now let us imagine this same body to move with the same uniform speed along the plane BC so that here also during a time-interval equal to that of descent along AB, it will traverse along BC extended a distance twice AB; but let us suppose that, at the very instant the body begins its ascent it is subjected, by its very nature, to the same influences which surrounded it during its descent from A along AB, namely, it descends from rest under the same acceleration as that which was effective in AB, and it traverses, during an equal interval of time, the same distance along this second plane as it did along AB; it is clear that, by thus superposing upon the body a uniform motion of ascent and an accelerated motion of descent, it will be carried along the plane BC as far as the point C where these two velocities become equal.

If now we assume any two points D and E, equally distant from the vertex B, we may then infer that the descent along BD takes place in the same time as the ascent along BE. Draw DF parallel to BC; we know that, after descent along AD, the body will ascend along DF; or, if, on reaching D, the body is carried along the horizontal DE, it will reach E with the same momentum with which it left D; hence from E the body will ascend as far as C, proving that the velocity at E is the same as that at D.

From this we may logically infer that a body which descends along any inclined plane and continues its motion along a plane inclined upwards will, on account of the momentum acquired, ascend to an equal

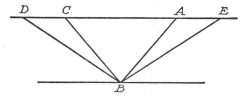

height above the horizontal; so that if the descent is along AB the body will be carried up the plane BC as far as the horizontal line ACD: and this is true whether the inclinations of the planes are the same or different, as in the case of the planes AB and BD. But by a previous postulate the speeds acquired by fall along variously inclined planes having the same vertical height are the same. If therefore the planes EB and BD have the same slope, the descent along EB will be able to drive the body along BD as far as D; and since this propulsion comes from the speed acquired on reaching the point B, it follows that this speed at B is the same whether the body has made its descent along AB or EB. Evidently then the body will be carried up BD whether the descent has been made along AB or along EB. The time of ascent along BD is however greater than that along BC, just as the descent along EB occupies more time than that along AB; moreover it has been demonstrated that the ratio between the lengths of these times is the same as that between the lengths of the planes.

Conclusion

SAGREDO. Indeed, I think we may concede to our Academician, without flattery, his claim that in the principle laid down in this treatise he has established a new science dealing with a very old subject. Observing with what ease and clearness he deduces from a single principle the proofs of so many theorems, I wonder not a little how such a question escaped the attention of Archimedes, Apollonius, Euclid and so many other mathematicians and illustrious philosophers, especially since so many ponderous tomes have been devoted to the subject of motion.

SALVIATI. There is a fragment of Euclid which treats of motion, but in it there is no indication that he ever began to investigate the property of acceleration and the manner in which it varies with slope. So that we may say the door is now opened, for the first time, to a new method fraught with numerous and wonderful results which in future years will command the attention of other minds.

SAGREDO. I really believe that just as, for instance, the few properties of the circle proven by Euclid in the Third Book of his *Elements* lead to many others more recondite, so the principles which are set forth in this little treatise will, when taken up by speculative minds, lead to many another more remarkable result; and it is to be believed that it will be so on account of the nobility of the subject, which is superior to any other in nature.

During this long and laborious day, I have enjoyed these simple theorems more than their proofs, many of which, for their complete comprehension, would require more than an hour each; this study, if you will be good enough to leave the book in my hands, is one which I mean to take up at my leisure after we have read the remaining portion which deals with the motion of projectiles; and this if agreeable to you we shall take up tomorrow.

SALVIATI. I shall not fail to be with you.

END OF THIRD DAY

FOURTH DAY

SALVIATI. Once more, Simplicio is here on time; so let us without delay take up the question of motion. The text of our Author is as follows:

THE MOTION OF PROJECTILES

In the preceding pages we have discussed the properties of motion naturally accelerated. I now propose to set forth those properties which belong to a body whose motion is compounded of two other motions, namely, one uniform and one naturally accelerated; these properties, well worth knowing, I propose to demonstrate in a rigid manner. This is the kind of motion seen in a moving projectile; its origin I conceive to be as follows:

Imagine any particle projected along a horizontal plane without friction; then we know, from what has been more fully explained in the preceding pages, that this particle will move along this same plane with a motion which is uniform and perpetual, provided the plane has no limits. But if the plane is limited and elevated, then the moving particle, which we imagine to be a heavy one, will on passing over the edge of the plane acquire, in addition to its previous uniform and perpetual motion, a downward propensity due to its own weight; so that the resulting motion which I call projection is compounded of one which is uniform and horizontal and of another which is vertical and naturally accelerated. We now proceed to demonstrate some of its properties, the first of which is as follows:

Theorem I, Proposition I

A projectile which is carried by a uniform horizontal motion compounded with a naturally accelerated vertical motion describes a path which is a semi-parabola.

SAGREDO. Here, Salviati, it will be necessary to stop a little while for my sake and, I believe, also for the benefit of Simplicio; for it so happens that I have not gone very far in my study of Apollonius and am merely aware of the fact that he treats of the parabola and other conic sections, without an understanding of which I hardly think one will be able to follow the proof of other propositions depending upon them. Since even in this first beautiful theorem the Author finds it necessary to prove that the path of a projectile is a parabola, and since, as I imagine, we shall have to deal with only this kind of curves, it will be absolutely necessary to have a thorough acquaintance, if not with all the properties which Apollonius has demonstrated for these figures, at least with those which are needed for the present treatment.

SIMPLICIO. Now even though Sagredo is, as I believe, well equipped for all his needs, I do not understand even the elementary terms; for although our philosophers have treated the motion of projectiles, I do not recall their having described the path of a projectile except to state in a general way that it is always a curved line, unless the projection be vertically upwards. But if the little Euclid which I have learned since our previous discussion does not enable me to understand the demonstrations which are to follow, then I shall be obliged to accept the theorems on faith without fully comprehending them.

SALVIATI. On the contrary, I desire that you should understand them from the Author himself, who, when he allowed me to see this work of his, was good enough to prove for me two of the principal properties of the parabola because I did not happen to have at hand the books of Apollonius. These properties, which are the only ones we shall need in the present discussion, he proved in such a way that no prerequisite knowledge was required. These theorems are, indeed, given by Apollonius, but after many preceding ones, to follow which would take a long while. I wish to shorten our task by deriving the first property purely and simply from the mode of generation of the parabola.

Beginning now with the first, imagine a right cone, erected upon the circular base *ibkc* with apex at *l*. The section of this cone made by a plane drawn parallel to the side *lk* is the curve which is called a *parabola*. The base of this parabola *bc* cuts at right angles the diameter *ik* of the circle *ibkc*, and the axis *ad* is parallel to the side *lk;* now having taken any point *f* in the curve *bfa* draw the straight line *fe* parallel to *bd;* then, I say, the square of *bd* is to the square of *fe* in the same ratio as the axis *ad* is to the portion *ae*.

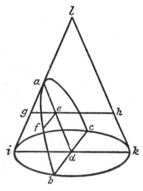

We can now resume the text and see how the Author demonstrates his first proposition in which he shows that a body falling with a motion compounded of a uniform horizontal and a naturally accelerated one describes a semi-parabola.

Let us imagine an elevated horizontal line or plane *ab* along which a body moves with uniform speed from *a* to *b*. Suppose this plane to end abruptly at *b;* then at this point the body will, on account of its weight, acquire also a natural motion downwards along the perpendicular *bn*. Draw the line *be* along the plane *ba* to represent the flow, or measure, of time; divide this line into a number of segments, *bc, cd, de*, representing equal intervals of time; from the points *b, c, d, e*, let fall lines which are parallel to the perpendicular *bn*. On the first of these lay off any distance *ci*, on the second a distance four times as long, *df;* on the third, one nine times as long, *eh;* and so on, in proportion to the squares of *cb, db, eb*, or, we may say, in the squared ratio of these same lines. Accordingly we see that while the body moves from *b* to *c* with uniform speed, it also falls perpendicularly through the distance *ci*, and at the end of the time-interval *bc* finds itself at the point *i*. In like manner at the end of the time-interval *bd*, which is the double of *bc*, the vertical fall will be four times the first distance *ci;* for it has been shown in a previous discussion that the distance traversed by a freely falling body varies as the square of the time; in like manner the space *eh* traversed during the time *be* will be nine times *ci;* thus it is evident that the distances *eh, df, ci* will be to one another as the squares of the lines *be, bd, bc.* Now from the points *i, f, h* draw the straight lines *io, fg, hl* parallel to *be;* these lines *hl, fg, io* are equal to *eb, db* and *cb,* respectively; so also are the lines *bo, bg, bl* respectively equal to *ci, df,* and *eh.* The square of *hl* is to that of *fg* as the line *lb* is to *bg;* and the square of *fg* is to that of *io* as *gb* is to *bo;* therefore the points *i, f, h,* lie on one and the same parabola. In like manner it may be shown that, if we take equal time-intervals of any size whatever, and if we imagine the particle to be carried by a similar compound motion, the positions of this particle, at the ends of these time-intervals, will lie on one and the same parabola.   Q.E.D.

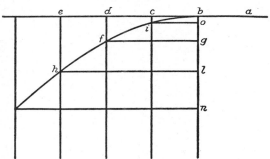

This conclusion follows the converse of the first of the two propositions given above. For, having drawn a parabola through the points *b* and *h,* any other two points, *f* and *i,* not falling on the parabola must lie either within or without; consequently the line *fg* is either longer or shorter than the line which terminates on the parabola. Therefore the square of *hl* will not bear to the square of *fg* the same ratio as the line *lb* to *bg,* but a greater or smaller; the fact is, however, that the square of *hl* does bear this same ratio to the square of *fg.* Hence the point *f* does lie on the parabola, and so do all the others.

SAGREDO. One cannot deny that the argument is new, subtle and conclusive, resting as it does upon this hypothesis, namely, that the horizontal motion remains uniform, that the vertical motion continues to be accelerated downwards in proportion to the square of the time, and that such motions and velocities as these combine without altering, disturbing, or hindering each other, so that as the motion proceeds the path of the projectile does not change into a different curve: but this, in my opinion, is impossible. For the axis of the parabola along which we imagine the natural motion of a falling body to take place stands perpendicular to a horizontal surface and ends at the center of the earth; and since the parabola deviates more and more from its axis no projectile can ever reach the center of the earth or, if it does, as seems necessary, then the path of the projectile must transform itself into some other curve very different from the parabola.

SIMPLICIO. To these difficulties, I may add others. One of these is that we suppose the horizontal plane, which slopes neither up nor down, to be represented by a straight line as if each point on this line were equally distant from the center, which is not the case; for as one starts from the middle [of the line] and goes toward either end, he departs farther and farther from the center [of the earth] and is therefore constantly going uphill. Whence it follows that the motion cannot remain uniform through any distance whatever, but must continually diminish. Besides, I do not see how it is possible to avoid the resistance of the medium which must destroy the uniformity of the horizontal motion and change the law of acceleration of falling bodies. These various difficulties render it highly improbable that a result derived from such unreliable hypotheses should hold true in practice.

SALVIATI. All these difficulties and objections which you urge are so well founded that it is impossible to remove them; and, as for me, I am ready to admit them all, which indeed I think our Author would also do. I grant that these conclusions proved in the abstract will be different when applied in the concrete and will be fallacious to this extent, that neither will the horizontal motion be uniform nor the natural acceleration be in the ratio assumed, nor the path of the projectile a parabola, etc. But, on the other hand, I ask you not to begrudge our Author that which other eminent men have assumed even if not strictly true. The authority of Archimedes alone will satisfy everybody. In his *Mechanics* and in his first quadrature of the parabola he takes for granted that the beam of a balance or steelyard is a straight line, every point of which is equidistant from the common center of all heavy bodies, and that the cords by which heavy bodies are suspended are parallel to each other.

Some consider this assumption permissible because, in practice, our instruments and the distances involved are so small in comparison with the enormous distance from the center of the earth that we may consider a minute of arc on a great circle as a straight line, and may regard the perpendiculars let fall from its two extremities as parallel. For if in actual practice one had to consider such small quantities, it would be necessary first of all to criticise the architects who presume, by use of a plumb line, to erect high towers with parallel sides. I may add that, in all their discussions, Archimedes and the others considered themselves as located at an infinite distance from the center of the earth, in which case their assumptions were not false, and therefore their conclusions were absolutely correct. When we wish to apply our proven conclusions to distances which, though finite, are very large, it is necessary for us to infer, on the basis of demonstrated truth, what correction is to be made for the fact that our distance from the center of the earth is not really infinite, but merely very great in comparison with the small dimensions of our apparatus. The largest of these will be the range of our projectiles—and even here we need consider only the artillery—which, however great, will never exceed four of those miles of which as many thousand separate us from the center of the earth; and since these paths terminate upon the surface of the earth only very slight changes can take place in their parabolic figure which, it is conceded, would be greatly altered if they terminated at the center of the earth.

As to the perturbation arising from the resistance of the medium this is more considerable and does not, on account of its manifold forms, submit to fixed laws and exact description. Thus if we consider only the resistance which the air offers to the motions studied by us, we shall see that it disturbs them all and disturbs them in an infinite variety of ways corresponding to the infinite variety in the form, weight, and velocity of the projectiles. For as to velocity, the greater this is, the greater will be the resistance offered by the air; a resistance which will be greater as the moving bodies become less dense. So that although the falling body ought to be displaced in proportion to the square of the duration of its motion, yet no matter how heavy the body, if it falls from a very considerable height, the resistance of the air will be such as to prevent any increase in speed and will render the motion uniform; and in proportion as the moving body is less dense this uniformity will be so much the more quickly attained and after a shorter fall. Even horizontal motion which, if no impediment were offered, would be uniform and constant is altered by the resistance of the air and finally ceases; and here again the less dense the body the quicker the process. Of these properties of weight, of velocity, and also of form, infinite in number, it is not possible to give any exact description; hence, in order to handle this matter in a scientific way, it is necessary to cut loose from these difficulties; and having discovered and demonstrated the theorems, in the case of no resistance, to use them and apply them with such limitations as experience will teach. And the advantage of this method will not be small; for the material and shape of the projectile may be chosen, as dense and round as possible, so that it will encounter the least resistance in the medium. Nor will the spaces and velocities in general be so great but that we shall be easily able to correct them with precision.

In the case of those projectiles which we use, made of dense material and round in shape, or of lighter material and cylindrical in shape, such as arrows, thrown from a sling or crossbow, the deviation from an exact parabolic path is quite insensible. Indeed, if you will allow me a little greater liberty, I can show you, by two experiments, that the dimensions of our apparatus are so small that these external and incidental resistances, among which that of the medium is the most considerable, are scarcely observable.

I now proceed to the consideration of motions through the air, since it is with these that we are now especially concerned; the resistance of the air exhibits itself in two ways: first by offering greater impedance to less dense than to very dense bodies, and secondly by offering greater resistance to a body in rapid motion than to the same body in slow motion.

Regarding the first of these, consider the case of two balls having the same dimensions, but one weighing ten or twelve times as much as the other; one, say, of lead, the other of oak, both allowed to fall from an elevation of 150 or 200 cubits.

Experiment shows that they will reach the earth with slight difference in speed, showing us that in both cases the retardation caused by the air is small; for if both balls start at the same moment and at the same elevation, and if the leaden one be slightly retarded and the wooden one greatly retarded, then the former ought to reach the earth a considerable distance in advance of the latter, since it is ten times as heavy. But this does not happen; indeed, the gain in distance of one over the other does not amount to the hundredth part of the entire fall. And in the case of a ball of stone weighing only a third or half as much as one of lead, the difference in their times of reaching the earth will be scarcely noticeable. Now since the speed acquired by a leaden ball in falling from a height of 200 cubits is so great that if the motion remained uniform the ball would, in an interval of time equal to that of the fall, traverse 400 cubits, and since this speed is so considerable in comparison with those which, by use of bows or other machines except firearms, we are able to give to our projectiles, it follows that we may, without sensible error, regard as absolutely true those propositions which we are about to prove without considering the resistance of the medium.

Passing now to the second case, where we have to show that the resistance of the air for a rapidly moving body is not very much greater than for one moving slowly, ample proof is given by the following experiment. Attach to two threads of equal length—say four or five yards—two equal leaden balls and suspend them from the ceiling; now pull them aside from the perpendicular, the one through 80 or more degrees, the other through not more than four or five degrees; so that, when set free, the one falls, passes through the perpendicular, and describes large but slowly decreasing arcs of 160, 150, 140 degrees, etc.; the other swinging through small and also slowly diminishing arcs of 10, 8, 6 degrees, etc.

In the first place it must be remarked that one pendulum passes through its arcs of 180°, 160°, etc., in the same time that the other swings through its 10°, 8°, etc., from which it follows that the speed of the first ball is 16 and 18 times greater than that of the second. Accordingly, if the air offers more resistance to the high speed than to the low, the frequency of vibration in the large arcs of 180° or 160°, etc., ought to be less than in the small arcs of 10°, 8°, 4°, etc., and even less than in arcs of 2°, or 1°; but this prediction is not verified by experiment; because if two persons start to count the vibrations, the one the large, the other the small, they will discover that after counting tens and even hundreds they will not differ by a single vibration, not even by a fraction of one.

This observation justifies the two following propositions, namely, that vibrations of very large and very small amplitude all occupy the same time and that the resistance of the air does not affect motions of high speed more than those of low speed, contrary to the opinion hitherto generally entertained.

SAGREDO. On the contrary, since we cannot deny that the air hinders both of these motions, both becoming slower and finally vanishing, we have to admit that the retardation occurs in the same proportion in each case. But how? How, indeed, could the resistance offered to the one body be greater than that offered to the other except by the impartation of more momentum and speed to the fast body than to the slow? And if this is so the speed with which a body moves is at once the cause and measure of the resistance which it meets. Therefore, all motions, fast or slow, are hindered and diminished in the same proportion; a result, it seems to me, of no small importance.

SALVIATI. We are able, therefore, in this second case to say that the errors, neglecting those which are accidental, in the results which we are about to demonstrate are small in the case of our machines where the velocities employed are mostly very great and the distances negligible in comparison with the semi-diameter of the earth or one of its great circles.

SIMPLICIO. I would like to hear your reason for putting the projectiles of firearms, i. e., those using powder, in a different class from the projectiles employed in bows, slings, and crossbows, on the ground of their not being equally subject to change and resistance from the air.

SALVIATI. I am led to this view by the excessive and, so to speak, supernatural violence with which such projectiles are launched; for, indeed, it appears to me that without exaggeration one might say that the speed of a ball fired either from a musket or from a piece of ordnance is supernatural. For if such a ball be allowed to fall from some great elevation its speed will, owing to the resistance of the air, not go on increasing indefinitely; that which happens to bodies of small density in falling through short distances—I mean the reduction of their motion to uniformity—will also happen to a ball of iron or lead after it has fallen a few thousand cubits; this terminal or final speed is the maximum which such a heavy body can naturally acquire in falling through the air. This speed I estimate to be much smaller than that impressed upon the ball by the burning powder.

An appropriate experiment will serve to demonstrate this fact. From a height of one hundred or more cubits fire a gun loaded with a lead bullet vertically downwards upon a stone pavement; with the same gun shoot against a similar stone from a distance of one or two cubits, and observe which of the two balls is the more flattened. Now if the ball which has come from the greater elevation is found to be the less flattened of the two, this will show that the air has hindered and diminished the speed initially imparted to the bullet by the powder, and that the air will not permit a bullet to acquire so great a speed, no matter from what height it falls; for if the speed impressed upon the ball by the fire does not exceed that acquired by it in falling freely then its downward blow ought to be greater rather than less.

This experiment I have not performed, but I am of the opinion that a musket ball or cannon shot, falling from a height as great as you please, will not deliver so strong a blow as it would if fired into a wall only a few cubits distant, i. e., at such a short range that the splitting or rending of the air will not be sufficient to rob the shot of that excess of super-natural violence given it by the powder.

The enormous momentum of these violent shots may cause some deformation of the trajectory, making the beginning of the parabola flatter and less curved than the end; but, so far as our Author is concerned, this is a matter of small consequence in practical operations, the main one of which is the preparation of a table of ranges for shots of high elevation, giving the distance attained by the ball as a function of the angle of elevation; and since shots of this kind are fired from mortars using small charges and imparting no supernatural momentum they follow their prescribed paths very exactly.

But now let us proceed with the discussion in which the Author invites us to the study and investigation of the motion of a body when that motion is compounded of two others; and first the case in which the two are uniform, the one horizontal, the other vertical.

Theorem II, Proposition II

> When the motion of a body is the resultant of two uniform motions, one horizontal, the other perpendicular, the square of the resultant momentum is equal to the sum of the squares of the two component momenta.

SIMPLICIO. At this point there is just one slight difficulty which needs to be cleared up; for it seems to me that the conclusion just reached contradicts a previous proposition in which it is claimed that the speed of a body coming from *a* to *b* is equal to that in coming from *a* to *c;* while now you conclude that the speed at *c* is greater than that at *b*.

SALVIATI. Both propositions, Simplicio, are true, yet there is a great difference between them. Here we are speaking of a body urged by a single motion which is the resultant of two uniform motions, while there we were speaking of two bodies each urged with naturally accelerated motions, one along the vertical *ab* the other along the inclined plane *ac*. Besides the time-intervals were there not supposed to be equal, that along the incline *ac* being greater than that along the vertical *ab;* but the motions of which we now speak, those along *ab, bc, ac,* are uniform and simultaneous.

SIMPLICIO. Pardon me; I am satisfied; pray go on.

SALVIATI. Our Author next undertakes to explain what happens when a body is urged by a motion compounded of one which is horizontal and uniform and of another which is vertical but naturally accelerated; from these two components results the path of a projectile, which is a parabola. The problem is to determine the speed of the projectile at each point. With this purpose in view our Author sets forth as follows the manner, or rather the method, of measuring such speed along the path which is taken by a heavy body starting from rest and falling with a naturally accelerated motion.

Theorem III, Proposition III

Let the motion take place along the line *ab,* starting from rest at *a,* and in this line choose any point *c.* Let *ac* represent the time, or the measure of the time, required for the body to fall through the space *ac;* let *ac* also represent the velocity at *c* acquired by a fall through the distance *ac.* In the line *ab* select any other point *b.* The problem now is to determine the velocity at *b* acquired by a body in falling through the distance *ab* and to express this in terms of the velocity at *c,* the measure of which is the length *ac.* Take as a mean proportional between *ac* and

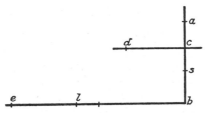

ab. We shall prove that the velocity at *b* is to that at *c* as the length *as* is to the length *ac.* Draw the horizontal line *cd,* having twice the length of *ac,* and *be,* having twice the length of *ba.* It then follows, from the preceding theorems, that a body falling through the distance *ac,* and turned so as to move along the horizontal *cd* with a uniform speed equal to that acquired on reaching *c,* will traverse the distance *cd* in the same interval of time as that required to fall with accelerated motion from *a* to *c.* Likewise *be* will be traversed in the same time as *ba.* But the time of descent through *ab* is *as;* hence the horizontal distance *be* is also traversed in the time *as.* Take a point *l* such that the time *as* is to the time *ac* as *be* is to *bl;* since the motion along *be* is uniform, the distance *bl,* if traversed with the speed acquired at *b,* will occupy the time *ac;* but in this same time-interval, *ac,* the distance *cd* is traversed with the speed acquired in *c.* Now two speeds are to each other as the distances traversed in equal intervals of time. Hence the speed at *c* is to the speed at *b* as *cd* is to *bl.* But since *dc* is to *be* as their halves, namely, as *ca* is to *ba,* and since *be* is to *bl* as *ba* is to *sa;* it follows that *dc* is to *bl* as *ca* is to *sa.* In other words, the speed at *c* is to that at *b* as *ca* is to *sa,* that is, as the time to fall through *ab.*

The method of measuring the speed of a body along the direction of its fall is thus clear; the speed is assumed to increase directly as the time.

Problem. Proposition IV

SALVIATI. Concerning motions and their velocities or momenta whether uniform or naturally accelerated, one cannot speak definitely until he has established a measure for such velocities and also for time. As for time we have the already widely adopted hours, first minutes and second minutes. So for velocities, just as for intervals of time, there is need of a common standard which shall be understood and accepted by everyone, and which shall be the same for all. As has already been stated, the Author considers the velocity of a freely falling body adapted to this purpose, since this velocity increases according to the same law in all parts of the world; thus for instance the speed acquired by a leaden ball of a pound weight starting from rest and falling vertically through the height of, say, a spear's length is the same in all places; it is therefore excellently adapted for representing the momentum acquired in the case of natural fall.

It still remains for us to discover a method of measuring momentum in the case of uniform motion in such a way that all who discuss the subject will form the same conception of its size and velocity. This will prevent one person from imagining it larger, another smaller, than it really is; so that in the composition of a given uniform motion with one which is accelerated different men may not obtain different values for the resultant. In order to determine and represent such a momentum and particular speed our Author has found no better method than to use the momentum acquired by a body in naturally accelerated motion. The speed of a body which has in this manner acquired any momentum whatever will, when converted into uniform motion, retain precisely such a speed as, during a time-interval equal to that of the fall, will carry the body through a distance equal to twice that of the fall. But since this matter is one which is fundamental in our discussion it is well that we make it perfectly clear by means of some particular example.

Let us consider the speed and momentum acquired by a body falling through the height, say, of a spear as a standard which we may use in the measurement of other speeds and momenta as occasion demands; assume for instance that the time of such a fall is four seconds; now in order to measure the speed acquired from a fall through any other height, whether greater or less, one must not conclude that these speeds bear to one another the same ratio as the heights of fall; for instance, it is not true that a fall through four times a given height confers a speed four times as great as that acquired by descent through the given height; because the speed of a naturally accelerated motion does not vary in proportion to the time. As has been shown above, the ratio of the spaces is equal to the square of the ratio of the times.

If, then, as is often done for the sake of brevity, we take the same limited straight line as the measure of the speed, and of the time, and also of the space traversed during that time, it follows that the duration of fall and the speed acquired by the same body in passing over any other distance, is not represented by this second distance, but by a mean proportional between the two distances. This I can better illustrate by an example. In the vertical line *ac,* lay off the portion *ab* to represent the distance traversed by a body falling freely with accelerated motion; the time of fall may be represented by any limited straight line, but for the sake of brevity, we shall represent it by the same length *ab;* this length may also be employed as a measure of the momentum and speed acquired during the motion; in short, let *ab* be a measure of the various physical quantities which enter this discussion.

Having agreed arbitrarily upon *ab* as a measure of these three different quantities, namely, space, time, and momentum, our next task is to find the time required for fall through a given vertical distance *ac,* also the momentum acquired at the terminal point *c,* both of which are to be expressed in terms of the time and momentum represented by *ab.* These two required quantities are obtained by laying off *ad,* a mean proportional between *ab* and *ac;* in other words, the time of fall from *a* to *c* is represented by *ad* on the same scale on which we agreed that the time of fall from *a* to *b* should be represented by *ab.* In like manner we may say that the momentum acquired at *c* is related to that acquired at *b,* in the same manner that the line *ad* is related to *ab,* since the velocity varies directly as the time, a conclusion which, although employed as a postulate in Proposition III, is here amplified by the Author.

This point being clear and well-established we pass to the consideration of the momentum in the case of two compound motions, one of which is compounded of a uniform horizontal and a uniform vertical motion, while the other is compounded of a uniform horizontal and a naturally accelerated vertical motion. If both components are uniform, and one at right angles to the other, we have already said that the square of the resultant is obtained by adding the squares of the components as will be clear from the following illustration.

Let us imagine a body to move along the vertical *ab* with a uniform momentum of 3, and on reaching *b* to move toward *c* with a momentum

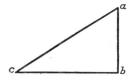

of 4, so that during the same time-interval it will traverse 3 cubits along the vertical and 4 along the horizontal. But a particle which moves with the resultant velocity will, in the same time, traverse the diagonal *ac,* whose length is not 7 cubits—the sum of *ab* (3) and *bc* (4)—but 5, which is *in potenza* equal to the sum of 3 and 4; that is, the squares of 3 and 4 when added make 25, which is the square of *ac,* and is equal to the sum of the squares of *ab* and *bc.* Hence *ac* is represented by the side—or we may say the root—of a square whose area is 25, namely 5.

As a fixed and certain rule for obtaining the momentum which results from two uniform momenta, one vertical, the other horizontal, we have therefore the following: take the square of each, add these together, and extract the square root of the sum, which will be the momentum resulting from the two. Thus, in the above example, the body which in virtue of its vertical motion would strike the horizontal plane with a momentum of 3, would owing to its horizontal motion alone strike at *c* with a momentum of 4; but if the body strikes with a momentum which is the resultant of these two, its blow will be that of a body moving with a momentum of 5; and such a blow will be the same at all points of the diagonal *ac,* since its components are always the same and never increase or diminish.

Let us now pass to the consideration of a uniform horizontal motion compounded with the vertical motion of a freely falling body starting from rest. It is at once clear that the diagonal which represents the motion compounded of these two is not a straight line, but, as has been demonstrated, a semi-parabola, in which the momentum is always increasing because the speed of the vertical component is always increasing. Wherefore, to determine the momentum at any given point in the parabolic diagonal, it is necessary first to fix upon the uniform horizontal momentum and then, treating the body as one falling freely, to find the vertical momentum at the given point; this latter can be determined only by taking into account the duration of fall, a consideration which does not enter into the composition of two uniform motions where the velocities and momenta are always the same; but here where one of the component motions has an initial value of zero and increases its speed in direct proportion to the time, it follows that the time must determine the speed at the assigned point. It only remains to obtain the momentum resulting from these two components (as in the case of uniform motions) by placing the square of the resultant equal to the sum of the squares of the two components.

To what has hitherto been said concerning the momenta, blows or shocks of projectiles, we must add another very important consideration; to determine the force and energy of the shock it is not sufficient to consider only the speed of the projectiles, but we must also take into account the nature and condition of the target which, in no small degree, determines the efficiency of the blow. First of all it is well known that the target suffers violence from the speed of the projectile in proportion as it partly or entirely stops the motion; because if the blow falls upon an object which yields to the impulse without resistance such a blow will be of no effect; likewise when one attacks his enemy with a spear and overtakes him at an instant when he is fleeing with equal speed there will be no blow but merely a harmless touch. But if the shock falls upon an object which yields only in part then the blow will not have its full effect, but the damage will be in proportion to the excess of the speed of the projectile over that of the receding body; thus, for example, if the shot reaches the target with a speed of 10 while the latter recedes with a speed of 4, the momentum and shock will be represented by 6. Finally the blow will be a maximum, in so far as the projectile is concerned, when the target does not recede at all but if possible completely resists and stops the motion of the projectile. I have said *in so far as the projectile is concerned* because if the target should approach the projectile the shock of collision would be greater in proportion as the sum of the two speeds is greater than that of the projectile alone.

Moreover it is to be observed that the amount of yielding in the target depends not only upon the quality of the material, as regards hardness, whether it be of iron, lead, wool, etc., but also upon its position. If the position is such that the shot strikes it at right angles, the momentum imparted by the blow will be a maximum; but if the motion be oblique, that is to say slanting, the blow will be weaker; and more and more so in proportion to the obliquity; for, no matter how hard the material of the target thus situated, the entire momentum of the shot will not be spent and stopped; the projectile will slide by and will, to some extent, continue its motion along the surface of the opposing body.

All that has been said above concerning the amount of momentum in the projectile at the extremity of the parabola must be understood to refer to a blow received on a line at right angles to this parabola or along the tangent to the parabola at the given point; for, even though the motion has two components, one horizontal, the other vertical, neither will the momentum along the horizontal nor that upon a plane perpendicular to the horizontal be a maximum, since each of these will be received obliquely.

SAGREDO. Your having mentioned these blows and shocks recalls to my mind a problem, or rather a question, in mechanics of which no author has given a solution or said anything which diminishes my astonishment or even partly relieves my mind.

My difficulty and surprise consist in not being able to see whence and upon what principle is derived the energy and immense force which makes its appearance in a blow; for instance we see the simple blow of a hammer, weighing not more than 8 or 10 lbs., overcoming resistances which, without a blow, would not yield to the weight of a body producing impetus by pressure alone, even though that body weighed many hundreds of pounds. I would like to discover a method of measuring the force of such a percussion. I can hardly think it infinite, but incline rather to the view that it has its limit and can be counterbalanced and measured by other forces, such as weights, or by levers or screws or other mechanical instruments which are used to multiply forces in a manner which I satisfactorily understand.

SALVIATI. You are not alone in your surprise at this effect or in obscurity as to the cause of this remarkable property. I studied this matter myself for a while in vain; but my confusion merely increased until finally meeting our Academician I received from him great consolation. First he told me that he also had for a long time been groping in the dark; but later he said that, after having spent some thousands of hours in speculating and contemplating thereon, he had arrived at some notions which are far removed from our earlier ideas and which are remarkable for their novelty. And since now I know that you would gladly hear what these novel ideas are I shall not wait for you to ask but promise that, as soon as our discussion of projectiles is completed, I will explain all these fantasies, or if you please, vagaries, as far as I can recall them from the words of our Academician. In the meantime we proceed with the propositions of the Author.

Theorem. Proposition V.

If projectiles describe semi-parabolas of the same amplitude, the momentum required to describe that one whose amplitude is double its altitude is less than that required for any other.

Let *bd* be a semi-parabola whose amplitude *cd* is double its altitude *cb;* on its axis extended upwards lay off *ba* equal to its altitude *bc.* Draw the line *ad* which will be a tangent to the parabola at *d* and will cut the

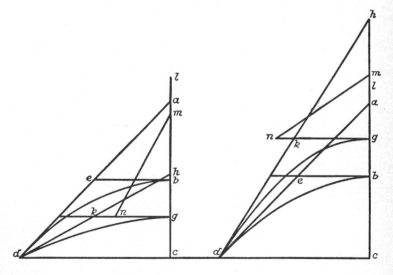

horizontal line *be* at the point *e,* making *be* equal to *bc* and also to *ba.* It is evident that this parabola will be described by a projectile whose uniform horizontal momentum is that which it would acquire at *b* in falling from rest at *a* and whose naturally accelerated vertical momentum is that of the body falling to c, from rest at b. From this it follows that the momentum at the terminal point d, compounded of these two, is represented by the diagonal ae, whose square is equal to the sum of the squares of the two components. Now let gd be any other parabola whatever having the same amplitude cd, but whose altitude cg is either greater or less than the altitude bc. Let hd be the tangent cutting the horizontal through g at k. Select a point l such that $hg:gk=gk:gl$. Then from a preceding proposition, it follows that gl will be the height from which a body must fall in order to describe the parabola gd.

Let gm be a mean proportional between ab and gl; then gm will represent the time and momentum acquired at g by a fall from l; for ab has been assumed as a measure of both time and momentum. Again let gn be a mean proportional between bc and cg; it will then represent the time and momentum which the body acquires at c in falling from g. If now we join m and n, this line mn will represent the momentum at d of the projectile traversing the parabola dg; which momentum is, I say, greater than that of the projectile travelling along the parabola bd whose measure was given by ae. For since gn has been taken as a mean proportional between bc and gc; and since bc is equal to be and also to kg (each of them being the half of dc) it follows that $cg:gn=gn:gk$, and as cg or (hg) is to gk so is ng^2 to gk^2: but by construction $hg:gk=gk:gl$. Hence $ng^2:gk^2=gk:gl$. But $gk:gl=gk^2:gm^2$, since gm is a mean proportional between kg and gl. Therefore the three squares ng, kg, mg form a continued proportion, $gn^2:gk^2=gk^2:gm^2$. And the sum of the two extremes which is equal to the square of mn is greater than twice the square of gk; but the square of ae is double the square of gk. Hence the square of mn is greater than the square of ae and the length mn is greater than the length ae.   Q.E.D.

Corollary

Conversely it is evident that less momentum will be required to send a projectile from the terminal point d along the parabola bd than along any other parabola having an elevation greater or less than that of the parabola bd, for which the tangent at d makes an angle of 45° with the horizontal. From which it follows that if projectiles are fired from the terminal point d, all having the same speed, but each having a different elevation, the maximum range, i. e., amplitude of the semi-parabola or of the entire parabola, will be obtained when the elevation is 45°: the other shots, fired at angles greater or less, will have a shorter range.

SAGREDO. The force of rigid demonstrations such as occur only in mathematics fills me with wonder and delight. From accounts given by gunners, I was already aware of the fact that in the use of cannon and mortars, the maximum range, that is, the one in which the shot goes farthest, is obtained when the elevation is 45° or, as they say, at the sixth point of the quadrant; but to understand why this happens far outweighs the mere information obtained by the testimony of others or even by repeated experiment.

SALVIATI. What you say is very true. The knowledge of a single fact acquired through a discovery of its causes prepares the mind to understand and ascertain other facts without need of recourse to experiment, precisely as in the present case, where by argumentation alone the Author proves with certainty that the maximum range occurs when the elevation is 45°. He thus demonstrates what has perhaps never been observed in experience, namely, that of other shots those which exceed or fall short of 45° by equal amounts have equal ranges; so that if the balls have been fired one at an elevation of 7 points, the other at 5, they will strike the level at the same distance: the same is true if the shots are fired at 8 and at 4 points, at 9 and at 3, etc.

SIMPLICIO. I am fully satisfied. So now Salviati can present the speculations of our Academician on the subject of impulsive forces.

SALVIATI. Let the preceding discussions suffice for today; the hour is already late and the time remaining will not permit us to clear up the subjects proposed; we may therefore postpone our meeting until another and more opportune occasion.

SAGREDO. I concur in your opinion, because after various conversations with intimate friends of our Academician I have concluded that this question of impulsive forces is very obscure, and I think that, up to the present, none of those who have treated this subject have been able to clear up its dark corners which lie almost beyond the reach of human imagination; among the various views which I have heard expressed one, strangely fantastic, remains in my memory, namely, that impulsive forces are indeterminate, if not infinite. Let us, therefore, await the convenience of Salviati.

END OF FOURTH DAY

THE ATOMIC THEORY

by

JOHN DALTON

CONTENTS

The Atomic Theory

JOHN DALTON

1766–1844

AT THE HEIGHT OF HIS FAME, John Dalton wrote the following note in the autograph album belonging to a friend of his:

The writer of this was born at the village of Eaglesfield, about two miles west of Cockermouth, Cumberland. Attended the village schools, there and in the neighborhood, till eleven years of age, at which period he had gone through a course of mensuration, surveying, navigation, etc.; began about twelve to teach the village school and continued it about two years; afterwards was occasionally employed in husbandry for a year or more; removed to Kendal at fifteen years of age as assistant in a boarding school; remained in that capacity for three or four years; then undertook the same school as principal and continued it for eight years; whilst at Kendal employed his leisure in studying Latin, Greek, French and the mathematics, with natural philosophy; removed thence to Manchester in 1793 as tutor in mathematics and natural philosophy in the New College; was six years in that engagement and after was employed as private and public teacher of mathematics and chemistry in Manchester, but occasionally by invitation in London, Edinburgh, Glasgow, Birmingham and Leeds.

Oct. 22, 1832   JOHN DALTON

These bare bones of biography can fortunately be clothed with flesh. Dalton was born in 1766, one of the six children of Joseph and Deborah Dalton, humble Quakers. Joseph Dalton was a hand-loom weaver and the farmer of a small patch of land which he owned. Nothing in the family life conduced to special refinement save the simple Quaker faith. The elder Daltons had benefited by neither formal education nor wealth; they differed little from their neighbors, most of them also plain, honest, rugged small farmers and tradespeople. The town schools provided only such provender as John Dalton was able to exhaust in a half dozen years, and required of a

teacher no further qualifications than Dalton was able to offer
when he was twelve. One may question his success as a
teacher at that age; it was evidently sufficient to persuade
him to elect teaching as his profession.

When he journeyed to Kendal to assist in a boarding
school, Dalton went on the invitation of a cousin who was
head of the school. He had, as he reports, leisure there to
study languages, mathematics, and natural philosophy. He
had also leisure to contribute vapid answers to vapid questions in two periodicals, the *Ladies' Diary* and the *Gentleman's Diary*. For example, to the question, Can one who has
loved sincerely love a second time? he replied with a curi-
ously silly essay.

Much more important, during these Kendal years Dalton
met John Gough. Gough was twice Dalton's age, and as a
result of smallpox had been blind from his infancy. Yet he
was a good classical scholar, and it was he who provoked
Dalton to study Greek and Latin. Well-informed about the
science of the day, he thought scientifically; and he taught his
younger friend to think similarly. He persuaded him to make
and record his first scientific observations, a series of local
weather data collected with the aid of homemade barometers,
thermometers, and hygroscopes. During these same years,
while Dalton was intermittently considering law and medicine as possible professions, he also collected and dried botani-
cal specimens, collected insects, experimented with his own
body to determine what proportion of food and drink in-
gested passed off as "insensible perspiration."

In 1793, through Gough's influence, Dalton was appointed
tutor in mathematics and natural philosophy at New College
in Manchester. Almost at once he published his *Meteorologi-
cal Observations and Essays* (Manchester, 1793). This opens
with an account of an aurora borealis he had observed in 1787
and a discussion of the causes and effects of auroras. One
essay considers the rise and fall of the barometer and the
causes therefor. The most important essay, historically, is the
one on evaporation, for in it he first states the idea now known
as Dalton's law, the law of partial pressures.

In 1794 the Manchester Literary and Philosophical Society elected Dalton to membership. The first paper he presented to the Society he titled "On Vision of Colour," and
in it he used data from his own and his brother's experiences.
They were both color-blind, as they had discovered when
they brought their mother, as a good Quaker present, a pair
of silk stockings of brilliant crimson. Later he presented to
the Society papers on rain and dew, on heat conduction, on
"Heat and Cold Produced by Mechanical Condensation and

Rarefaction of Air." In all of these papers Dalton relied for data on his own loose experiments and his own inaccurate instruments. His numerical results have not been confirmed by later students. Yet the essays are valuable, for the experiments are most sagaciously interpreted, and Dalton exercised in them his wonderful faculty for happy generalization. Thus, in 1803, in a paper "On the Tendency of Elastic Fluids to Diffuse Through Each Other," from quite insufficient data he evolved the final form of the law of partial pressures. Similarly, in a paper on the expansion of gases by heat, he anticipated by six months Gay-Lussac's conclusions.

During these years in Manchester, Dalton was teaching mechanics, algebra, geometry, bookkeeping, chemistry, and natural philosophy to private students as well as in New College. He traveled very little—only occasionally to Bristol and to London, which he thought the "most disagreeable place for one of a contemplative turn to exist in"—and his contact with the intellectual and scientific world was wholly through the books available to him in the free library of Manchester. Yet his papers were attracting such attention that in 1803 he was invited to give a course of lectures at the Royal Institution in London, and his teaching was drawing to him so many private pupils that he withdrew from New College.

Between 1803 and 1820, after which Dalton's powers faded and his production diminished, he prepared studies on fog, on alloys, on sulphuric ether, on respiration, and on animal heat. Most important, he developed his atomic theory. He first presented his ideas on atoms in a series of lectures given in Glasgow in 1807; and in a second course of lectures at the Royal Institution in London, in 1809–10, he explained how he had come to his conclusions. The real publication came, however, in the first volume of his *New System of Chemical Philosophy,* 1808. From this volume pertinent passages are here reprinted.

In person, Dalton was of middle height, robust, muscular, and awkward. His mouth was firm, his voice gruff, his chin massive. He was said to resemble Newton. His mode of living was always quiet, adjusted to the contemplative life he preferred. For thirty years he occupied the same lodgings in Manchester (he never married) going thence daily to his rooms at the Literary and Philosophical Society to receive his pupils and do his own experimenting. On Sundays he faithfully attended the Quaker services, and on Thursdays he played a weekly game of bowls.

Dalton's theory of the atomic composition of all matter won quick recognition and acceptance. It earned him such high regard from the scientific and academic world that in his last years honors showered upon him. In 1816 he was elected a corresponding member of the French Academy of Science; in 1822 he was elected Fellow of the Royal Society; in 1826 he was the first recipient of the annual royal medal and prize recently established by George IV; in 1832 Oxford made him a Doctor of Common Law; in 1833 the government awarded him a pension for life, and in the announcement of the grant he was named "one of the greatest legislators of chemical science." He held also a degree as Doctor of Law from Edinburgh, and memberships in learned societies in Munich, Moscow, and Berlin. When he visited Paris in 1822, Biot, Ampère, Arago, Fresnel, Laplace, Cuvier, and other French scientists combined their efforts to honor him.

Many of Dalton's ideas in chemistry have been superseded. His theories of heat are as out-of-date as his use of *elastic fluid* for "gas," *azotic gas* for "nitrogen," *oxygenous gas* for "oxygen," et cetera. His fame is nevertheless secure. It rests upon his discovery of a simple principle, universally applicable to the facts of chemistry—that elements combine always in fixed proportions. Sir Humphry Davy rightly said that in laying the foundation for future labors, Dalton's labors in chemistry resembled those of Kepler in astronomy.

THE ATOMIC THEORY

I. ON THE CONSTITUTION OF BODIES

THERE ARE three distinctions in the kinds of bodies, or three states, which have more especially claimed the attention of philosophical chemists; namely, those which are marked by the terms *elastic fluids, liquids, and solids.* A very familiar instance is exhibited to us in water, of a body, which, in certain circumstances, is capable of assuming all the three states. In steam we recognise a perfectly elastic fluid, in water, a perfect liquid, and in ice, a complete solid. These observations have tacitly led to the conclusion which seems universally adopted, that all bodies of sensible magnitude, whether liquid or solid, are constituted of a vast number of extremely small particles, or atoms of matter bound together by a force of attraction, which is more or less powerful according to circumstances, and which, as it endeavours to prevent their separation, is very properly called, in that view, *attraction of cohesion;* but as it collects them from a dispersed state (as from steam into water) it is called, *attraction of aggregation,* or, more simply, *affinity.* Whatever names it may go by, they still signify one and the same power. It is not my design to call in question this conclusion, which appears completely satisfactory; but to shew that we have hitherto made no use of it, and that the consequence of the neglect has been a very obscure view of chemical agency, which is daily growing more so in proportion to the new lights attempted to be thrown upon it.

Whether the ultimate particles of a body, such as water, are all alike, that is, of the same figure, weight, &c., is a question of some importance. From what is known, we have no reason to apprehend a diversity in these particulars: if it does exist in water, it must equally exist in the elements constituting water, namely, hydrogen and oxygen. Now it is scarcely possible to conceive how the aggregates of dissimilar particles should be so uniformly the same. If some of the particles of water were heavier than others, if a parcel of the liquid on any occasion were constituted principally of these heavier particles, it must be supposed to affect the specific gravity of the mass, a circumstance not known. Similar observations may be made on other substances. Therefore we may conclude that *the ultimate particles of all homogeneous bodies are perfectly alike in weight, figure, &c.* In other words, every particle of water is like every other particle of water; every particle of hydrogen is like every other particle of hydrogen, &c.

Besides the force of attraction, which, in one character or another, belongs universally to ponderable bodies, we find another force that is likewise universal, or acts upon all matter which comes under our cognisance, namely, a force of repulsion. This is now generally, and I think properly, ascribed to the agency of heat. An atmosphere of this subtile fluid constantly surrounds the atoms of all bodies, and prevents them from being drawn into actual contact. This appears to be satisfactorily proved by the observation that the bulk of a body may be diminished by abstracting some of its heat; but it should seem that enlargement and diminution of bulk depend perhaps more on the arrangement than on the size of the ultimate particles.

We are now to consider how these two great antagonist powers of attraction and repulsion are adjusted, so as to allow of the three different states of *elastic fluids, liquids, and solids.* We shall divide the subject into four Sections; namely, first, *on the constitution of pure elastic fluids;* second, *on the constitution of mixed elastic fluids;* third, *on the constitution of liquids,* and fourth, *on the constitution of solids.*

Section 1. On the Constitution of Pure Elastic Fluids

A pure elastic fluid is one, the constituent particles of which are all alike, or in no way distinguishable. Steam, or aqueous vapour, hydrogenous gas, oxygenous gas, azotic gas, and several others are of this kind. These fluids are constituted of particles possessing very diffuse atmospheres of heat, the capacity or bulk of the atmosphere being often one or two thousand times that of the particle in a liquid or solid form. Whatever therefore may be the shape or figure of the solid atom abstractedly, when surrounded by such an atmosphere it must be globular; but as all the globules in any small given volume are subject to the same pressure, they must be equal in bulk, and will therefore be arranged in horizontal strata, like a pile of shot. A volume of elastic fluid is found to expand whenever the pressure is taken off. This proves that the repulsion exceeds the attraction in such case. The absolute attraction and repulsion of the particles of an elastic fluid, we have no means of estimating, though we can have little doubt but that the cotemporary energy of both is great; but the excess of the repulsive energy above the attractive can be estimated, and the law of increase and diminution be ascertained in many cases. Thus, in steam, the density may be taken at $\frac{1}{1728}$ that of water; consequently each particle of steam has 12 times the diameter that one of water has, and must press upon 144 particles of a watery surface; but the pressure upon each is equivalent to that of a column of water of 34 feet; therefore the excess of the elastic force in a particle of steam is equal to the weight of a column of particles of water, whose height is $34 \times 144 = 4896$ feet. And further, this elastic force decreases as the distance of the particles increases. With respect to steam and other elastic fluids then, the force of cohesion is entirely counteracted by that of repulsion, and the only force which is efficacious to move the particles is the excess of the repulsion above the attraction. Thus, if the attraction be as 10 and the repulsion as 12, the effective repulsive force is as 2. It appears, then that an elastic fluid, so far from requiring any force to separate its particles, always requires a force to retain them in their situation, or to prevent their separation.

Some elastic fluids, as hydrogen, oxygen, &c., resist any pressure that has yet been applied to them. In such then it is evident the repulsive force of heat is more than a match for the affinity of the particles and the external pressure united. To what extent this would continue we cannot say; but from analogy we might apprehend that a still greater pressure would succeed in giving the attractive force the superiority, when the elastic fluid would become a liquid or solid. In other elastic fluids, as steam, upon the application of compression to a certain degree, the elasticity apparently ceases altogether, and the particles collect in small drops of liquid, and fall down. This phenomenon requires explanation.

The constitution of a liquid, as water, must then be conceived to be that of an aggregate of particles, exercising in a most powerful manner the forces of attraction and repulsion, but nearly in an equal degree.—Of this more in the sequel.

Section 2. On the Constitution of Mixed Elastic Fluids

When two or more elastic fluids, whose particles do not unite chemically upon mixture, are brought together, one measure of each, they occupy the space of two measures, but become uniformly diffused through each other, and remain so, whatever may be their specific gravities. The fact admits of no doubt; but explanations have been given in various ways, and none of them completely satisfactory. As the subject is one of primary importance in forming a system of chemical principles, we must enter somewhat more fully into the discussion.

Dr. Priestley was one of the earliest to notice the fact: it naturally struck him with surprise that two elastic fluids, having apparently no affinity for each other, should not arrange themselves according to their specific gravities, as liquids do in like circumstances. Though he found this was not the case after the elastic fluids had once been thoroughly mixed, yet he suggests it as probable that if two of such fluids could be exposed to each other without agitation, the one specifically heavier would retain its lower situation. He does not so much as hint at such gases being retained in a mixed state by affinity. With regard to his suggestion of two gases being carefully exposed to each other without agitation, I made a series of experiments expressly to determine the question. From these it seems to be decided that gases always intermingle and gradually diffuse themselves amongst each other, if exposed ever so carefully; but it requires a considerable time to produce a complete intermixture, when the surface of communication is small. This time may vary from a minute to a day or more, according to the quantity of the gases and the freedom of communication.

When or by whom the notion of mixed gases being held together by chemical affinity was first propagated, I do not know; but it seems probable that the notion of water being dissolved in air led to that of air being dissolved in air.—Philosophers found that water gradually disappeared or evaporated in air, and increased its elasticity; but steam at a low temperature was known to be unable to overcome the resistance of the air, therefore the agency of affinity was necessary to account for the effect. In the permanently elastic fluids indeed, this agency did not seem to be so much wanted, as they are all able to support themselves; but the diffusion through each other was a circumstance which did not admit of an easy solution any other way. In regard to the solution of water in air, it was natural to suppose, nay, one might almost have been satisfied without the aid of experiment, that the different gases would have had different affinities for water, and that the quantities of water, dissolved in like circumstances, would have varied according to the nature of the gas. Saussure found however that there was no difference in this respect in the solvent powers of carbonic acid, hydrogen gas, and common air.—It might be expected that at least the *density* of the gas would have some influence upon its solvent powers, that air of half density would take half the water, or the quantity of water would diminish in some proportion to the density; but even here again we are disappointed; whatever be the rarefaction, if water be present, the vapour produces the same elasticity, and the hygrometer finally settles at extreme moisture, as in air of common density in like circumstances. These facts are sufficient to create extreme difficulty in the conception how any principle of affinity or *cohesion* between air and water can be the agent. It is truly astonishing that the same quantity of vapour should cohere to *one* particle of air in a given space as to *one thousand* in the same space. But the wonder does not cease here; a Torricellian vacuum dissolves water; and in this instance we have vapour existing independently of air at all temperatures; what makes it still more remarkable is, the vapour in such vacuum is precisely the same in quantity and force as in the like volume of any kind of air of extreme moisture.

These and other considerations which occurred to me some years ago were sufficient to make me altogether abandon the hypothesis of air dissolving water, and to explain the phenomena some other way, or to acknowledge they were inexplicable. In the autumn of 1801, I hit upon an idea which seemed to be exactly calculated to explain the phenomena of vapour; it gave rise to a great variety of experiments.

The distinguishing feature of the new theory was that the particles of one gas are not elastic or repulsive in regard to the particles of another gas, but only to the particles of their own kind. Consequently when a vessel contains a mixture of two such elastic fluids, each acts independently upon the vessel, with its proper elasticity, just as if the other were absent, whilst no mutual action between the fluids themselves is observed. This position most effectually provided for the existence of vapour of any temperature in the atmosphere, because it could have nothing but its own weight to support; and it was perfectly obvious why neither more nor less vapour could exist in air of extreme moisture than in a vacuum of the same temperature. So far then the great object of the theory was attained. The law of the condensation of vapour in the atmosphere by cold was evidently the same on this scheme as that of the condensation of pure steam, and experience was found to confirm the conclusion at all temperatures. The only thing now wanting to completely establish the independent existence of aqueous vapour in the atmosphere was the conformity of other liquids to water, in regard to the diffusion and condensation of their vapour. This was found to take place in several liquids, and particularly in sulphuric ether, one which was most likely to shew any anomaly to advantage if it existed, on account of the great change of expansibility in its vapour at ordinary temperatures. The existence of vapour in the atmosphere and its occasional condensation were thus accounted for; but another question remained, how does it rise from a surface of water subject to the pressure of the atmosphere?

From the novelty, both in the theory and the experiments, and their importance, provided they were correct, the new facts and experiments were highly valued, some of the latter were repeated, and found correct, and none of the results, as far as I know, have been controverted; but the theory was almost universally misunderstood, and consequently reprobated. This must have arisen partly at least from my being too concise, and not sufficiently clear in its exposition.

Dr. Thomson was the first, as far as I know, who publicly animadverted upon the theory; this gentleman, so well known for his excellent *System of Chemistry,* observed in the first edition of that work that the theory would not account for the equal distribution of gases; but that, granting the supposition of one gas neither attracting nor repelling another, the two must still arrange themselves according to their specific gravity. But the most general objection to it was quite of a different kind; it was admitted that the theory was adapted so as to obtain the most uniform and permanent diffusion of gases; but it was urged that as one gas was as a vacuum to another, a measure of any gas being put to a measure of another, the two measures ought to occupy the space of one measure only. Finding that my views on the subject were thus misapprehended, I wrote an illustration of the theory, which was published in the 3d Vol. of *Nicholson's Journal,* for November, 1802. In that paper I endeavoured to point out the conditions of mixed gases more at large, according to my hypothesis; and particularly touched upon the discriminating feature of it, that of two particles of any gas A, repelling each other by the known stated law, whilst one or more particles of another gas B were interposed in a direct line, without at all affecting the reciprocal action of the said two particles of A. Or, if any particle of B were casually to come in contact with one of A, and press against it, this pressure did not preclude the cotemporary action of all the surrounding particles of A upon the one in contact with B. In this respect the mutual action of particles of the same gas was represented as resembling magnetic action, which is not disturbed by the intervention of a body not magnetic.

Berthollet in his *Chemical Statics* (1804) has given a chapter on the constitution of the atmosphere, in which he has entered largely into a discussion of the new theory. This celebrated chemist, upon comparing the results of experiments made by De Luc, Saussure, Volta, Lavoisier, Watt, &c., together with those of Gay-Lussac, and his own, gives his full assent to the fact that vapours of every kind increase the elasticity of each species of gas alike, and just as much as the force of the said vapours in vacuo; and not only so, but that the specific gravity of vapour in air and vapour in vacuo is in all cases the same (Vol. 1. Sect. 4). Consequently he adopts the theorem for finding the quantity of vapour which a given volume of air can dissolve, which I have laid down; namely,

$$ s = \frac{p}{p-f} $$

where p represents the pressure upon a given volume (1) of dry air, expressed in inches of mercury, $f =$ the force of the vapour in vacuo at the temperature, in inches of mercury, and $s =$ the space which the mixture of air and vapour occupies under the given pressure, p, after saturation. So far therefore we perfectly agree: but he objects to the theory by which I attempt to explain these phenomena, and substitutes another of his own.

The first objection I shall notice is one that clearly shews Berthollet either does not understand or does not rightly apply the theory he opposes; he says, "If one gas occupied the interstices of another, as though they were vacancies, there would not be any augmentation of volume when aqueous or ethereal vapour was combined with the air; nevertheless there is one proportional to the quantity of vapour added: humidity should increase the specific gravity of the air, whereas it renders it specifically lighter, as has been already noticed by Newton." This is the objection which has been so frequently urged. Let a tall cylindrical glass vessel containing dry air be inverted over mercury, and a portion of the air drawn out by a syphon, till an equilibrium of pressure is established within and without; let a small portion of water, ether, &c., be then thrown up into the vessel; the vapour rises and occupies the interstices of the air as a void; but what is the obvious consequence? Why, the surface of the mercury being now pressed both by the dry air and by the new raised vapour is more pressed within than without, and an enlargement of the volume of air is unavoidable, in order to restore the equilibrium. Again, in the open air: suppose there were no aqueous atmosphere around the earth, only an azotic one = 23 inches of mercury, and an oxygenous one = 6 inches. The air being thus perfectly dry, evaporation would commence with great speed. The vapour first formed, being constantly urged to ascend by that below, and as constantly resisted by the air, must, in the first instance, dilate the other two atmospheres (for the ascending steam adds its force to the upward elasticity of the two gases, and in part alleviates their pressure, the necessary consequence of which is dilatation). At last, when all the vapour has ascended that the temperature will admit of, the aqueous atmosphere attains an equilibrium; it no longer presses upon the other two, but upon the earth; the others return to their original density and pressure throughout. In this case, it is true, there would not be any augmentation of volume when aqueous vapour was combined with the air; humidity would increase the weight of the congregated atmospheres, but diminish their specific gravity under a given pressure. One would have thought that this solution of the phenomenon upon my hypothesis was too obvious to escape the notice of anyone in any degree conversant with pneumatic chemistry.

Another objection is derived from the very considerable time requisite for a body of hydrogen to descend into one of carbonic acid; if one gas were as a vacuum for another, why is the equilibrium not instantly established? This objection is certainly plausible; we shall consider it more at large hereafter.

In speaking of the pressure of the atmosphere retaining water in a liquid state, which I deny, Berthollet adopts the idea of Lavoisier, "that without it the moleculæ would be infinitely dispersed, and that nothing would limit their separation, unless their own weight should collect them to form an atmosphere." This, I may remark, is not the language dictated by a correct notion on the subject. Suppose our atmosphere were annihilated, and the waters on the surface of the globe were instantly expanded into steam; surely the action of gravity would collect the moleculæ into an atmosphere of similar constitution to the one we now possess; but suppose the whole mass of water evaporated amounted in weight to 30 inches of mercury, how could it support its own weight at the common temperature? It would in a short time be condensed into water merely by its weight, leaving a small portion, such as the temperature could support, amounting perhaps to half an inch of mercury in weight, as a permanent atmosphere, which would effectually prevent any more vapour from rising, unless there were an increase of temperature. Does not everyone know that water and other liquids can exist in a Torricellian vacuum at low temperatures solely by the pressure of vapour arising from them? What need then of the pressure of the atmosphere in order to prevent an excess of vapourisation?

The experiments of Fontana on the distillation of water and ether in close vessels containing air are adduced to prove that vapours do not penetrate air without resistance. This is true no doubt; vapour cannot make its way in such circumstances through a long and circuitous route without time, and if the external atmosphere keep the vessel cool, the vapour may be condensed by its sides, and fall down in a liquid form as fast as it is generated, without ever penetrating in any sensible quantity to its remote extremity.

Dr. Thomson, in the 3d Edition of his *System of Chemistry,* has entered into a discussion on the subject of mixed gases; he seems to comprehend the excellence and defects of my notions on these subjects, with great acuteness. He does not conclude with Berthollet that, on my hypothesis, "there would not be any augmentation of volume when aqueous and ethereal vapour was combined with the air," which has been so common an objection. There is however one objection which this gentleman urges that shews he does not completely understand the mechanism of my hypothesis. At page 448, Vol. 3, he observes that from the principles of hydrostatics, "each particle of a fluid sustains the whole pressure. Nor can I perceive any reason why this principle should not hold, even on the supposition that Dalton's hypothesis is well founded." Upon this I would observe that when once an equilibrium is established in any mixture of gases, each particle of gas is pressed as if by the surrounding particles *of its own kind only*. It is in the renunciation of that hydrostatical principle that the leading feature of the theory consists. The lowest particle of oxygen in the atmosphere sustains the weight of all the particles of oxygen above it, and the weight of no other. It was therefore a maxim with me that every particle of gas is equally pressed in every direction, but the pressure arises from the particles of its own kind only. Indeed when a measure of oxygen is put to a measure of azote, at the moment the two surfaces come in contact, the particles of each gas press against those of the other with their full force; but the two gases get gradually intermingled, and the force which each particle has to sustain proportionally diminishes, till at last it becomes the same as that of the original gas dilated to twice its volume. The ratio of the forces is as the cube root of the spaces inversely; that is, $\sqrt[3]{2} : 1$, or as 1.26 : 1 nearly. In such a mixture as has just been mentioned, then, the common hypothesis supposes the pressure of each particle of gas to be 1.26; whereas mine supposes it only to be 1; but the sum of the pressure of both gases on the containing vessel, or any other surface, is exactly the same on both hypotheses.

With regard to the objection that one gas makes a more durable resistance to the entrance of another than it ought to do on my hypothesis: This occurred to me in a very early period of my speculations; I devised the train of reasoning which appeared to obviate the objection; but it being necessarily of a mathematical nature, I did not wish to obtrude it upon the notice of chemical philosophers, but rather to wait till it was called for.—The resistance which any medium makes to the motion of a body depends upon the surface of that body, and is greater as the surface is greater, all other circumstances being the same. A ball of lead 1 inch in diameter meets with a certain resistance in falling through the air; but the same ball, being made into a thousand smaller ones of $\frac{1}{10}$ of an inch diameter, and falling with the same velocity, meets with 10 times the resistance it did before: because the force of gravity increases as the *cube* of the diameter of any particle, and the resistance only as the *square* of the diameter. Hence it appears that in order to increase the resistance of particles moving in any medium, it is only necessary to divide them, and that the resistance will be a maximum when the division is a maximum. We have only then to consider particles of lead falling through air by their own gravity, and we may have an idea of the resistance of one gas entering another, *only the particles of lead must be conceived to be infinitely small,* if I may be allowed the expression. Here we shall find great resistance, and yet no one, I should suppose, will say that the air and the lead are mutually elastic.

Mr. Murray has lately edited a system of chemistry, in which he has given a very clear description of the phenomena of the atmosphere, and of other similar mixtures of elastic fluids. He has ably discussed the different theories that have been proposed on the subject, and given a perspicuous view of mine, which he thinks is ingenious, and calculated to explain several of the phenomena well, but, upon the whole, not equally satisfactory with that which he adopts. He does not object to the mechanism of my hypothesis in regard to the independent elasticity of the several gases entering into any mixture, but argues that the phenomena do not require so extraordinary a postulatum; and more particularly disapproves of the application of my theory to account for the evaporation.

The principal feature in Mr. Murray's theory, and which he thinks distinguishes it from mine, is "that between mixed gases, which are capable, under any circumstances of combining, an attraction must always be exerted."

Before we animadvert on these principles, it may be convenient to extend the first a little farther, and to adopt as a maxim, "that between the particles of *pure* gases, which are capable under any circumstances of combining, an attraction must always be exerted." This, Mr. Murray cannot certainly object to, in the case of steam, a pure elastic fluid, the particles of which are known in certain circumstances to combine. Nor will it be said that steam and a permanent gas are different; for he justly observes, "this distinction (between gases and vapours) is merely relative, and arises from the difference of temperature at which they are formed; the state with regard to each, while they exist in it, is precisely the same." Is steam then constituted of particles in which the attraction is so far exerted as to prevent their separation? No: they exhibit no traces of attraction, more than the like number of particles of oxygen do, when in the gaseous form. What then is the conclusion? It is this: *notwithstanding it must be allowed that all bodies, at all times, and in every situation, attract one another; yet in certain circumstances, they are likewise actuated by a repulsive power; the only efficient motive force is then the difference of these two powers.*

From the circumstance of gases mixing together without experiencing any sensible diminution of volume, the advocates for the agency of chemical affinity characterise it as a "slight action," and "a weak reciprocal action." So far I think they are consistent; but when we hear of this affinity being so far exerted as to prevent the separation of elastic particles, I do not conceive with what propriety it can be called weak. Suppose this affinity should be exercised in the case of steam of 212°; then the attraction becoming equal to the repulsion, the force which any one particle would exercise must be equal to the weight of a column of water of 4896 feet high.

It is somewhat remarkable that those gases which are known to combine occasionally, as azote and oxygen, and those which are never known to combine, as hydrogen and carbonic acid, should dissolve one another with equal facility; nay, these last exercise this solvent power with more effect than the former; for hydrogen can draw up carbonic acid from the bottom to the top of any vessel, notwithstanding the latter is 20 times the specific gravity of the former. One would have thought that a force of adhesion was more to be expected in the particles of steam than in a mixture of hydrogen and carbonic acid. But it is the business of those who adopt the theory of the mutual solution of gases to explain these difficulties.

In a mixture where are 8 particles of oxygen for 1 of hydrogen, it is demonstrable that the central distances of the particles of hydrogen are at a medium twice as great as those of oxygen. Now supposing the central distance of two adjacent particles of hydrogen to be denoted by 12, query, what is supposed to be the central distance of any one particle of hydrogen from that one particle, or those particles of oxygen with which it is connected by this weak chemical union? It would be well if those who understand and maintain the doctrine of chemical solution would represent how they conceive this to be; it would enable those who are desirous to learn, to obtain a clear idea of the system, and those who are dissatisfied with it, to point out its defects with more precision.

In discussing the doctrines of elastic fluids mixed with vapour, Mr. Murray seems disposed to question the accuracy of the fact that the quantity of vapour is the same in vacuo as in air, though he has not attempted to ascertain in which case it more abounds. This is certainly the touchstone of the mechanical and chemical theories; and I had thought that whoever admitted the truth of the fact must unavoidably adopt the mechanical theory. Berthollet however, convinced from his own experience that the fact was incontrovertible, attempts to reconcile it, inimical as it is, to the chemical theory; with what success it is left to others to judge. Mr. Murray joins with Berthollet in condemning as extravagant the position which I maintain, that if the atmosphere were annihilated, we should have little more aqueous vapour than at present exists in it. Upon which I shall only remark that if either of those gentlemen will calculate, or give a rough estimate upon their hypothesis, of the quantity of aqueous vapour that would be collected around the earth, on the said supposition, I will engage to discuss the subject with them more at large.

In 1802, Dr. Henry announced a very curious and important discovery, which was afterwards published in the *Philosophical Transactions;* namely, *that the quantity of any gas absorbed by water is increased in direct proportion to the pressure of the gas on the surface of the water.* Previously to this, I was engaged in an investigation of the quantity of carbonic acid in the atmosphere; it was matter of surprise to me that lime water should so readily manifest the presence of carbonic acid in the air, whilst pure water, by exposure for any length of time, gave not the least traces of that acid. I thought that length of time ought to compensate for weakness of affinity. In pursuing the subject I found that the quantity of this acid taken up by water was greater or less in proportion to its greater or less density in the gaseous mixture, incumbent upon the surface, and therefore ceased to be surprised at water absorbing so insensible a portion from the atmosphere. I had not however entertained any suspicion that this law was generally applicable to the gases till Dr. Henry's discovery was announced. Immediately upon this, it struck me as essentially necessary, in ascertaining the quantity of any gas which a given volume of water will absorb, that we must be careful the gas is perfectly pure or unmixed with any other gas whatever; otherwise the maximum effect for any given pressure cannot be produced. This thought was suggested to Dr. Henry, and found to be correct; in consequence of which it became expedient to repeat some of his experiments relating to the quantity of gas absorbed under a given pressure. Upon due consideration of all these phenomena, Dr. Henry became convinced that there was no system of elastic fluids which gave so simple, easy and intelligible a solution of them as the one I adopt, namely, that each gas in any mixture exercises a distinct pressure, which continues the same if the other gases are withdrawn.

I shall now proceed to give my present views on the subject of mixed gases, which are somewhat different from what they were when the theory was announced, in consequence of the fresh lights which succeeding experience has diffused. In prosecuting my enquiries into the nature of elastic fluids, I soon perceived it was necessary, if possible, to ascertain whether the atoms or ultimate particles of the different gases are of the same size or volume in like circumstances of temperature and pressure. By the size or volume of an ultimate particle, I mean, in this place, the space it occupies in the state of a pure elastic fluid; in this sense the bulk of the particle signifies the bulk of the supposed impenetrable nucleus, together with that of its surrounding repulsive atmosphere of heat. At the time I formed the theory of mixed gases, I had a confused idea, as many have, I suppose, at this time, that the particles of elastic fluids are all of the same size; that a given volume of oxygenous gas contains just as many particles as the same volume of hydrogenous; or, if not, that we had no data from which the question could be solved. But from a train of reasoning I became convinced that different gases have *not* their particles of the same size; and that the following may be adopted as a maxim, till some reason appears to the contrary: namely,—

That every species of pure elastic fluid has its particles globular and all of a size; but that no two species agree in the size of their particles, the pressure and temperature being the same.

When we contemplate upon the disposition of the globular particles in a volume of pure elastic fluid, we perceive it must be analogous to that of a square pile of shot; the particles must be disposed into horizontal strata, each four particles forming a square: in a superior stratum, each particle rests upon four particles below, the points of its contact with all four being 45° above the horizontal plane, or that plane which passes through the centres of the four particles. On this account the pressure is steady and uniform throughout. But when a measure of one gas is presented to a measure of another in any vessel, we have then a surface of elastic globular particles of one size in contact with an equal surface of particles of another: in such case the points of contact of the heterogeneous particles must vary all the way from 40° to 90°; an intestine motion must arise from this inequality, and the particles of one kind be propelled amongst those of the other. The same cause which prevented the two elastic surfaces from maintaining an equilibrium will always subsist, the particles of one kind being from their size unable to apply properly to the other, so that no equilibrium can ever take place amongst the heterogeneous particles. The intestine motion must therefore continue till the particles arrive at the opposite surface of the vessel against any point of which they can rest with stability, and the equilibrium at length is acquired when each gas is uniformly diffused through the other. In the open atmosphere no equilibrium can take place in such case till the particles have ascended so far as to be restrained by their own weight; that is, till they constitute a distinct atmosphere.

It is remarkable that when two equal measures of different gases are thus diffused, and sustain an invaried pressure, as that of the atmosphere, the pressure upon each particle after the mixture is less than before. This points out the active principle of diffusion; for particles of fluids are always disposed to move to that situation where the pressure is least. Thus, in a mixture of equal measures of oxygen and hydrogen, the common pressure on each particle before mixture being denoted by 1, that after the mixture, when the gas becomes of half its density, will be denoted by $\sqrt[3]{1/2} = .794$.

This view of the constitution of mixed gases agrees with that which I have given before, in the two following particulars, which I consider as essential to every theory on the subject to give it plausibility.

1st. The diffusion of gases through each other is effected by means of the repulsion belonging to the homogenous particles; or to that principle which is always energetic to produce the dilatation of the gas.

2d. When any two or more mixed gases acquire an equilibrium, the elastic energy of each against the surface of the vessel or of any liquid is precisely the same as if it were the only gas present occupying the whole space, and all the rest were withdrawn.

In other respects I think the last view accords better with the phenomena.

Section 3. On the Constitution of Liquids, and the Mechanical Relations betwixt Liquids and Elastic Fluids

A liquid or inelastic fluid may be defined to be a body, the parts of which yield to a very small impression, and are easily moved one upon another. This definition may suffice for the consideration of liquids in an hydrostatical sense, but not in a chemical sense. Strictly speaking, there is no substance inelastic; but we commonly apply the word elastic to such fluids only as have the property of condensation in a very conspicuous degree. Water is a liquid or inelastic fluid; but if it is compressed by a great force, it yields a little, and again recovers its original bulk when the pressure is removed. We are indebted to Mr. Canton for a set of experiments by which the compressibility of several liquids is demonstrated. Water, he found, lost about $\frac{1}{21740}$th part of its bulk by the pressure of the atmosphere.

When we consider the origin of water from steam, we have no reason to wonder at its compressibility, and that in a very small degree; it would be wonderful if water had not this quality. The force of steam at 212° is equal to the pressure of the atmosphere; what a prodigious force must it have when condensed 15 or 18 hundred times? The truth is, water, and, by analogy, other liquids, must be considered as bodies, under the control of two most powerful and energetic agents, attraction and repulsion, between which there is an equilibrium. If any compressing force is applied, it yields, indeed, but in such a manner as a strong spring would yield when wound up almost to the highest pitch. When we attempt to separate one portion of liquid from another, the case is different: here the attraction is the antagonist force, and that being balanced by the repulsion of the heat, a moderate force is capable of producing the separation. But even here we perceive the attractive force to prevail, there being a manifest cohesion of the particles. Whence does this arise? It should seem that when two particles of steam coalesce to form water, they take their station so as to effect a perfect equilibrium between the two opposite powers; but if any foreign force intervene, so as to separate the two molecules an evanescent space, the repulsion decreases faster than the attraction, and consequently this last acquires a superiority or excess, which the foreign force has to overcome. If this were not the case, why do they at first, or upon the formation of water, pass from the greater to the less distance?

With regard to the collocation and arrangement of particles in an aggregate of water or any other liquid, I have already observed that this is not, in all probability, the same as in air. It seems highly improbable from the phenomena of the expansion of liquids by heat. The law of expansion is unaccountable for, if we confine liquids to one and the same arrangement of their ultimate particles in all temperatures; for we cannot avoid concluding, if that were the case, the expansion would go on in a progressive way with the heat, like as in air; and there would be no such thing observed as a point of temperature at which the expansion was stationary.

RECIPROCAL PRESSURE OF LIQUIDS AND ELASTIC FLUIDS

When an elastic fluid is confined by a vessel of certain materials, such as wood, earthenware, &c., it is found slowly to communicate with the external air, to give and receive successively, till a complete intermixture takes place. There is no doubt but this is occasioned by those vessels being porous, so as to transmit the fluids. Other vessels, as those of metal, glass, &c., confine air most completely. These therefore cannot be porous;

or rather, their pores are too small to admit of the passage of air. I believe no sort of vessel has yet been found to transmit one gas and confine another; such a one is a desideratum in practical chemistry. All the gases appear to be completely porous, as might be expected, and therefore operate very temporarily in confining each other. How are liquids in this respect? Do they resemble glass, or earthenware, or gases, in regard to their power of confining elastic fluids? Do they treat all gases alike, or do they confine some and transmit others? These are important questions: they are not to be answered in a moment. We must patiently examine the facts.

Before we can proceed, it will be necessary to lay down a rule, if possible, by which to distinguish the *chemical* from the *mechanical* action of a liquid upon an elastic fluid. I think the following cannot well be objected to: *When an elastic fluid is kept in contact with a liquid, if any change is perceived, either in the elasticity or any other property of the elastic fluid, so far the mutual action must be pronounced* CHEMICAL: *but if* NO *change is perceived, either in the elasticity or any other property of the elastic fluid, then the mutual action of the two must be pronounced wholly* MECHANICAL.

If a quantity of lime be kept in water and agitated, upon standing a sufficient time, the lime falls down, and leaves the water transparent: but the water takes a small portion of the lime which it permanently retains, contrary to the Laws of specific gravity. Why? Because that portion of lime is dissolved by the water. If a quantity of air be put to water and agitated, upon standing a sufficient time, the air rises up to the surface of the water and leaves it transparent; but the water permanently retains a portion of air, contrary to the Laws of specific gravity. Why? Because that small portion of air is dissolved by the water. So far the two explanations are equally satisfactory. But if we place the two portions of water under the receiver of an air pump, and exhaust the incumbent air, the whole portion of air absorbed by the water ascends, and is drawn out of the receiver; whereas the lime remains still in solution as before. If now the question be repeated, why is the air retained in the water? The answer must be, because there is an elastic force on the surface of the water which holds it in. The water appears passive in the business. But, perhaps, the pressure on the surface of the water may have some effect upon its affinity for air, and none on that for lime? Let the air be drawn off from the surfaces of the two portions of water, and another species induced without alleviating the pressure. The lime water remains unchanged; the air escapes from the other much the same as in vacuo. The question of the relation of water to air appears by this fact to be still more difficult; at first the air seemed to be retained by the attraction of the water; in the second case, the water seemed indifferent; in the third, it appears as if repulsive to the air; yet in all three, it is the same air that has to act on the same water. From these facts, there seems reason then for maintaining three opinions on the subject of the mutual action of air and water; namely, that water attracts air, that water does not attract it, and that water repels air. One of these must be true; but we must not decide hastily. Dr. Priestley once imagined that the clay of a porous earthen retort, when red hot, "destroys for a time the aërial form of whatever air is exposed to the outside of it; which aërial form it recovers, after it has been transmitted in combination from one part of the clay to another, till it has reached the inside of the retort." But he soon discarded so extravagant an opinion.

From the recent experiments of Dr. Henry, with those of my own, there appears reason to conclude that a given volume of water absorbs the following parts of its bulk of the several gases.

Bulk of gas absorbed.

1	= 1	Carbonic acid
1	= 1	Sulphuretted hydrogen
1	= 1	Nitrous oxide
$\frac{1}{8}$	= .125	Olefiant gas
$\frac{1}{27}$	= .037	Oxygenous gas
$\frac{1}{27}$	= .037	Nitrous gas
$\frac{1}{27}$	= .037	Carburetted hydrogen
$\frac{1}{27}$	= .037	Carbonic oxide?
$\frac{1}{64}$	= .0156	Azotic gas
$\frac{1}{64}$	= .0156	Hydrogenous gas
$\frac{1}{64}$	= .0156	Carbonic oxide?

These fractions are the cubes of $\frac{1}{1}$, $\frac{1}{2}$, $\frac{1}{3}$, $\frac{1}{4}$, &c. This shews the distances of the gaseous particles in the water to be always same multiple of the distances without.

In a mixture of two or more gases, the rule holds the same as when the gases are alone; that is, the quantity of each absorbed is the same as if it was the only gas present.

As the quantity of any gas in a given volume is subject to variation from pressure and temperature, it is natural to enquire whether any change is induced in the absorption of these circumstances; the experiments of Dr. Henry have decided this point, by ascertaining that if the exterior gas is condensed or rarefied in any degree, the gas absorbed is condensed or rarefied in the same degree; so that the proportions absorbed given above are absolute.

One remarkable fact, which has been hinted at, is that no one gas is capable of retaining another in water; it escapes, not indeed instantly, like as in a vacuum, but gradually, like as carbonic acid escapes into the atmosphere from the bottom of a cavity communicating with it.

It remains now to decide whether the relation between water and the above-mentioned gases is of a *chemical* or *mechanical* nature. From the facts just stated, it appears evident that the elasticity of carbonic acid and the other two gases of the first class is not at all affected by the water. It remains exactly of the same energy whether the water is present or absent. All the other properties of those gases continue just the same, as far as I know, whether they are alone or blended with water: we must therefore,

I conceive, if we abide by the Law just laid down, pronounce the mutual action between these gases and water to be *mechanical.*

In the other gases it is very remarkable their density within the water should be such as to require the distance of the particles to be just 2, 3 or 4 times what it is without. In olefiant gas, the distance of the particles within is just twice that without, as is inferred from the density being $\frac{1}{8}$. In oxygenous gas, &c., the distance is 3 times as great, and in hydrogenous, &c., 4 times. This is certainly curious, and deserves further investigation; but at present we have only to decide whether the general phenomena denote the relation to be of a chemical or mechanical nature. In no case whatever does it appear that the elasticity of any of these gases is affected; if water takes $\frac{1}{27}$ of its bulk of any gas, the gas so absorbed exerts $\frac{1}{27}$ of the elasticity that the exterior gas does, and of course it escapes from the water when the pressure is withdrawn from its surface, or when a foreign one is induced, against which it is not a proper match. As far as is known too, all the other properties of the gases continue the same; thus, if water containing oxygenous gas be admitted to nitrous gas, the union of the two gases is certain; after which the water takes up $\frac{1}{27}$ of its bulk of nitrous gas, as it would have done, if this circumstance had not occurred. It seems clear then that the relation is a *mechanical* one.

Carbonic acid gas then presses upon water in the first instance with its whole force; in a short time it partly enters the water, and then the reaction of the part entered contributes to support the incumbent atmosphere. Finally, the gas gets completely diffused through the water, so as to be of the same density within as without; the gas within the water then presses on the containing vessel only, and reacts upon the incumbent gas. The water then sustains no pressure either from the gas within or without. In olefiant gas the surface of the water supports $\frac{7}{8}$ of the pressure, in oxygenous, &c., $\frac{26}{27}$, and in hydrogenous, &c., $\frac{63}{64}$.

When any gas is confined in a vessel over water in the pneumatic trough, so as to communicate with the atmosphere through the medium of water, that gas must constantly be filtring through the water into the atmosphere, whilst the atmospheric air is filtring through the water the contrary way, to supply its place in the vessel; so that in due time the air in the vessel becomes atmospheric, as various chemists have experienced. Water in this respect is like an earthenware retort: it admits the gases to go both ways at the same time.

It is not easy to assign a reason why water should be so permeable to carbonic acid, &c., and not to the other gases; and why there should be those differences observable in the others. The densities $\frac{1}{8}$, $\frac{1}{27}$ and $\frac{1}{64}$ have most evidently a reference to a mechanical origin, but none whatever to a chemical one. No mechanical equilibrium could take place if the densities of the gases within were not regulated by this law; but why the gases should not all agree in some one of these forms, I do not see any reason.

Upon the whole it appears that water, like earthenware, is incapable of forming a perfect barrier to any kind of air; but it differs from earthenware in one respect; the last is alike permeable to all the gases, but water is much more permeable to some gases than to others. Other liquids have not been sufficiently examined in this respect.

Section 4.   On the Constitution of Solids

A solid body is one, the particles of which are in a state of equilibrium betwixt two great powers, attraction and repulsion, but in such a manner that no change can be made in their distances without considerable force.

Notwithstanding the *hardness* of solid bodies, or the difficulty of moving the particles one amongst another, there are several that admit of such motion without fracture, by the application of proper force, especially if assisted by heat. The ductility and malleability of the metals need only to be mentioned. It should seem the particles glide along each other's surface, somewhat like a piece of polished iron at the end of a magnet, without being at all weakened in their cohesion. The absolute force of cohesion, which constitutes the *strength* of bodies, is an enquiry of great practical importance. It has been found by experiment that wires of the several metals beneath, being each $\frac{1}{10}$ of an inch in diameter, were just broken by the annexed weights.

Lead	$29\frac{1}{4}$
Tin	$49\frac{1}{4}$
Copper	$299\frac{1}{4}$
Brass	360
Silver	370
Iron	450
Gold	500

} Pounds.

A piece of good oak, an inch square and a yard ,ong, will just bear in the middle 330 lbs. But such a piece of wood should not in practice be trusted, for any length of time, with above $\frac{1}{3}$ or $\frac{1}{4}$ of that weight. Iron is about 10 times as strong as oak, of the same dimensions.

One would be apt to suppose that *strength* and *hardness* ought to be found proportionate to each other; but this is not the case. Glass is harder than iron, yet the latter is much the stronger of the two.

Crystallization exhibits to us the effects of the natural arrangement of the ultimate particles of various compound bodies; but we are scarcely yet sufficiently acquainted with chemical synthesis and analysis to understand the rationale of this process. The rhomboidal form may arise from the proper position of 4, 6, 8, or 9 globular particles, the cubic form from 8 particles, the triangular form from 3, 6 or 10 particles, the hexahedral prism from 7 particles, &c. Perhaps, in due time, we may be enabled to ascertain the number and order of elementary particles, constituting any given compound element, and from that determine the figure which it will prefer on crystallization, and *vice versa;* but it seems premature to form any theory on this subject till we have discovered from other principles the number and order of the primary elements which combine to form some of the compound elements of most frequent occurrence; the method for which we shall endeavour to point out in the ensuing chapter.

II. ON CHEMICAL SYNTHESIS

WHEN any body exists in the elastic state, its ultimate particles are separated from each other to a much greater distance than in any other state; each particle occupies the centre of a comparatively large sphere, and supports its dignity by keeping all the rest, which by their gravity, or otherwise, are disposed to encroach up it, at a respectful distance. When we attempt to conceive the *number* of particles in an atmosphere, it is somewhat like attempting to conceive the number of stars in the universe; we are confounded with the thought. But if we limit the subject, by taking a given volume of any gas, we seem persuaded that, let the divisions be ever so minute, the number of particles must be finite; just as in a given space of the universe, the number of stars and planets cannot be infinite.

Chemical analysis and synthesis go no farther than to the separation of particles one from another, and to their reunion. No new creation or destruction of matter is within the reach of chemical agency. We might as well attempt to introduce a new planet into the solar system, or to annihilate one already in existence, as to create or destroy a particle of hydrogen. All the changes we can produce consist in separating particles that are in a state of cohesion or combination, and joining those that were previously at a distance.

In all chemical investigations, it has justly been considered an important object to ascertain the relative *weights* of the simples which constitute a compound. But unfortunately the enquiry has terminated here; whereas from the relative weights in the mass, the relative weights of the ultimate particles or atoms of the bodies might have been inferred, from which their number and weight in various other compounds would appear, in order to assist and to guide future investigations, and to correct their results. Now it is one great object of this work to shew the importance and advantage of ascertaining *the relative weights of the ultimate particles, both of simple and compound bodies, the number of simple elementary particles which constitute one compound particle, and the number of less compound particles which enter into the formation of one more compound particle.*

If there are two bodies, A and B, which are disposed to combine, the following is the order in which the combinations may take place, beginning with the most simple: namely,

1 atom of A + 1 atom of B = 1 atom of C, binary.
1 atom of A + 2 atoms of B = 1 atom of D, ternary.
2 atoms of A + 1 atom of B = 1 atom of E, ternary.
1 atom of A + 3 atoms of B = 1 atom of F, quaternary.
3 atoms of A + 1 atom of B = 1 atom of G, quaternary.

&c. &c.

The following general rules may be adopted as guides in all our investigations respecting chemical synthesis.

1st. When only one combination of two bodies can be obtained, it must be presumed to be a *binary* one, unless some cause appear to the contrary.

2d. When two combinations are observed, they must be presumed to be a *binary* and a *ternary*.

3d. When three combinations are obtained, we may expect one to be a *binary,* and the other two *ternary*.

4th. When four combinations are observed, we should expect one *binary,* two *ternary,* and one *quaternary,* &c.

5th. A *binary* compound should always be specifically heavier than the mere mixture of its two ingredients.

6th. A *ternary* compound should be specifically heavier than the mixture of a binary and a simple, which would, if combined, constitute it; &c.

7th. The above rules and observations equally apply when two bodies, such as C and D, D and E, &c., are combined.

From the application of these rules to the chemical facts already well ascertained, we deduce the following conclusions: 1st. That water is a binary compound of hydrogen and oxygen, and the relative weights of the two elementary atoms are as 1:7, nearly; 2d. That ammonia is a binary compound of hydrogen and azote, and the relative weights of the two atoms are as 1:5, nearly; 3d. That nitrous gas is a binary compound of azote and oxygen, the atoms of which weigh 5 and 7 respectively; that nitric acid is a binary or ternary compound according as it is derived, and consists of one atom of azote and two of oxygen, together weighing 19; that nitrous oxide is a compound similar to nitric acid, and consists of one atom of oxygen and two of azote, weighing 17; that nitrous acid is a binary compound of nitric acid and nitrous gas, weighing 31; that oxynitric acid is a binary compound of nitric acid and oxygen, weighing 26; 4th. That carbonic oxide is a binary compound, consisting of one atom of charcoal and one of oxygen, together weighing nearly 12; that carbonic acid is a ternary compound (but sometimes binary), consisting of one atom of charcoal and two of oxygen, weighing 19; &c., &c. In all these cases the weights are expressed in atoms of hydrogen, each of which is denoted by unity.

From the novelty as well as importance of the ideas suggested in this chapter, it is deemed expedient to give a plate exhibiting the mode of combination in some of the more simple cases. The elements or atoms of such bodies as are conceived at present to be simple are denoted by a small circle, with some distinctive mark; and the combinations consist in the juxtaposition of two or more of these; when three or more particles of elastic fluids are combined together in one, it is to be supposed that the particles of the same kind repel each other, and therefore take their stations accordingly.

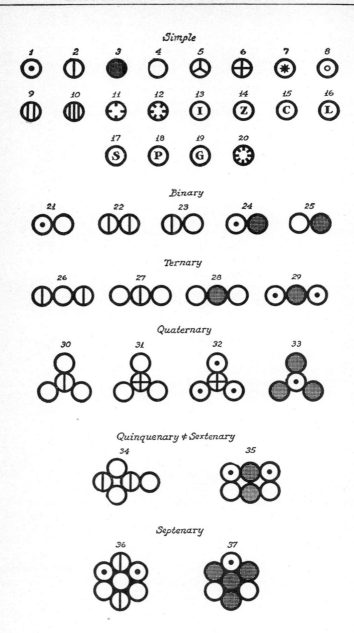

EXPLANATION OF PLATE

This plate contains the arbitrary marks or signs chosen to represent the several chemical elements or ultimate particles.

1.	Hydrog. its rel. weight ...	1	11.	Strontites	46
2.	Azote	5	12.	Barytes	68
3.	Carbone or charcoal	5	13.	Iron	38
4.	Oxygen	7	14.	Zinc	56
5.	Phosphorus	9	15.	Copper	56
6.	Sulphur	13	16.	Lead	95
7.	Magnesia	20	17.	Silver	100
8.	Lime	23	18.	Platina	100
9.	Soda	28	19.	Gold	140
10.	Potash	42	20.	Mercury	167

21. An atom of water or steam, composed of 1 of oxygen and 1 of hydrogen, retained in physical contact by a strong affinity, and supposed to be surrounded by a common atmosphere of heat; its relative weight = ... 8
22. An atom of ammonia, composed of 1 of azote and 1 of hydrogen 6
23. An atom of nitrous gas, composed of 1 of azote and 1 of oxygen 12
24. An atom of olefiant gas, composed of 1 of carbone and 1 of hydrogen 6
25. An atom of carbonic oxide composed of 1 of carbone and 1 of oxygen 12
26. An atom of nitrous oxide, 2 azote+1 oxygen 17
27. An atom of nitric acid, 1 azote+2 oxygen 19
28. An atom of carbonic acid, 1 carbone+2 oxygen 19
29. An atom of carburetted hydrogen, 1 carbone+2 hydrogen 7
30. An atom of oxynitric acid, 1 azote+3 oxygen 26
31. An atom of sulphuric acid, 1 sulphur+3 oxygen 34
32. An atom of sulphuretted hydrogen, 1 sulphur+3 hydrogen 16
33. An atom of alcohol, 3 carbone+1 hydrogen 16
34. An atom of nitrous acid, 1 nitric acid+1 nitrous gas 31
35. An atom of acetous acid, 2 carbone+2 water 26
36. An atom of nitrate of ammonia, 1 nitric acid+1 ammonia+1 water 33
37. An atom of sugar, 1 alcohol+1 carbonic acid 35

Enough has been given to shew the method; it will be quite unnecessary to devise characters and combinations of them to exhibit to view in this way all the subjects that come under investigation; nor is it necessary to insist upon the accuracy of all these compounds, both in number and weight; the principle will be entered into more particularly hereafter, as far as respects the individual results. It is not to be understood that all those particles marked as simple substances are necessarily such by the theory;

they are only necessarily of such weights. Soda and potash, such as they are found in combination with acids, are 28 and 42 respectively in weight; but according to Mr. Davy's very important discoveries, they are metallic oxides; the former then must be considered as composed of an atom of metal, 21, and one of oxygen, 7; and the latter, of an atom of metal, 35, and one of oxygen, 7. Or, soda contains 75 per cent metal and 25 oxygen; potash, 83.3 metal and 16.7 oxygen. It is particularly remarkable that according to the above-mentioned gentleman's essay on the Decomposition and Composition of the fixed alkalies in the *Philosophical Transactions* (a copy of which essay he has just favoured me with), it appears that "the largest quantity of oxygen indicated by these experiments was, for potash 17, and for soda, 26 parts in 100, and the smallest 13 and 19."

EXPERIMENTAL RESEARCHES
IN ELECTRICITY

by

MICHAEL FARADAY

CONTENTS

Experimental Researches in Electricity

MICHAEL FARADAY

1791–1867

THE FARADAYS cherished a tradition that a progenitor had come from Ireland into northern England. There, in Westmorland, the family first appears in eighteenth-century records as members of a Sandemanian (or Glassite) congregation. James Faraday, born in 1761, became a blacksmith, married Margaret Hastwell, and removed to London. His four children were born in London or in Surrey, near by. Michael, the third child, was born in Newington, Surrey, in 1791. Because James never earned much, and was besides afflicted in health, the children grew up in poverty. Michael later reported that his formal education was confined to instruction in the three Rs at a common day school, and that he spent his free hours at home or in the street. When he was twelve he entered the service of a bookbinder and bookseller as errand boy, having practically the duties of a newspaper boy. The following year he was apprenticed to the same bookbinder for a seven-year period.

Faraday's true education began during these years of apprenticeship. He read the books he was binding, he attended the evening lectures of Mr. Tatam, founder of a mutual improvement group called the City Philosophical Society, and he cultivated the acquaintance of several young men who shared his ardency for education and self-improvement. Of his reading, Faraday wrote that he "delighted in Marcet's *Conversations in Chemistry,* and the electrical treatises in the *Encyclopaedia Britannica.*" In his lodgings with his master, he performed such simple experiments in chemistry as he could finance for a few pennies, and he actually built an electrical machine and other bits of electrical apparatus.

About the time Faraday's apprenticeship was ending, in 1812, a customer of his master's took him to hear Sir Humphry Davy lecture at the Royal Institution. The young man's interest was so fired that he attended more of Davy's lectures, took notes on them, elaborated and illustrated his notes with drawings, and resolved to become a scientist rather than a bookbinder. He had the audacity to write to Sir Humphry, asking for an opportunity to work in science, and he enclosed his illustrated lecture notes. Sir Humphry was impressed. He talked to the young man, liked him, advised him not to devote his life to science—which he described as a hard mistress—laughed at his notion that men of science had the highest and purest moral motives, and offered him an assistantship at the Royal Institution. An assistant was granted a salary of twenty-five shillings a week and two rooms at the top of the house. Faraday accepted the offer.

Davy used Faraday's services in his experiments with the explosive nitrogen trichloride, and thought so well of him that when, in the fall of 1813, he decided to go to the Continent for an extended tour, he took him along as his amanuensis. Unfortunately, Davy's valet withdrew at the last moment, and his duties fell upon Faraday. He squirmed; but he persisted in completing the trip with Sir Humphry and Lady Davy, for he was aware that association with the great man was in itself an education. So for two years he traveled through France and Switzerland and the Tyrol and Italy, studying French and Italian diligently, assisting Sir Humphry in the performance of experiments and demonstrations—one of the most fascinating was the burning, at Florence, of a diamond in an atmosphere of oxygen, using the great lenses belonging to the Duke of Florence as a burning glass—making the acquaintance of such scientists as Volta and the elder de la Rive, and writing voluminous letters home to England promising that once back there he would never leave again.

In 1815, Sir Humphry and his party returned to England. Very soon Faraday was back at the Royal Institution as a laboratory assistant and superintendent of apparatus. He had now thirty shillings a week and decent living quarters. At once he called in his old friends of the apprentice days to continue with him their activities for mutual educational improvement. Now a member of the City Philosophical Society, he lectured before it for the first time in 1816, his subject being "The General Properties of Matter." Thereafter he studied elocution with a teacher and devoted some part of his attention to means of making himself a good lecturer. As one of his duties at the Institution, he attended all lectures given there. How much he profited by observing the methods of successful speakers appears from his own success when he first lectured at the Institution in 1827. His series begun then continued for more than thirty years. Europe has never had in science a more practiced, brilliant, and successful popular instructor.

In 1816, Faraday made his first positive contribution to scientific literature, an analysis of native caustic lime from Tuscany. He printed the paper in the *Quarterly Journal of Science;* in the same *Journal,* during the next four years, he printed thirty-seven articles and notes. These were on various subjects in physics and chemistry, for he had not yet settled upon electricity as his special interest. In 1823 he succeeded in liquefying chlorine. The experiment had grown out of a suggestion of Davy's; and Davy claimed that credit for the accomplishment belonged to him. Only Faraday's modesty and disinterestedness prevented a break between the two men. In the following year, when Faraday was nominated to a fellowship in the Royal Society, Davy displayed ill will often interpreted as jealousy. Despite his opposition, Faraday was elected, and the friction between the two lessened quickly. In 1825 it was Davy who nominated Faraday to become the director of the laboratory at the Royal Institution.

While investigating the condensed oil gas manufactured by the Portable Gas Company, Faraday discovered benzol (which he called bicarburet of hydrogen). Some of his biographers have made the rather extravagant claim that he is therefore responsible for the whole enormous aniline trade industry. About the same time, in 1829, he became a lecturer at the Royal Military Academy at Woolwich and a member of the Scientific Advising Committee of the Admiralty. A few years later he became Scientific Adviser to Trinity House. Almost until his death he retained these connections with the government, generally receiving no stipend for the advice and decisions he gave on the ventilation of lighthouses, the purchase and manufacture of optical equipment, the selection of paints, cottons, oils, lightning conductors for lighthouses, and so on. He thought that a good subject owed such services to his government.

Though he had begun some experiments on magnetism and electricity as early as 1823, not until some years later did Faraday devote himself to the great experiments in electricity for which he is principally famous. In 1831 he discovered electromagnetic induction. His results he gave to the Royal Society in his First Series of *Experimental Researches in Electricity.* In the years following he contributed further series of papers regularly. From these the following selections are taken.

The publication of the *Experimental Researches in Electricity* established Faraday's reputation with the non-scientific world. Immediately commerce and industry began to bid for his services. In the next year, by his advisory work, he added a full thousand pounds to his two-hundred-pound stipend from the Institution. The following year he earned more. Then he made up his mind that he could serve only one master, and that he preferred science to wealth. In subsequent years he accepted employment apart from the pure research and lecturing of the Institution at a sharply declining rate; after 1845 he never accepted a penny for any industrial work.

Faraday had married in 1821 the daughter of an elder in the Sandemanian Congregation of which he was a member. With her he lived a life compounded of the sweetest sympathy and understanding. Both were extremely devout, for Faraday kept his religious convictions—the Sandemanians held to doctrines which would now be labeled fundamentalist—and his scientific views strictly apart. In 1840 he was elected an elder in his church, and thus had pressed upon him the duty of preaching a sermon on alternate Sundays. Possibly it was this addition to his already great intellectual load which caused him to suffer a partial breakdown in 1841. He suffered particularly from loss of memory; he had to take a long holiday, and for three years he abandoned his studies.

The long vacation obviously did not impair his powers. In 1845 he discovered the influence of a magnetic field of force on polarized light, and in the same year he established the distinction between magnetic and diamagnetic substances. The two great accomplishments won for him, in 1846, from the Royal Society, both the Royal and the Rumford medals. Such honors were by this time no novelties to him. Perhaps, indeed, no other scientist has ever been equally recognized, feted, and decorated in his own lifetime. He received no fewer than ninety-five honorary titles and marks of distinction from the learned societies of Europe and America. He deserved them. For among the incredibly numerous discoveries credited to him, four must be characterized as massive: magneto-electric induction, the chemical phenomena of the electric current, the magnetization of light, and diamagnetism. And only compared with these are his studies in the liquefaction of gases, in frictional electricity, in regelation, of small importance.

Twice Faraday did refuse honors. In 1835 he refused a government pension—which he was subsequently persuaded to accept. And twice he declined to become president of the Royal Society. He did not refuse the house on Hampton Court Green which Queen Victoria, through the good offices of the Prince Consort, offered him in 1858. There he spent his declining years. In 1865 he made his last report to Trinity House and relinquished his duties at the Royal Institution. In 1867 he died.

Faraday's skill as an experimenter and his success as a

lecturer depended in no small degree on his remarkable sense of order, his pertinacity, and his control over a kind of Celtic impulsiveness. His biographer Tyndall, who was his successor at the Royal Institution and his great personal friend, remarks that the man was never swallowed up in the scientist. He speaks eloquently of Faraday's long friendships with Davy, Biot, the two de la Rives, Arago, Humboldt, and a host of students and assistants. To sum up the man, Tyndall quotes from St. Paul: "blameless, vigilant, sober, of good behaviour, apt to teach, not given to filthy lucre."

EXPERIMENTAL RESEARCHES
IN ELECTRICITY

I. IDENTITY OF ELECTRICITIES DERIVED FROM DIFFERENT SOURCES

THE PROGRESS of the electrical researches which I have had the honour to present to the Royal Society brought me to a point at which it was essential for the further prosecution of my inquiries that no doubt should remain of the identity or distinction of electricities excited by different means. I have satisfied myself that they are identical, and I hope the experiments which I have to offer, and the proofs flowing from them, will be found worthy the attention of the Royal Society.

The various phenomena exhibited by electricity may, for the purposes of comparison, be arranged under two heads; namely, those connected with electricity of tension, and those belonging to electricity in motion. This distinction is taken at present not as philosophical, but merely as convenient. The effect of electricity of tension, at rest, is either attraction or repulsion at sensible distances. The effects of electricity in motion or electrical currents may be considered as 1st, Evolution of heat; 2nd, Magnetism; 3rd, Chemical decomposition; 4th, Physiological phenomena; 5th, Spark. It will be my object to compare electricities from different sources, and especially common and voltaic electricities, by their power of producing these effects.

1. Voltaic Electricity

Tension.—When a voltaic battery of 100 pairs of plates has its extremities examined by the ordinary electrometer, it is well known that they are found positive and negative, the gold leaves at the same extremity repelling each other, the gold leaves at different extremities attracting each other, even when half an inch or more of air intervenes.

That ordinary electricity is discharged by points with facility through air, that it is readily transmitted through highly rarefied air, and also through heated air, as for instance a flame, is due to its high tension. I sought, therefore, for similar effects in the discharge of voltaic electricity, using as a test of the passage of the electricity either the galvanometer or chemical action produced by the arrangement hereafter to be described.

The voltaic battery I had at my disposal consisted of 140 pairs of plates four inches square, with double coppers. It was insulated through-out, and diverged a gold-leaf electrometer about one third of an inch. On endeavouring to discharge this battery by delicate points very nicely ar-ranged and approximated, either in the air or in an exhausted receiver, I could obtain no indications of a current, either by magnetic or chemi-cal action. In this, however, was found no point of discordance between voltaic and common electricity; for when a Leyden battery was charged so as to deflect the gold-leaf electrometer to the same degree, the points were found equally unable to discharge it with such effect as to produce either magnetic or chemical action. This was not because common elec-tricity could not produce both these effects, but because when of such low intensity the quantity required to make the effects visible (being enormously great) could not be transmitted in any reasonable time. In conjunction with the other proofs of identity hereafter to be given, these effects of points also prove identity instead of difference between voltaic and common electricity.

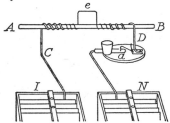

FIG. I.

As heated air discharges common electricity with far greater facility than points, I hoped that voltaic electricity might in this way also be discharged. An apparatus was therefore constructed (Fig. 1), in which A B is an insulated glass rod upon which two copper wires, C, D, are fixed firmly; to these wires are soldered two pieces of fine platina wire, the ends of which are brought very close to each other at e, but without touching; the copper wire C was connected with the positive pole of a voltaic battery, and the wire D with a decomposing apparatus, from which the communication was completed to the negative pole of the bat-tery. In these experiments only two troughs, or twenty pairs of plates, were used.

Whilst in the state described, no decomposition took place at the point a, but when the side of a spirit-lamp flame was applied to the two platina extremities at e, so as to make them bright red-hot, decomposition occurred; iodine soon appeared at the point a, and the transference of electricity through the heated air was established. On raising the tempera-ture of the points e by a blowpipe, the discharge was rendered still more free, and decomposition took place instantly. On removing the source of heat, the current immediately ceased. On putting the ends of the wires very close by the side of and parallel to each other, but not touching, the effects were perhaps more readily obtained than before. On using a larger voltaic battery, they were also more freely obtained.

These effects, not hitherto known or expected under this form, are only cases of the discharge which takes place through air between the charcoal terminations of the poles of a powerful battery, when they are gradually separated after contact. Then the passage is through heated air exactly as with common electricity, and Sir H. Davy has recorded that with the original battery of the Royal Institution this discharge passed through a space of at least four inches. In the exhausted receiver the electricity would *strike* through nearly half an inch of space, and the combined effect of rarefaction and heat was such upon the inclosed air as to enable it to conduct the electricity through a space of six or seven inches.

The instantaneous charge of a Leyden battery by the poles of a voltaic apparatus is another proof of the tension, and also the quantity, of electricity evolved by the latter. Sir H. Davy says, "When the two conductors from the ends of the combination were connected with a Leyden battery, one with the internal, the other with the external coating, the battery instantly became charged; and on removing the wires and making the proper connections, either a shock or a *spark* could be perceived: and the least possible time of contact was sufficient to renew the charge to its full intensity."

In motion: i. *Evolution of heat.*—The evolution of heat in wires and fluids by the voltaic current is matter of general notoriety.

ii. *Magnetism.*—No fact is better known to philosophers than the power of the voltaic current to deflect the magnetic needle, and to make magnets according to *certain laws;* and no effect can be more distinctive of an electrical current.

iii. *Chemical decomposition.*—The chemical powers of the voltaic current, and their subjection to *certain laws,* are also perfectly well known.

iv. *Physiological effects.*—The power of the voltaic current, when strong, to shock and convulse the whole animal system, and when weak to affect the tongue and the eyes, is very characteristic.

v. *Spark.*—The brilliant star of light produced by the discharge of a voltaic battery is known to all as the most beautiful light that man can produce by art.

That these effects may be almost infinitely varied, some being exalted whilst others are diminished, is universally acknowledged; and yet without any doubt of the identity of character of the voltaic currents thus made to differ in their effect. The beautiful explication of these variations afforded by Cavendish's theory of quantity and intensity requires no support at present, as it is not supposed to be doubted.

In consequence of the comparisons that will hereafter arise between wires carrying voltaic and ordinary electricities, and also because of certain views of the condition of a wire or any other conducting substance connecting the poles of a voltaic apparatus, it will be necessary to give some definite expression of what is called the voltaic current, in contradistinction to any supposed peculiar state of arrangement, not progressive, which the wire or the electricity within it may be supposed to assume. If two voltaic troughs P N, P' N', Fig. 2, be symmetrically arranged and insulated, and the ends N P' connected by a wire, over which a magnetic needle is suspended, the wire will exert no effect over the needle; but immediately that the ends P N' are connected by another wire, the needle will be deflected, and will remain so as long as the circuit is complete. Now if the troughs merely act by causing a peculiar arrangement in the wire either of its particles or its electricity, that arrangement constituting its electrical and magnetic state, then the wire N P' should be in a similar state of arrangement *before* P and N' were connected to what it is afterwards, and should have deflected the needle, although less powerfully, perhaps to one half the extent which would result when the communication is complete throughout. But if the magnetic effects depend upon a current, then it is evident why they could not be produced in *any* degree

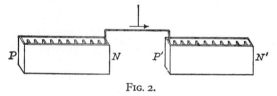

FIG. 2.

before the circuit was complete; because prior to that no current could exist.

By *current,* I mean anything progressive, whether it be a fluid of electricity, or two fluids moving in opposite directions, or merely vibrations, or, speaking still more generally, progressive forces. By *arrangement,* I understand a local adjustment of particles, or fluids, or forces, not progressive. Many other reasons might be urged in support of the view of a *current* rather than an *arrangement,* but I am anxious to avoid stating unnecessarily what will occur to others at the moment.

2. Ordinary Electricity

By ordinary electricity I understand that which can be obtained from the common machine, or from the atmosphere, or by pressure, or cleavage of crystals, or by a multitude of other operations; its distinctive character being that of great intensity, and the exertion of attractive and repulsive powers, not merely at sensible but at considerable distances.

Tension.—The attractions and repulsions at sensible distances, caused by ordinary electricity, are well known to be so powerful in certain cases as to surpass, almost infinitely, the similar phenomena produced by electricity, otherwise excited. But still those attractions and repulsions are exactly of the same nature as those already referred to under the head *Tension, Voltaic electricity;* and the difference in degree between them is not greater than often occurs between cases of ordinary electricity only.

The discharge of common electricity through heated air is a well-known fact. The parallel case of voltaic electricity has already been described.

In motion: i. *Evolution of heat.*—The heating power of common electricity, when passed through wires or other substances, is perfectly well known. The accordance between it and voltaic electricity is in this respect complete.

ii. *Magnetism.*—Voltaic electricity has most extraordinary and exalted magnetic powers. If common electricity be identical with it, it ought to have the same powers. In rendering needles or bars magnetic, it is found to agree with voltaic electricity, and the *direction* of the magnetism, in both cases, is the same; but in deflecting the magnetic needle, common electricity has been found deficient, so that sometimes its power has been denied altogether, and at other times distinctions have been hypothetically assumed for the purpose of avoiding the difficulty.

M. Colladon, of Geneva, considered that the difference might be due to the use of insufficient quantities of common electricity in all the experiments before made on this head; and in a memoir read to the Académie des Sciences in 1826, describes experiments in which, by the use of a battery, points, and a delicate galvanometer, he succeeded in obtaining deflections, and thus establishing identity in that respect. I am happy to say that my results fully confirm those by M. Colladon, and I should have had no occasion to describe them, but that they are essential as proofs of the accuracy of the final and general conclusions I am enabled to draw respecting the magnetic and chemical action of electricity.

The plate electrical machine I have used is fifty inches in diameter; it has two sets of rubbers; its prime conductor consists of two brass cylinders connected by a third, the whole length being twelve feet, and the surface in contact with air about 1422 square inches. When in good excitation, one revolution of the plate will give ten or twelve sparks from the conductors, each an inch in length. Sparks or flashes from ten to fourteen inches in length may easily be drawn from the conductors. Each turn of the machine, when worked moderately, occupies about four fifths of a second.

The electric battery consisted of fifteen equal jars. They are coated eight inches upwards from the bottom, and are twenty-three inches in circumference, so that each contains 184 square inches of glass, coated on both sides; this is independent of the bottoms, which are of thicker glass, and contain each about fifty square inches.

A good *discharging train* was arranged by connecting metallically a sufficiently thick wire with the metallic gas pipes of the house, with the metallic gas pipes belonging to the public gasworks of London, and also with the metallic water pipes of London. It was so effectual in its office as to carry off instantaneously electricity of the feeblest tension, even that of a single voltaic trough, and was essential to many of the experiments.

It was to the retarding power of bad conductors, with the intention of diminishing its *intensity* without altering its *quantity,* that I first looked with the hope of being able to make common electricity assume more of the characters and power of voltaic electricity than it is usually supposed to have.

The coating and armour of the galvanometer were first connected with the discharging train; the end B (Fig. 3) of the galvanometer wire was connected with the outside coating of the battery, and then both these with the discharging train; the end A of the galvanometer wire was connected with a discharging rod by a wet thread four feet long; and finally, when the battery had been positively charged by about forty turns of the machine, it was discharged by the rod and the thread through the galvanometer. The needle immediately moved.

FIG. 3.

During the time that the needle completed its vibration in the first direction and returned, the machine was worked, and the battery recharged; and when the needle in vibrating resumed its first direction, the discharge was again made through the galvanometer. By repeating this action a few times, the vibrations soon extended to above 40° on each side of the line of rest.

This effect could be obtained at pleasure. Nor was it varied, apparently, either in direction or degree, by using a short thick string, or even four short thick strings in place of the long fine thread. With a more delicate galvanometer, an excellent swing of the needle could be obtained by one discharge of the battery.

On reversing the galvanometer communications so as to pass the discharge through from B to A, the needle was equally well deflected, but in the opposite direction.

The deflections were in the same direction as if a voltaic current had been passed through the galvanometer, i.e. the positively charged surface of the electric battery coincided with the positive end of the voltaic apparatus, and the negative surface of the former with the negative end of the latter.

The battery was then thrown out of use, and the communications so arranged that the current could be passed from the prime conductor, by the discharging rod held against it, through the wet string, through the galvanometer coil, and into the discharging train, by which it was finally dispersed. This current could be stopped at any moment, by removing the discharging rod, and either stopping the machine or connecting the prime conductor by another rod with the discharging train; and could be as instantly renewed. The needle was so adjusted that, whilst vibrating in moderate and small arcs, it required time equal to twenty-five beats of a watch to pass in one direction through the arc, and of course an equal time to pass in the other direction.

Thus arranged, and the needle being stationary, the current, direct from the machine, was sent through the galvanometer for twenty-five beats, then interrupted for other twenty-five beats, renewed for twenty-five beats more, again interrupted for an equal time, and so on continually. The needle soon began to vibrate visibly, and after several alternations of this kind, the vibration increased to 40° or more.

On changing the direction of the current through the galvanometer, the direction of the deflection of the needle was also changed. In all cases the motion of the needle was in direction the same as that caused either by the use of the electric battery or a voltaic trough.

I now rejected the wet string, and substituted a copper wire, so that the electricity of the machine passed at once into wires communicating directly with the discharging train, the galvanometer coil being one of the wires used for the discharge. The effects were exactly those obtained above.

Instead of passing the electricity through the system, by bringing the discharging rod at the end of it into contact with the conductor, four points were fixed on to the rod; when the current was to pass, they were held about twelve inches from the conductor, and when it was not to pass, they were turned away. Then operating as before, except with this variation, the needle was soon powerfully deflected, and in perfect consistency with the former results. Points afforded the means by which Colladon, in all cases, made his discharges.

Finally, I passed the electricity first through an exhausted receiver, so as to make it there resemble the aurora borealis, and then through the galvanometer to the earth; and it was found still effective in deflecting the needle, and apparently with the same force as before.

From all these experiments, it appears that a current of common electricity, whether transmitted through water or metal, or rarefied air, or by means of points in common air, is still able to deflect the needle; the only requisite being, apparently, to allow time for its action: that it is, in fact, just as magnetic in every respect as a voltaic current, and that in this character therefore no distinction exists.

iii. *Chemical decomposition.*—The chemical action of voltaic electricity is characteristic of that agent, but not more characteristic than are the *laws* under which the bodies evolved by decomposition arrange themselves at the poles. Dr. Wollaston showed that common electricity resembled it in these effects, and "that they are both essentially the same."

I first repeated Wollaston's fourth experiment, in which the ends of coated silver wires are immersed in a drop of sulphate of copper. By passing the electricity of the machine through such an arrangement, that end in the drop which received the electricity became coated with metallic copper. One hundred turns of the machine produced an evident effect; two hundred turns a very sensible one. The decomposing action was, however, very feeble. Very little copper was precipitated, and no sensible trace of silver from the other pole appeared in the solution.

A much more convenient and effectual arrangement for chemical decompositions by common electricity is the following. Upon a glass plate, Fig. 4, placed over but raised above a piece of white paper, so that shadows may not interfere, put two pieces of tinfoil *a, b;* connect one of these by an insulated wire *c,* or wire and string, with the machine, and the other, *g,* with the discharging train or the negative conductor; provide two pieces of fine platina wire, bent as in Fig. 5, so that the part *d, f* shall be

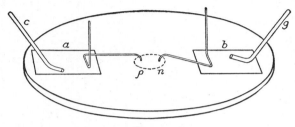

FIG. 4.

nearly upright, whilst the whole is resting on the three bearing points *p, c, f;* place these as in Fig. 4; the points *p, n* then become the decomposing poles. In this way surfaces of contact, as minute as possible, can be obtained at pleasure, and the connection can be broken or renewed in a moment, and the substances acted upon examined with the utmost facility.

A coarse line was made on the glass with solution of sulphate of copper, and the terminations *p* and *n* put into it; the foil *a* was connected

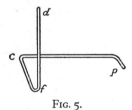

FIG. 5.

with the positive conductor of the machine by wire and wet string, so that no sparks passed: twenty turns of the machine caused the precipitation of so much copper on the end *n* that it looked like copper wire; no apparent change took place at *p.*

On combining a piece of litmus with a piece of turmeric paper, wetting both with solution of sulphate of soda, and putting the paper on the glass, so that *p* was on the litmus and *n* on the turmeric, a very few turns of the machine sufficed to show the evolution of acid at the former and alkali at the latter, exactly in the manner effected by a volta-electric current.

Decompositions took place equally well, whether the electricity passed from the machine to the foil *a,* through water, or through wire only; by *contact* with the conductor, or by *sparks* there; provided the sparks were not so large as to cause the electricity to pass in sparks from *p* to *n*, or towards *n*; and I have seen no reason to believe that in cases of true electro-chemical decomposition by the machine, the electricity passed in sparks from the conductor, or at any part of the current, is able to do more, because of its tension, than that which is made to pass merely as a regular current.

Finally, the experiment was extended into the following form, supplying in this case the fullest analogy between common and voltaic electricity. Three compound pieces of litmus and turmeric paper were moistened in solution of sulphate of soda, and arranged on a plate of glass with platina wires, as in Fig. 6. The wire *m* was connected with the prime conductor of the machine, the wire *t* with the discharging train,

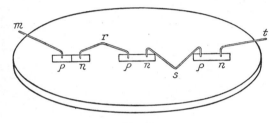

FIG. 6.

and the wires *r* and *s* entered into the course of the electrical current by means of the pieces of moistened paper; they were so bent as to rest each on three points, *n, r, p; n, s, p,* the points *r* and *s* being supported by the glass, and the others by the papers: the three terminations *p, p, p,* rested on the litmus, and the other three *n, n, n* on the turmeric paper. On working the machine for a short time only, acid was evolved at *all* the poles or terminations *p, p, p,* by which the electricity entered the solution, and alkali at the other poles *n, n, n,* by which the electricity left the solution.

I have been the more anxious to assign the true value of this experiment as a test of electro-chemical action, because I shall have occasion to refer to it in cases of supposed chemical action by magneto-electric and other electric currents and elsewhere. But, independent of it, there cannot be now a doubt that Dr. Wollaston was right in his general conclusion; and that voltaic and common electricity have powers of chemical decomposition, alike in their nature, and governed by the same law of arrangement.

iv. *Physiological effects.*—The power of the common electric current to shock and convulse the animal system, and when weak to affect the tongue and the eyes, may be considered as the same with the similar power of voltaic electricity, account being taken of the intensity of the one electricity and duration of the other. When a wet thread was interposed in the course of the current of common electricity from the battery charged by eight or ten revolutions of the machine in good action, and the discharge made by platina spatulas through the tongue or the gums, the effect upon the tongue and eyes was exactly that of a momentary feeble voltaic circuit.

v. *Spark.*—The beautiful flash of light attending the discharge of common electricity is well known. It rivals in brilliancy, if it does not even very much surpass, the light from the discharge of voltaic electricity; but it endures for an instant only, and is attended by a sharp noise like that of a small explosion. Still no difficulty can arise in recognising it to be the same spark as that from the voltaic battery, especially under certain circumstances. The eye cannot distinguish the difference between a voltaic and a common electricity spark, if they be taken between amalgamated surfaces of metal, at intervals only, and through the same distance of air.

3. Magneto-Electricity

Tension.—The attractions and repulsions due to the tension of ordinary electricity have been well observed with that evolved by magneto-electric induction. M. Pixii, by using an apparatus, clever in its construction and powerful in its action, was able to obtain great divergence of the gold leaves of an electrometer.

In motion: i. *Evolution of heat.*—The current produced by magneto-electric induction can heat a wire in the manner of ordinary electricity. At the British Association of Science at Oxford, in June of the present year, I had the pleasure, in conjunction with Mr. Harris, Professor Daniell, Mr. Duncan, and others, of making an experiment, for which the great magnet in the museum, Mr. Harris's new electrometer and the magneto-electric coil were put in requisition. The latter had been modified in the manner I have elsewhere described, so as to produce an electric spark when its contact with the magnet was made or broken. The terminations of the spiral, adjusted so as to have their contact with each other broken when the spark was to pass, were connected with the wire in the electrometer, and it was found that each time the magnetic contact was made and broken, expansion of the air within the instrument occurred, indicating an increase, at the moment, of the temperature of the wire.

ii. *Magnetism.*—These currents were discovered by their magnetic power.

iii. *Chemical decomposition.*—I have made many endeavours to effect chemical decomposition by magneto-electricity, but unavailingly. The apparatus of M. Pixii already referred to has, however, in the hands of himself and M. Hachette, given decisive chemical results, so as to complete this link in the chain of evidence. Water was decomposed by it, and the oxygen and hydrogen obtained in separate tubes according to the law governing volta-electric and machine-electric decomposition.

iv. *Physiological effects.*—A frog was convulsed in the earliest experiments on these currents. The sensation upon the tongue, and the flash before the eyes, which I at first obtained only in a feeble degree, have

been since exalted by more powerful apparatus, so as to become even disagreeable.

v. *Spark*.—The feeble spark which I first obtained with these currents has been varied and strengthened by Signori Nobili and Antinori,
and others, so as to leave no doubt as to its identity with the common
electric spark.

4. *Thermo-Electricity*

With regard to thermo-electricity (that beautiful form of electricity
discovered by Seebeck), the very conditions under which it is excited
are such as to give no ground for expecting that it can be raised like common electricity to any high degree of tension; the effects, therefore, due
to that state are not to be expected. The sum of evidence respecting its
analogy to the electricities already described is, I believe, as follows:—
Tension. The attractions and repulsions due to a certain degree of tension
have not been observed. *In currents:* i. *Evolution of heat*. I am not aware
that its power of raising temperature has been observed. ii. *Magnetism*.
It was discovered, and is best recognised, by its magnetic powers. iii.
Chemical decomposition has not been effected by it. iv. *Physiological
effects*. Nobili has shown that these currents are able to cause contrac-
tions in the limbs of a frog. v. *Spark*. The spark has not yet been seen.

Only those effects are weak or deficient which depend upon a certain
high degree of intensity; and if common electricity be reduced in that
quality to a similar degree with the thermo-electricity, it can produce no
effects beyond the latter.

5. *Animal Electricity*

After an examination of the experiments of Walsh, Ingenhousz,
Cavendish, Sir H. Davy, and Dr. Davy, no doubt remains on my mind
as to the identity of the electricity of the torpedo with common and
voltaic electricity; and I presume that so little will remain on the minds
of others as to justify my refraining from entering at length into the
philosophical proofs of that identity. At present the sum of evidence is as
follows:—

Tension.—No sensible attractions or repulsions due to tension have
been observed.

In motion: i. *Evolution of heat;* not yet observed; I have little or no
doubt that Harris's electrometer would show it.

ii. *Magnetism*.—Perfectly distinct. According to Dr. Davy, the current deflected the needle and made magnets under the same law, as to
direction, which governs currents of ordinary and voltaic electricity.

iii. *Chemical decomposition*.—Also distinct; and though Dr. Davy
used an apparatus of similar construction with that of Dr. Wollaston, still
no error in the present case is involved, for the decompositions were

polar, and in their nature truly electro-chemical. By the direction of the magnet, it was found that the under surface of the fish was negative, and the upper positive; and in the chemical decompositions, silver and lead were precipitated on the wire connected with the under surface, and not on the other; and when these wires were either steel or silver, in solution of common salt, gas (hydrogen?) rose from the negative wire, but none from the positive.

iv. *Physiological effects.*—These are so characteristic that by them the peculiar powers of the torpedo and gymnotus are principally recognised.

v. *Spark.*—The electric spark has not yet been obtained.

In concluding this summary of the powers of torpedinal electricity, I cannot refrain from pointing out the enormous absolute quantity of electricity which the animal must put in circulation at each effort. It is doubtful whether any common electrical machine has as yet been able to supply electricity sufficient in a reasonable time to cause true electro-chemical decomposition of water, yet the current from the torpedo has done it. The same high proportion is shown by the magnetic effects. These circumstances indicate that the torpedo has power (in the way probably that Cavendish describes) to continue the evolution for a sensible time, so that its successive discharges rather resemble those of a voltaic arrangement, intermitting in its action, than those of a Leyden apparatus, charged and discharged many times in succession. In reality, however, there is *no philosophical difference* between these two cases.

The *general conclusion* which must, I think, be drawn from this collection of facts is that *electricity, whatever may be its source, is identical in its nature.* The phenomena in the five kinds of species quoted differ, not in their character but only in degree; and in that respect vary in proportion to the variable circumstances of *quantity* and *intensity* which can at pleasure be made to change in almost any one of the kinds of electricity as much as it does between one kind and another.

Table of the experimental Effects common to the Electricities derived from different Sources.

	Physiological Effects.	Magnetic Deflection.	Magnets Made.	Spark.	Heating Power.	True Chemical Action.	Attraction and Repulsion.	Discharge by Hot Air.
1. Voltaic electricity	×	×	×	×	×	×	×	×
2. Common electricity	×	×	×	×	×	×	×	×
3. Magneto-electricity	×	×	×	×	×	×	×	
4. Thermo-electricity	×	×	+	+	+	+		
5. Animal electricity	×	×	×	+	+	×		

II. NEW CONDITIONS OF ELECTRO-CHEMICAL
DECOMPOSITION

THE TENSION of machine electricity causes it, however small in quantity, to pass through any length of water, solutions, or other substances classing with these as conductors, as fast as it can be produced, and therefore, in relation to quantity, as fast as it could have passed through much shorter portions of the same conducting substance. With the voltaic battery the case is very different, and the passing current of electricity supplied by it suffers serious diminution in any substance, by considerable extension of its length, but especially in such bodies as those mentioned above.

I endeavoured to apply this facility of transmitting the current of electricity through any length of a conductor to an investigation of the transfer of the elements in a decomposing body, in contrary directions, towards the poles. The general form of apparatus used in these experiments has been already described; and also a particular experiment, in which, when a piece of litmus paper and a piece of turmeric paper were combined and moistened in solution of sulphate of soda, the point of the wire from the machine (representing the positive pole) put upon the litmus paper, and the receiving point from the discharging train, representing the negative pole, upon the turmeric paper, a very few turns of the machine sufficed to show the evolution of acid at the former, and alkali at the latter, exactly in the manner effected by a volta-electric current.

The pieces of litmus and turmeric paper were *now* placed each upon a separate plate of glass, and connected by an insulated string four feet long, moistened in the same solution of sulphate of soda: the terminal decomposing wire points were placed upon the papers as before. On working the machine, the same evolution of acid and alkali appeared as in the former instance, and with equal readiness, notwithstanding that the places of their appearance were four feet apart from each other. Finally, a piece of string, seventy feet long, was used. It was insulated in the air by suspenders of silk, so that the electricity passed through its entire length: decomposition took place exactly as in former cases, alkali and acid appearing at the two extremities in their proper places.

The negative point of the discharging train, the turmeric paper, and the string were then removed; the positive point was left resting upon the litmus paper, and the latter touched by a piece of moistened string held in the hand. A few turns of the machine evolved acid at the positive point as freely as before.

These experiments were varied so as to include the action of only one metallic pole, but that not the pole connected with the machine. Turmeric paper was moistened in solution of sulphate of soda, placed upon glass, and connected with the discharging train by a decomposing wire; a piece of wet string was hung from it, the lower extremity of which was brought opposite a point connected with the positive prime conductor of the machine. The machine was then worked for a few turns, and alkali immediately appeared at the point of the discharging train which rested on the turmeric paper. Corresponding effects took place at the negative conductor of a machine.

These cases are abundantly sufficient to show that electro-chemical decomposition does not depend upon the simultaneous action of two metallic poles, since a single pole might be used, decomposition ensue, and one or other of the elements liberated, pass to the pole, according as it was positive or negative. In considering the course taken by, and the final arrangement of, the other element, I had little doubt that I should find it had receded towards the other extremity, and that the air itself had acted as a pole, an expectation which was fully confirmed in the following manner.

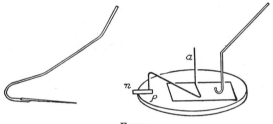

Fig. 7.

A piece of turmeric paper, not more than 0.4 of an inch in length and 0.5 of an inch in width, was moistened with sulphate of soda and placed upon the edge of a glass plate opposite to, and about two inches from, a point connected with the discharging train (Fig. 7); a piece of tinfoil, resting upon the same glass plate, was connected with the machine, and also with the turmeric paper, by a decomposing wire *a*. The machine was then worked, the positive electricity passing into the turmeric paper at the point *p*, and out at the extremity *n*. After forty or fifty turns of the machine, the extremity *n* was examined, and the two points or angles found deeply coloured by the presence of free alkali.

Arrangements were then made in which no metallic communication with the decomposing matter was allowed, but both poles (if they might

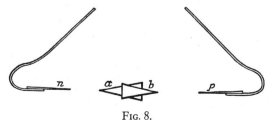

Fig. 8.

now be called by that name) formed of air only. A piece of turmeric paper *a*, Fig. 8, and a piece of litmus paper *b* were dipped in solution of sulphate of soda, put together so as to form one moist pointed conductor, and supported on wax between two needle points, one *p* connected by a wire with the conductor of the machine, and the other, *n*, with the discharging train. The interval in each case between the points was about half an inch: the positive point *p* was opposite the litmus paper; the negative point *n* opposite the turmeric. The machine was then worked for a time, upon which evidence of decomposition quickly appeared, for the point of the litmus *b* became reddened from acid evolved there, and the point of the turmeric *a* red from a similar and simultaneous evolution of alkali.

Upon turning the paper conductor round, so that the litmus point should now give off the positive electricity, and the turmeric point receive it, and working the machine for a short time, both the red spots disappeared, and as on continuing the action of the machine no red spot was re-formed at the litmus extremity, it proved that in the first instance the effect was not due to the action of brushes or mere electric discharges causing the formation of nitric acid from the air.

If the combined litmus and turmeric paper in this experiment be considered as constituting a conductor independent of the machine or the discharging train, and the final places of the elements evolved be considered in relation to this conductor, then it will be found that the acid collects at the *negative* or receiving end or pole of the arrangement, and the alkali at the *positive* or delivering extremity.

Finally, a series of four small compound conductors, consisting of litmus and turmeric paper (Fig. 9) moistened in solution of sulphate of

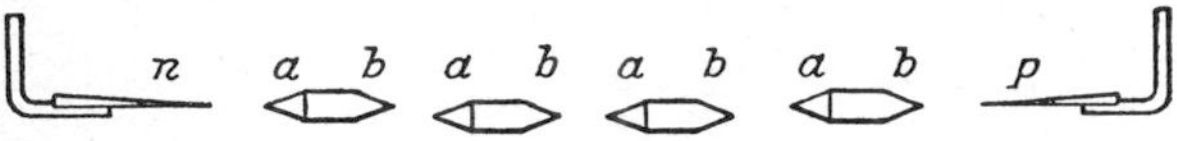

FIG. 9.

soda, were supported on glass rods, in a line at a little distance from each other, between the points *p* and *n* of the machine and discharging train, so that the electricity might pass in succession through them, entering in at the litmus points *b, b* and passing out at the turmeric points *a, a*. On working the machine carefully, so as to avoid sparks and brushes, I soon obtained evidence of decomposition in each of the moist conductors, for all the litmus points exhibited free acid, and the turmeric points equally showed free alkali.

These cases of electro-chemical decomposition are in their nature exactly of the same kind as those affected under ordinary circumstances by the voltaic battery, notwithstanding the great differences as to the presence or absence, or at least as to the nature, of the parts usually called poles; and also of the final situation of the elements eliminated at the electrified boundary surfaces. They indicate at once an internal action of the parts suffering decomposition, and appear to show that the power which is effectual in separating the elements is exerted there, and not at the poles.

Theory of Electro-chemical Decomposition

The extreme beauty and value of electro-chemical decompositions have given to that power which the voltaic pile possesses of causing their occurrence an interest surpassing that of any other of its properties; for the power is not only intimately connected with the continuance, if not with the production, of the electrical phenomena, but it has furnished us with the most beautiful demonstrations of the nature of many compound bodies; has in the hands of Becquerel been employed in compounding substances; has given us several new combinations, and sustains us with the hope that when thoroughly understood it will produce many more.

What may be considered as the general facts of electro-chemical decomposition are agreed to by nearly all who have written on the subject. They consist in the separation of the decomposable substance acted upon into its proximate or sometimes ultimate principles, whenever both poles of the pile are in contact with that substance in a proper condition; in the evolution of these principles at distant points, *i.e.* at the poles of the pile, where they are either finally set free or enter into union with the substance of the poles; and in the constant determination of the evolved elements or principles to particular poles according to certain well-ascertained laws.

But the views of men of science vary much as to the nature of the action by which these effects are produced; and as it is certain that we shall be better able to apply the power when we really understand the manner in which it operates, this difference of opinion is a strong inducement to further inquiry. I have been led to hope that the following investigations might be considered, not as an increase of that which is doubtful, but a real addition to this branch of knowledge.

That electro-chemical decomposition does not depend upon any direct attraction and repulsion of the poles (meaning thereby the metallic terminations either of the voltaic battery or ordinary electrical machine arrangements) upon the elements in contact with or near to them appeared very evident from the experiments made in air, when the substances evolved did not collect about any poles, but, in obedience to the direction of the current, were evolved, and I would say ejected, at the extremities of the decomposing substance. But notwithstanding the extreme dissimilarity in the character of air and metals, and the almost total difference existing between them as to their mode of conducting electricity and becoming charged with it, it might perhaps still be contended, although quite hypothetically, that the bounding portions of air were now the surfaces or places of attraction, as the metals had been supposed to be before. In illustration of this and other points, I endeavoured to devise an arrangement by which I could decompose a body against a surface of water, as well as against air or metal, and succeeded in doing so unexceptionably in the following manner. As the experiment for very natural reasons requires many precautions to be successful, and will be referred to hereafter in illustration of the views I shall venture to give, I must describe it minutely.

A glass basin (Fig. 10), four inches in diameter and four inches deep, had a division of mica *a* fixed across the upper part so as to descend one inch and a half below the edge, and be perfectly watertight at the sides: a plate of platina *b,* three inches wide, was put into the basin on one side of the division *a,* and retained there by a glass block below, so that any gas produced by it in a future stage of the experiment should not ascend beyond the mica and cause currents in the liquid on that side. A strong solution of sulphate of magnesia was carefully poured without splashing into the basin, until it rose a little above the lower edge of the mica division *a,* great care being taken that the glass or mica on the unoccupied or

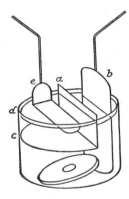

Fig. 10.

c side of the division in the figure should not be moistened by agitation of the solution above the level to which it rose. A thin piece of clean cork, well wetted in distilled water, was then carefully and lightly placed on the solution at the *c* side, and distilled water poured gently onto it until a stratum the eighth of an inch in thickness appeared over the sulphate of magnesia; all was then left for a few minutes, that any solution adhering to the cork might sink away from it, or be removed by the water on which it now floated; and then more distilled water was added in a similar manner, until it reached nearly to the top of the glass. In this way solution of the sulphate occupied the lower part of the glass, and also the upper on the right-hand side of the mica; but on the left-hand side of the division a stratum of water from *c* to *d,* one inch and a half in depth, reposed upon it, the two presenting, when looked through horizontally, a comparatively definite plane of contact. A second platina pole *e* was arranged so as to be just under the surface of the water, in a position nearly horizontal, a little inclination being given to it, that gas evolved during decomposition might escape: the part immersed was three inches and a half long by one inch wide, and about seven eighths of an inch of water intervened between it and the solution of sulphate of magnesia.

The latter pole *e* was now connected with the negative end of a voltaic battery, of forty pairs of plates four inches square, whilst the former pole *b* was connected with the positive end. There was action and gas evolved at both poles; but from the intervention of the pure water, the decomposition was very feeble compared to what the battery would have effected in a uniform solution. After a little while (less than a minute), magnesia also appeared at the negative side: *it did not make its appearance at the negative metallic pole, but in the water,* at the plane where the solution and the water met; and on looking at it horizontally, it could be there perceived lying in the water upon the solution, not rising more than the fourth of an inch above the latter, whilst the water between it and the negative pole was perfectly clear. On continuing the action, the bubbles of hydrogen rising upwards from the negative pole impressed a circulatory movement on the stratum of water, upwards in the middle, and downwards at the side, which gradually gave an ascending form to the cloud of magnesia in the part just under the pole, having an appearance as if it were there attracted to it; but this was altogether an effect of the currents, and did not occur until long after the phenomena looked for were satisfactorily ascertained.

After a little while the voltaic communication was broken, and the platina poles removed with as little agitation as possible from the water and solution, for the purpose of examining the liquid adhering to them. The pole *e,* when touched by turmeric paper, gave no traces of alkali, nor could anything but pure water be found upon it. The pole *b,* though drawn through a much greater depth and quantity of fluid, was found so acid as to give abundant evidence to litmus paper, the tongue, and other tests. Hence there had been no interference of alkaline salts in any way, undergoing first decomposition, and then causing the separation of the magnesia at a distance from the pole by mere chemical agencies. This experiment was repeated again and again, and always successfully.

As, therefore, the substances evolved in cases of electro-chemical decomposition may be made to appear against air—which, according to common language, is not a conductor, nor is decomposed—or against water, which is a conductor, and can be decomposed—as well as against the metal poles, which are excellent conductors, but undecomposable—there appears but little reason to consider the phenomena generally, as due to the *attraction* or attractive powers of the latter, when used in the ordinary way, since similar attractions can hardly be imagined in the former instances.

If the wires of a galvanometer be terminated by plates, and these be immersed in dilute acid, contained in a regularly formed rectangular glass trough, connected at each end with a voltaic battery by poles equal to the section of the fluid, a part of the electricity will pass through the instrument and cause a certain deflection. And if the plates are always retained at the *same distance from each other* and from the sides of the trough, are always parallel to each other, and uniformly placed relative to the fluid, then, whether they are immersed near the middle of the decomposing solution or at one end, still the instrument will indicate the same deflection, and consequently the same electric influence.

It is very evident that when the width of the decomposing conductor varies, as is always the case when mere wires or plates, as poles, are dipped into or are surrounded by solution, no constant expression can be given as to the action upon a single particle placed in the course of the current, nor any conclusion of use, relative to the supposed attractive or repulsive force of the poles, be drawn. The force will vary as the distance from the pole varies; as the particle is directly between the poles or more or less on one side; and even as it is nearer to or further from the sides of the containing vessels, or as the shape of the vessel itself varies; and, in fact, by making variations in the form of the arrangement, the force upon any single particle may be made to increase, or diminish, or remain constant, whilst the distance between the particle and the pole shall remain the same; or the force may be made to increase, or diminish, or remain constant, either as the distance increases or as it diminishes.

From numerous experiments, I am led to believe the following general expression to be correct; but I purpose examining it much further, and would therefore wish not to be considered at present as pledged to its accuracy. The *sum of chemical decomposition is constant* for any section taken across a decomposing conductor, uniform in its nature, at whatever distance the poles may be from each other or from the section; or however that section may intersect the currents, whether directly across them or so oblique as to reach almost from pole to pole, or whether it be plane, or curved, or irregular in the utmost degree; provided the current of electricity be retained constant in quantity, and that the section passes through every part of the current through the decomposing conductor.

I have reason to believe that the statement might be made still more general, and expressed thus: That *for a constant quantity of electricity, whatever the decomposing conductor may be, whether water, saline solutions, acids, fused bodies, etc., the amount of electro-chemical action is also a constant quantity,* i.e. *would always be equivalent to a standard chemical effect founded upon ordinary chemical affinity.* I have this investigation in hand, with several others, and shall be prepared to give it in the next part of these *Researches.*

Electro-chemical decomposition is well known to depend essentially upon the *current* of electricity. I have shown that in certain cases the decomposition is proportionate to the quantity of electricity passing, whatever may be its intensity or its source, and that the same is probably true for all cases, even when the utmost generality is taken on the one hand and great precision of expression on the other.

Passing to the consideration of electro-chemical decomposition, it appears to me that the effect is produced by an *internal corpuscular action,* exerted according to the direction of the electric current, and that it is due to a force either *superadded to* or *giving direction to the ordinary chemical affinity* of the bodies present. The body under decomposition may be considered as a mass of acting particles, all those which are included in the course of the electric current contributing to the final effect: and it is because the ordinary chemical affinity is relieved, weakened, or partly neutralised by the influence of the electric current in one direction parallel to the course of the latter, and strengthened or added to in the opposite direction, that the combining particles have a tendency to pass in opposite courses.

In this view the effect is considered as *essentially dependent* upon the *mutual chemical affinity* of the particles of opposite kinds. Particles *a a*, Fig. 11, could not be transferred or travel from one pole N towards the other P unless they found particles of the opposite kind *b b*, ready to pass in the contrary direction: for it is by virtue of their increased affinity for those particles, combined with their diminished affinity for such as are behind them in their course, that they are urged forward: and when any one particle *a*, Fig. 12, arrives at the pole, it is excluded or set free, be-

FIG. 11.   FIG. 12.

cause the particle *b* of the opposite kind, with which it was the moment before in combination, has, under the superinducing influence of the current, a greater attraction for the particle *a*, which is before it in its course, than for the particle *a*, towards which its affinity has been weakened.

As far as regards any single compound particle, the case may be considered as analogous to one of ordinary decomposition, for in Fig. 12, *a* may be conceived to be expelled from the compound *a b* by the superior attraction of *a* for *b*, that superior attraction belonging to it in consequence of the relative position of *a b* and *a* to the direction of the axis of electric power superinduced by the current. But as all the compound particles in the course of the current, except those actually in contact with the poles, act conjointly, and consist of elementary particles, which whilst they are in one direction expelling are in the other being expelled, the case becomes more complicated but not more difficult of comprehension.

It is not here assumed that the acting particles must be in a right line between the poles. The lines of action which may be supposed to represent the electric currents passing through a decomposing liquid have in many experiments very irregular forms; and even in the simplest case of two wires or points immersed as poles in a drop or larger single portion of fluid, these lines must diverge rapidly from the poles; and the direction in which the chemical affinity between particles is most powerfully modified will vary with the direction of these lines, according constantly with them. But even in reference to these lines or currents, it is not supposed that the particles which mutually affect each other must of necessity be parallel to them, but only that they shall accord generally with their direction. Two particles, placed in a line perpendicular to the electric current passing in any particular place, are not supposed to have their ordinary chemical relations towards each other affected; but as the line joining them is inclined one way to the current their mutual affinity is increased; as it is inclined in the other direction it is diminished; and the effect is a maximum, when that line is parallel to the current.

That the actions, of whatever kind they may be, take place frequently in oblique directions is evident from the circumstance of those particles being included which in numerous cases are not in a line between the poles. Thus, when wires are used as poles in a glass of solution, the decompositions and recompositions occur to the right or left of the direct line between the poles, and indeed in every part to which the currents extend, as is proved by many experiments, and must therefore often occur between particles obliquely placed as respects the current itself; and when a metallic vessel containing the solution is made one pole, whilst a mere point or wire is used for the other, the decompositions and recompositions must frequently be still more oblique to the course of the currents.

I hope I have now distinctly stated, although in general terms, the view I entertain of the cause of electro-chemical decomposition, *as far as that cause can at present be traced and understood.* I conceive the effects to arise from forces which are *internal,* relative to the matter under decomposition—and not *external,* as they might be considered, if directly dependent upon the poles. I suppose that the effects are due to a modification, by the electric current, of the chemical affinity of the particles through or by which that current is passing, giving them the power of acting more forcibly in one direction than in another, and consequently making them travel by a series of successive decompositions and recompositions in opposite directions, and finally causing their expulsion or exclusion at the boundaries of the body under decomposition, in the direction of the current, *and that* in larger or smaller quantities, according as the current is more or less powerful. I think, therefore, it would be more philosophical, and more directly expressive of the facts, to speak of such a body in relation to the current passing through it, rather than to the poles, as they are usually called, in contact with it; and say that whilst under decomposition, oxygen, chlorine, iodine, acids, etc., are rendered at its negative extremity, and combustibles, metals, alkalies, bases, etc., at its positive extremity. I do not believe that a substance can be transferred in the electric current beyond the point where it ceases to find particles with which it can combine; and I may refer to the experiments made in air, and in water, already quoted, for facts illustrating these views in the first instance.

The theory I have ventured to put forth appears to me to explain all the prominent features of electro-chemical decomposition in a satisfactory manner.

In the first place, it explains why, in all ordinary cases, the evolved substances *appear only at the poles;* for the poles are the limiting surfaces of the decomposing substance, and except at them, every particle finds other particles having a contrary tendency with which it can combine.

Then it explains why, in numerous cases, the elements or evolved substances are not *retained* by the poles; and this is no small difficulty in those theories which refer the decomposing effect directly to the attractive power of the poles. If, in accordance with the usual theory, a piece of platina be supposed to have sufficient power to attract a particle of hydrogen from the particle of oxygen with which it was the instant before combined, there seems no sufficient reason, nor any fact, except those to be explained, which shows why it should not, according to analogy with all ordinary attractive forces, as those of gravitation, magnetism, cohesion, chemical affinity, etc., *retain* that particle which it had just before taken from a distance and from previous combination. Yet it does not do so, but allows it to escape freely. Nor does this depend upon its assuming the gaseous state, for acids and alkalies, etc., are left equally at liberty to diffuse themselves through the fluid surrounding the pole, and show no particular tendency to combine with or adhere to the latter.

But in the theory that I have just given, the effect appears to be a natural consequence of the action: the evolved substances are *expelled* from the decomposing mass, not *drawn out by an attraction* which ceases to act on one particle without any assignable reason, while it continues to act on another of the same kind: and whether the poles be metal, water, or air, still the substances are evolved, and are sometimes set free, whilst at others they unite to the matter of the poles, according to the chemical nature of the latter, *i.e.* their chemical relation to those particles which are leaving the substance under operation.

The theory accounts for the *transfer of elements* in a manner which seems to me at present to leave nothing unexplained; and it was, indeed, the phenomena of transfer in the numerous cases of decomposition of bodies rendered fluid by heat, which, in conjunction with the experiments in air, led to its construction.

Chloride of silver furnishes a beautiful instance, especially when decomposed by silver-wire poles. Upon fusing a portion of it on a piece of glass, and bringing the poles into contact with it, there is abundance of silver evolved at the negative pole, and an equal abundance absorbed at the positive pole, for no chlorine is set free: and by careful management, the negative wire may be withdrawn from the fused globule as the silver is reduced there, the latter serving as the continuation of the pole, until a wire or thread of revived silver, five or six inches in length, is produced; at the same time the silver at the positive pole is as rapidly dissolved by the chlorine, which seizes upon it, so that the wire has to be continually advanced as it is melted away. The whole experiment includes the action of only two elements, silver and chlorine, and illustrates in a beautiful manner their progress in opposite directions, parallel to the electric current, which is for the time giving a uniform general direction to their mutual affinities.

According to my theory, an element or a substance not decomposable under the circumstances of the experiment (as, for instance, a dilute acid or alkali) should not be transferred, or pass from pole to pole, unless it be in chemical relation to some other element or substance tending to pass in the opposite direction, for the effect is considered as essentially due to the mutual relation of such particles.

In support of these arguments, it may be observed that as yet no determination of a substance to a pole, or tendency to obey the electric current, has been observed (that I am aware of) in cases of mere mixture; *i.e.* a substance diffused through a fluid, but having no sensible chemical affinity with it or with substances that may be evolved from it during the action, does not in any case seem to be affected by the electric current. Pulverised charcoal was diffused through dilute sulphuric acid, and subjected with the solution to the action of a voltaic battery, terminated by platina poles; but not the slightest tendency of the charcoal to the negative pole could be observed. Sublimed sulphur was diffused through similar acid, and submitted to the same action, a silver plate being used as the negative pole; but the sulphur had no tendency to pass to that pole, the silver was not tarnished, nor did any sulphuretted hydrogen appear. The case of magnesia and water, with those of comminuted metals in certain solutions, is also of this kind; and, in fact, substances which have the instant before been powerfully determined towards the pole, as magnesia from sulphate of magnesia, become entirely *indifferent to it* the moment they assume their independent state, and pass away, diffusing themselves through the surrounding fluid.

It may be expressed as a general consequence that the more directly bodies are opposed to each other in chemical affinity, the more *ready* is their separation from each other in cases of electro-chemical decomposition, *i.e.* provided other circumstances, as insolubility, deficient conducting power, proportions, etc., do not interfere. This is well known to be the case with water and saline solutions; and I have found it to be equally true with *dry* chlorides, iodides, salts, etc., rendered subject to electro-chemical decomposition by fusion. So that in applying the voltaic battery for the purpose of decomposing bodies not yet resolved into forms of matter simpler than their own, it must be remembered that success may depend not upon the weakness, or failure upon the strength, of the affinity by which the elements sought for are held together, but contrariwise; and then modes of application may be devised by which, in *association* with ordinary chemical powers, and the assistance of fusion, we may be able to penetrate much further than at present into the constitution of our chemical elements.

Some of the most beautiful and surprising cases of electro-chemical decomposition and *transfer* which Sir Humphry Davy described in his celebrated paper were those in which acids were passed through alkalies, and alkalies or earths through acids; and the way in which substances having the most powerful attractions for each other were thus prevented from combining, or, as it is said, had their natural affinity destroyed or suspended throughout the whole of the circuit, excited the utmost astonishment. But if I be right in the view I have taken of the effects, it will appear that that which made the *wonder* is in fact the *essential condition* of transfer and decomposition, and that the more alkali there is in the course of an acid, the more will the transfer of that acid be facilitated from pole to pole; and perhaps a better illustration of the difference between the theory I have ventured and those previously existing cannot be offered than the views they respectively give of such facts as these.

III. ELECTRO-CHEMICAL DECOMPOSITION—*Continued*

The theory which I believe to be a true expression of the facts of electrochemical decomposition, and which I have therefore detailed in a former part of these *Researches,* is so much at variance with those previously advanced that I find the greatest difficulty in stating results, as I think, correctly, whilst limited to the use of terms which are current with a certain accepted meaning. Of this kind is the term *pole,* with its prefixes of positive and negative, and the attached ideas of attraction and repulsion. The general phraseology is that the positive pole *attracts* oxygen, acids, etc., or, more cautiously, that it *determines* their evolution upon its surface; and that the negative pole acts in an equal manner upon hydrogen, combustibles, metals, and bases. According to my view, the determining force is *not* at the poles, but *within* the body under decomposition; and the oxygen and acids are rendered at the *negative* extremity of that body, whilst hydrogen, metals, etc., are evolved at the *positive* extremity.

To avoid, therefore, confusion and circumlocution, and for the sake of greater precision of expression than I can otherwise obtain, I have deliberately considered the subject with two friends, and with their assistance and concurrence in framing them, I purpose henceforward using certain other terms, which I will now define. The *poles,* as they are usually called, are only the doors or ways by which the electric current passes into and out of the decomposing body; and they, of course, when in contact with that body, are the limits of its extent in the direction of the current. The term has been generally applied to the metal surfaces in contact with the decomposing substance; but whether philosophers generally would also apply it to the surfaces of air and water, against which I have effected electro-chemical decomposition, is subject to doubt. In place of the term pole, I propose using that of *Electrode,* and I mean thereby that substance, or rather surface, whether of air, water, metal, or any other body, which bounds the extent of the decomposing matter in the direction of the electric current.

The surfaces at which, according to common phraseology, the electric current enters and leaves a decomposing body are most important places of action, and require to be distinguished apart from the poles, with which they are mostly, and the electrodes, with which they are always, in contact. Wishing for a natural standard of electric direction to which I might refer these, expressive of their difference and at the same time free from all theory, I have thought it might be found in the earth. If the magnetism of the earth be due to electric currents passing round it, the latter must be in a constant direction, which, according to present usage of speech, would be from east to west, or, which will strengthen this help to the memory, that in which the sun appears to move. If in any case of electro-decomposition we consider the decomposing body as placed so that the current passing through it shall be in the same direction, and parallel to that supposed to exist in the earth, then the surfaces at which the electricity is passing into and out of the substance would have an invariable reference, and exhibit constantly the same relations of powers. Upon this notion we purpose calling that towards the east the *anode,* and that towards the west the *cathode;* and whatever changes may take place in our views of the nature of electricity and electrical action, as they must affect the *natural standard* referred to, in the same direction, and to an equal amount with any decomposing substances to which these terms may at any time be applied, there seems no reason to expect that they will lead to confusion or tend in any way to support false views. The *anode* is therefore that surface at which the electric current, according to our present expression, enters: it is the *negative* extremity of the decomposing body; is where oxygen, chlorine, acids, etc., are evolved; and is against or opposite the positive electrode. The *cathode* is that surface at which the current leaves the decomposing body, and is its *positive* extremity; the combustible bodies, metals, alkalies, and bases, are evolved there, and it is in contact with the negative electrode.

I shall have occasion in these *Researches,* also, to class bodies together according to certain relations derived from their electrical actions; and wishing to express those relations without at the same time involving the expression of any hypothetical views, I intend using the following names and terms. Many bodies are decomposed directly by the electric current, their elements being set free; these I propose to call *electrolytes.* Water, therefore, is an electrolyte. The bodies which, like nitric or sulphuric acids, are decomposed in a secondary manner are not included under this term. Then, for *electro-chemically decomposed,* I shall often use the term *electrolysed,* derived in the same way, and implying that the body spoken of is separated into its components under the influence of electricity: it is analogous in its sense and sound to *analyse,* which is derived in a similar manner. The term *electrolytical* will be understood at once: muriatic acid is electrolytical, boracic acid is not.

Finally, I require a term to express those bodies which can pass to the *electrodes,* or, as they are usually called, the poles. Substances are frequently spoken of as being *electro-negative* or *electro-positive,* according as they go under the supposed influence of a direct attraction to the positive or negative pole. But these terms are much too significant for the use to which I should have to put them; for though the meanings are perhaps right, they are only hypothetical, and may be wrong; and then, through a very imperceptible, but still very dangerous, because continual, influence, they do great injury to science, by contracting and limiting the habitual views of those engaged in pursuing it. I propose to distinguish such bodies by calling those *anions* which go to the *anode* of the decomposing body; and those passing to the *cathode, cations;* and when I have occasion to speak of these together, I shall call them *ions.* Thus the chloride of lead is an *electrolyte,* and when *electrolysed* evolves the two *ions,* chlorine and lead, the former being an *anion* and the latter a *cation.*

On a new Measurer of Volta-electricity

I have already said, when introducing my theory of electro-chemical decomposition, that the chemical decomposing action of a current *is constant for a constant quantity of electricity,* notwithstanding the greatest variations in its sources, in its intensity, in the size of the *electrodes* used, in the nature of the conductors (or non-conductors) through which it is passed, or in other circumstances. The conclusive proofs of the truth of these statements shall be given almost immediately.

I endeavoured upon this law to construct an instrument which should measure out the electricity passing through it, and which, being interposed in the course of the current used in any particular experiment, should serve at pleasure, either as a *comparative standard* of effect or as a *positive measurer* of this subtile agent.

There is no substance better fitted, under ordinary circumstances, to be the indicating body in such an instrument than water; for it is decomposed with facility when rendered a better conductor by the addition of acids or salts; its elements may in numerous cases be obtained and collected without any embarrassment from secondary action, and, being gaseous, they are in the best physical condition for separation and measurement.

The first precaution needful in the construction of the instrument was to avoid the recombination of the evolved gases, an effect which the positive electrode has been found so capable of producing. For this purpose various forms of decomposing apparatus were used. The first consisted of straight tubes, each containing a plate and wire of platina soldered together by gold, and fixed hermetically in the glass at the closed extremity of the tube (Fig. 13). The tubes were about eight inches long, 0.7 of an inch in diameter, and graduated. The platina plates were about an inch long, as wide as the tubes would permit, and adjusted as near to the mouths of the tubes as was consistent with the safe collection of the gases evolved. In certain cases, where it was required to evolve the elements upon as small a surface as possible, the metallic extremity, instead of being a plate, consisted of the wire bent into the form of a ring (Fig.

FIG. 13.

FIG. 14.

14). When these tubes were used as measurers, they were filled with the dilute sulphuric acid, inverted in a basin of the same liquid (Fig. 15), and placed in an inclined position, with their mouths near to each other, that as little decomposing matter should intervene as possible; and also in such a direction that the platina plates should be in vertical planes.

FIG. 15.

Another form of apparatus is that delineated (Fig. 16). The tube is bent in the middle; one end is closed; in that end is fixed a wire and plate, *a*, proceeding so far downwards that, when in the position figured, it shall be as near to the angle as possible, consistently with the collection, at the closed extremity of the tube, of all the gas evolved against it. The plane of this plate is also perpendicular. The other metallic termination, *b*, is introduced at the time decomposition is to be effected, being

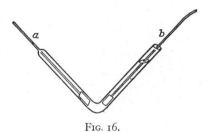

FIG. 16.

brought as near the angle as possible, without causing any gas to pass from it towards the closed end of the instrument. The gas evolved against it is allowed to escape.

The third form of apparatus contains both electrodes in the same tube; the transmission, therefore, of the electricity and the consequent decomposition is far more rapid than in the separate tubes. The resulting gas is the sum of the portions evolved at the two electrodes, and the instrument is better adapted than either of the former as a measurer of the quantity of voltaic electricity transmitted in ordinary cases. It consists of a straight tube (Fig. 17) closed at the upper extremity, and graduated, through the sides of which pass platina wires (being fused into the glass), which are connected with two plates within. The tube is fitted by grinding into one mouth of a double-necked bottle. If the latter be one half or two thirds full of the dilute sulphuric acid, it will, upon inclination of the whole, flow into the tube and fill it. When an electric current is passed through the instrument, the gases evolved against the plates collect in the

upper portion of the tube and are not subject to the recombining power
of the platina.

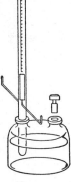

FIG. 17.

Another form of the instrument is given in Fig. 18.

A fifth form is delineated (Fig. 19). This I have found exceedingly
useful in experiments continued in succession for days together, and
where large quantities of indicating gas were to be collected. It is fixed on
a weighted foot, and has the form of a small retort containing the two
electrodes: the neck is narrow and sufficiently long to deliver gas issuing
from it into a jar placed in a small pneumatic trough. The electrode
chamber, sealed hermetically at the part held in the stand, is five inches
in length and o.6 of an inch in diameter; the neck about nine inches in
length and o.4 of an inch in diameter internally. The figure will fully
indicate the construction.

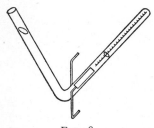

FIG. 18.

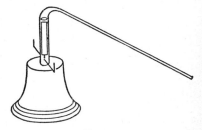

FIG. 19.

Next to the precaution of collecting the gases, if mingled, out of
contact with the platina was the necessity of testing the law of a *definite electrolytic* action, upon water at least, under all varieties of condition; that, with a conviction of its certainty, might also be obtained a
knowledge of those interfering circumstances which would require to be
practically guarded against.

The first point investigated was the influence or indifference of extensive variations in the size of the electrodes, for which purpose instruments like those last described were used. One of these had plates 0.7 of an inch wide and nearly four inches long; another had plates only 0.5 of an inch wide and 0.8 of an inch long; a third had wires 0.02 of an inch in diameter and three inches long; and a fourth, similar wires only half an inch in length. Yet when these were filled with dilute sulphuric acid, and, being placed in succession, had one common current of electricity passed through them, very nearly the same quantity of gas was evolved in all. The difference was sometimes in favour of one and sometimes on the side of another; but the general result was that the largest quantity of gases was evolved at the smallest electrodes, namely, those consisting merely of platina wires.

Experiments of a similar kind were made with the single-plate straight tubes, and also with the curved tubes, with similar consequences; and when these, with the former tubes, were arranged together in various ways, the result, as to the equality of action of large and small metallic surfaces when delivering and receiving the same current of electricity, was constantly the same. As an illustration, the following numbers are given. An instrument with two wires evolved 74.3 volumes of mixed gases; another with plates, 73.25 volumes; whilst the sum of the oxygen and hydrogen in two separate tubes amounted to 73.65 volumes. In another experiment the volumes were 55.3, 55.3, and 54.4.

But it was observed in these experiments that in single-plate tubes more hydrogen was evolved at the negative electrode than was proportionate to the oxygen at the positive electrode; and generally, also, more than was proportionate to the oxygen and hydrogen in a double-plate tube. Upon more minutely examining these effects, I was led to refer them, and also the differences between wires and plates, to the solubility of the gases evolved, especially at the positive electrode.

With the intention of avoiding this solubility of the gases as much as possible, I arranged the decomposing plates in a vertical position, that the bubbles might quickly escape upwards and that the downward currents in the fluid should not meet ascending currents of gas. This precaution I found to assist greatly in producing constant results, and especially in experiments to be hereafter referred to, in which other liquids than dilute sulphuric acid, as for instance solution of potash, were used.

The irregularities in the indications of the measurer proposed, arising from the solubility just referred to, are but small, and may be very nearly corrected by comparing the results of two or three experiments. They may also be almost entirely avoided by selecting that solution which is found to favour them in the least degree; and still further by collecting the hydrogen only, and using that as the indicating gas; for, being much less soluble than oxygen, being evolved with twice the rapidity and in larger bubbles, it can be collected more perfectly and in greater purity.

From the foregoing and many other experiments, it results that *variation in the size of the electrodes causes no variation in the chemical action of a given quantity of electricity upon water.*

The next point in regard to which the principle of constant electro-chemical action was tested was *variation of intensity*. In the first place, the preceding experiments were repeated, using batteries of an *equal* number of plates, *strongly* and *weakly* charged; but the results were alike. They were then repeated, using batteries sometimes containing forty and at other times only five pairs of plates; but the results were still the same. *Variations therefore in the intensity,* caused by difference in the strength of charge or in the number of alternations used, *produced no difference as to the equal action of large and small electrodes.*

The *third point,* in respect to which the principle of equal electro-chemical action on water was tested, was *variation of the strength of the solution used.* In order to render the water a conductor, sulphuric acid had been added to it; and it did not seem unlikely that this substance, with many others, might render the water more subject to decomposi-tion, the electricity remaining the same in quantity. But such did not prove to be the case. Diluted sulphuric acid, of different strengths, was introduced into different decomposing apparatus and submitted simulta-neously to the action of the same electric current. Slight differences oc-curred, as before, sometimes in one direction, sometimes in another; but the final result was that *exactly the same quantity of water was decom-posed in all the solutions by the same quantity of electricity,* though the sulphuric acid in some was seventyfold what it was in others. The strengths used were of specific gravity 1.495, and downwards.

Although not necessary for the practical use of the instrument I am describing, yet as connected with the important point of constant electro-chemical action upon water, I now investigated the effects produced by an electric current passing through aqueous solutions of acids, salts, and compounds, exceedingly different from each other in their nature, and found them to yield astonishingly uniform results. But many of them which are connected with a secondary action will be more usefully de-scribed hereafter.

When solutions of caustic potassa or soda, or sulphate of magnesia, or sulphate of soda were acted upon by the electric current, just as much oxygen and hydrogen was evolved from them as from the diluted sul-phuric acid, with which they were compared. When a solution of am-monia, rendered a better conductor by sulphate of ammonia, or a solution of subcarbonate of potassa was experimented with, the *hydrogen* evolved was in the same quantity as that set free from the diluted sulphuric acid with which they were compared. Hence *changes in the nature of the solution do not alter the constancy of electrolytic action upon water.*

I consider the foregoing investigation as sufficient to prove the very extraordinary and important principle with respect to WATER, *that when subjected to the influence of the electric current, a quantity of it is de-composed exactly proportionate to the quantity of electricity which has passed,* notwithstanding the thousand variations in the conditions and circumstances under which it may at the time be placed; and further, that when the interference of certain secondary effects, together with the solution or recombination of the gas and the evolution of air, is guarded against, *the products of the decomposition may be collected with such accuracy as to afford a very excellent and valuable measurer of the electricity concerned in their evolution.*

The forms of instrument which I have given, Figs. 17, 18, 19, are probably those which will be found most useful, as they indicate the quantity of electricity by the largest volume of gases, and cause the least obstruction to the passage of the current. The fluid which my present experience leads me to prefer is a solution of sulphuric acid of specific gravity about 1.336, or from that to 1.25; but it is very essential that there should be no organic substance, nor any vegetable acid, nor other body, which, by being liable to the action of the oxygen or hydrogen evolved at the electrodes, shall diminish their quantity or add other gases to them.

In many cases when the instrument is used as a *comparative standard,* or even as a *measurer,* it may be desirable to collect the hydrogen only, as being less liable to absorption or disappearance in other ways than the oxygen; whilst at the same time its volume is so large as to render it a good and sensible indicator. In such cases the first and second form of apparatus have been used, Figs. 15, 16. The indications obtained were very constant, the variations being much smaller than in those forms of apparatus collecting both gases; and they can also be procured when solutions are used in comparative experiments, which, yielding no oxygen or only secondary results of its action, can give no indications if the educts at both electrodes be collected. Such is the case when solutions of ammonia, muriatic acid, chlorides, iodides, acetates or other vegetable salts, etc., are employed.

In a few cases, as where solutions of metallic salts liable to reduction at the negative electrode are acted upon, the oxygen may be advantageously used as the measuring substance. This is the case, for instance, with sulphate of copper.

There are therefore two general forms of the instrument which I submit as a measurer of electricity; one in which both the gases of the water decomposed are collected, and the other in which a single gas, as the hydrogen only, is used. When referred to as a *comparative instrument* (a use I shall now make of it very extensively), it will not often require particular precaution in the observation; but when used as an *absolute measurer,* it will be needful that the barometric pressure and the temperature be taken into account, and that the graduation of the instruments should be to one scale; the hundredths and smaller divisions of a cubical inch are quite fit for this purpose, and the hundredth may be very conveniently taken as indicating a DEGREE of electricity.

It can scarcely be needful to point out further than has been done how this instrument is to be used. It is to be introduced into the course of the electric current, the action of which is to be exerted anywhere else, and if 60° or 70° of electricity are to be measured out, either in one or several portions, the current, whether strong or weak, is to be continued until the gas in the tube occupies that number of divisions or hundredths of a cubical inch. Or if a quantity competent to produce a certain effect is to be measured, the effect is to be obtained, and then the indication read off. In exact experiments it is necessary to correct the volume of gas for changes in temperature and pressure, and especially for moisture. For the latter object the volta-electrometer (Fig. 19) is most accurate, as its gas can be measured over water, whilst the others retain it over acid or saline solutions.

I have not hesitated to apply the term *degree* in analogy with the use made of it with respect to another most important imponderable agent, namely, heat; and as the definite expansion of air, water, mercury, etc., is there made use of to measure heat, so the equally definite evolution of gases is here turned to a similar use for electricity.

The instrument offers the only *actual measurer* of voltaic electricity which we at present possess. For without being at all affected by variations in time or intensity, or alterations in the current itself, of any kind, or from any cause, or even of intermissions of action, it takes note with accuracy of the quantity of electricity which has passed through it, and reveals that quantity by inspection; I have therefore named it a VOLTA-ELECTROMETER.

On the primary or secondary character of the bodies evolved at the Electrodes

Before the *volta-electrometer* could be employed in determining, as a *general law,* the constancy of electro-decomposition, it became necessary to examine a distinction, already recognised among scientific men, relative to the products of that action, namely, their primary or secondary character; and, if possible, by some general rule or principle, to decide when they were of the one or the other kind. It will appear hereafter that great mistakes respecting electro-chemical action and its consequences have arisen from confounding these two classes of results together.

When a substance under decomposition yields at the electrodes those bodies uncombined and unaltered which the electric current has separated, then they may be considered as primary results, even though themselves compounds. Thus the oxygen and hydrogen from water are primary results; and so also are the acid and alkali (themselves compound bodies) evolved from sulphate of soda. But when the substances separated by the current are changed at the electrodes before their appearance, then they give rise to secondary results, although in many cases the bodies evolved are elementary.

These secondary results occur in two ways, being sometimes due to the mutual action of the evolved substance and the matter of the electrode, and sometimes to its action upon the substances contained in the body itself under decomposition. Thus, when carbon is made the positive electrode in dilute sulphuric acid, carbonic oxide and carbonic acid occasionally appear there instead of oxygen; for the latter, acting upon the matter of the electrode, produces these secondary results. Or if the positive electrode, in a solution of nitrate or acetate of lead, be platina, then peroxide of lead appears there, equally a secondary result with the former, but now depending upon an action of the oxygen on a substance in the solution. Again, when ammonia is decomposed by platina electrodes, nitrogen appears at the *anode;* but though an *elementary* body, it is a *secondary* result in this case, being derived from the chemical action of the oxygen electrically evolved there upon the ammonia in the surrounding solution. In the same manner, when aqueous solutions of metallic salts are decomposed by the current, the metals evolved at the *cathode,* though elements, are *always* secondary results, and not immediate consequences of the decomposing power of the electric current.

But when we take to our assistance the law of *constant electro-chemical action* already proved with regard to water, and which I hope to extend satisfactorily to all bodies, and consider the *quantities* as well as the *nature* of the substances set free, a generally accurate judgment of the primary or secondary character of the results may be formed: and this important point, so essential to the theory of electrolysation, since it decides what are the particles directly under the influence of the current (distinguishing them from such as are not affected) and what are the results to be expected, may be established with such degree of certainty as to remove innumerable ambiguities and doubtful considerations from this branch of the science.

Let us apply these principles to the case of ammonia, and the supposed determination of nitrogen to one or the other *electrode.* A pure strong solution of ammonia is as bad a conductor, and therefore as little liable to electrolysation, as pure water; but when sulphate of ammonia is dissolved in it, the whole becomes a conductor; nitrogen *almost* and occasionally *quite* pure is evolved at the *anode,* and hydrogen at the *cathode;* the ratio of the volume of the former to that of the latter varying, but being as 1 to about 3 or 4. This result would seem at first to imply that the electric current had decomposed ammonia, and that the nitrogen had been determined towards the positive electrode. But when the electricity used was measured out by the volta-electrometer, it was found that the hydrogen obtained was exactly in the proportion which would have been supplied by decomposed water, whilst the nitrogen had no certain or constant relation whatever. When, upon multiplying experiments, it was found that, by using a stronger or weaker solution, or a more or less powerful battery, the gas evolved at the *anode* was a mixture of oxygen and nitrogen, varying both in proportion and absolute quantity, whilst the hydrogen at the *cathode* remained constant, no doubt could be entertained that the nitrogen at the *anode* was a secondary result, depending upon the chemical action of the nascent oxygen, determined to that surface by the electric current, upon the ammonia in solution. It was the water, therefore, which was electrolysed, not the ammonia.

I have experimented upon many bodies, with a view to determine whether the results were primary or secondary. I have been surprised to find how many of them, in ordinary cases, are of the latter class, and how frequently water is the only body electrolysed in instances where other substances have been supposed to give way. Some of these results I will give in as few words as possible.

Nitric acid.—When very strong, it conducted well, and yielded oxygen at the positive electrode. No gas appeared at the negative electrode; but nitrous acid, and apparently nitric oxide, was formed there, which, dissolving, rendered the acid yellow or red, and at last even effervescent, from the spontaneous separation of nitric oxide. Upon diluting the acid with its bulk or more of water, gas appeared at the negative electrode. Its quantity could be varied by variations, either in the strength of the acid or of the voltaic current: for that acid from which no gas separated at the *cathode,* with a weak voltaic battery, did evolve gas there with a stronger; and that battery which evolved no gas there with a strong acid, did cause its evolution with an acid more dilute. The gas at the *anode* was always oxygen; that at the *cathode* hydrogen. When the quantity of products was examined by the volta-electrometer, the oxygen, whether from strong or weak acid, proved to be in the same proportion as from water. When the acid was diluted to specific gravity 1.24, or less, the hydrogen also proved to be the same in quantity as from water. Hence I conclude that the nitric acid does not undergo electrolysation, but the water only; that the oxygen at the *anode* is always a primary result, but that the products at the *cathode* are often secondary, and due to the reaction of the hydrogen upon the nitric acid.

Nitre.—A solution of this salt yields very variable results, according as one or other form of tube is used, or as the electrodes are large or small. Sometimes the whole of the hydrogen of the water decomposed may be obtained at the negative electrode; at other times, only a part of it, because of the ready formation of secondary results. The solution is a very excellent conductor of electricity.

Muriatic acid.—A strong solution gave hydrogen at the negative electrode and chlorine only at the positive electrode; of the latter, a part acted on the platina and a part was dissolved. A minute bubble of gas remained; it was not oxygen, but probably air previously held in solution.

It was an important matter to determine whether the chlorine was a primary result or only a secondary product, due to the action of the oxygen evolved from water at the *anode* upon the muriatic acid; *i.e.* whether the muriatic acid was electrolysable, and, if so, whether the decomposition was *definite*.

The muriatic acid was gradually diluted. One part with six of water gave only chlorine at the *anode*. One part with eight of water gave only chlorine; with nine of water, a little oxygen appeared with the chlorine: but the occurrence or non-occurrence of oxygen at these strengths depended, in part, on the strength of the voltaic battery used. With fifteen parts of water, a little oxygen, with much chlorine, was evolved at the *anode*. As the solution was now becoming a bad conductor of electricity, sulphuric acid was added to it: this caused more ready decomposition, but did not sensibly alter the proportion of chlorine and oxygen.

The muriatic acid was now diluted with 100 times its volume of dilute sulphuric acid. It still gave a large proportion of chlorine at the *anode,* mingled with oxygen; and the result was the same, whether a voltaic battery of forty pairs of plates or one containing only five pairs were used. With acid of this strength, the oxygen evolved at the *anode* was to the hydrogen at the *cathode,* in volume, as 17 is to 64; and therefore the chlorine would have been thirty volumes had it not been dissolved by the fluid.

Next with respect to the quantity of elements evolved. On using the volta-electrometer, it was found that, whether the strongest or the weakest muriatic acid were used, whether chlorine alone or chlorine mingled with oxygen appeared at the *anode,* still the hydrogen evolved at the *cathode* was a constant quantity, *i.e.* exactly the same as the hydrogen which the *same quantity of electricity* could evolve from water.

This constancy does not decide whether the muriatic acid is electrolysed or not, although it proves that if so, it must be in definite proportions to the quantity of electricity used. Other considerations may, however, be allowed to decide the point. The analogy between chlorine and oxygen, in their relations to hydrogen, is so strong as to lead almost to the certainty that, when combined with that element, they would perform similar parts in the process of electro-decomposition. They both unite with it in single proportional or equivalent quantities. In other binary compounds of chlorine also, where nothing equivocal depending on the simultaneous presence of it and oxygen is involved, the chlorine is directly eliminated at the *anode* by the electric current. Such is the case with the chloride of lead, which may be justly compared with protoxide of lead, and stands in the same relation to it as muriatic acid to water. The chlorides of potassium, sodium, barium, etc., are in the same relation to the protoxides of the same metals and present the same results under the influence of the electric current.

From all the experiments, combined with these considerations, I conclude that muriatic acid is decomposed by the direct influence of the electric current, and that the quantities evolved are, and therefore the chemical action is, *definite for a definite quantity of electricity.* For though I have not collected and measured the chlorine, in its separate state, at the *anode,* there can exist no doubt as to its being proportional to the hydrogen at the *cathode;* and the results are therefore sufficient to establish the general law of *constant electro-chemical action* in the case of muriatic acid.

In the dilute acid, I conclude that a part of the water is electro-chemically decomposed, giving origin to the oxygen, which appears mingled with the chlorine at the *anode.* The oxygen *may* be viewed as a secondary result; but I incline to believe that it is not so: for, if it were, it might be expected in largest proportion from the stronger acid, whereas the reverse is the fact. This consideration, with others, also leads me to conclude that muriatic acid is more easily decomposed by the electric current than water; since, even when diluted with eight or nine times its

quantity of the latter fluid, it alone gives way, the water remaining unaffected.

Chlorides.—On using solutions of chlorides in water—for instance,
the chlorides of sodium or calcium—there was evolution of chlorine only
at the positive electrode, and of hydrogen, with the oxide of the base, as
soda or lime, at the negative electrode. The process of decomposition may
be viewed as proceeding in two or three ways, all terminating in the same
results. Perhaps the simplest is to consider the chloride as the substance
electrolysed, its chlorine being determined to and evolved at the *anode,*
and its metal passing to the *cathode,* where, finding no more chlorine, it
acts upon the water, producing hydrogen and an oxide as secondary
results. As the discussion would detain me from more important matter,
and is not of immediate consequence, I shall defer it for the present. It is,
however, of *great consequence* to state that, on using the volta-electrometer, the hydrogen in both cases was definite; and if the results do not
prove the definite decomposition of chlorides (which shall be proved elsewhere), they are not in the slightest degree opposed to such a conclusion
and do support the *general law.*

Tartaric acid.—Pure solution of tartaric acid is almost as bad a conductor as pure water. On adding sulphuric acid, it conducted well, the
results at the positive electrode being primary or secondary in different
proportions, according to variations in the strength of the acid and the
power of the electric current. Alkaline tartrates gave a large proportion
of secondary results at the positive electrode. The hydrogen at the negative electrode remained constant unless certain triple metallic salts were
used.

Solutions, of salts containing other vegetable acids, as the benzoates;
of sugar, gum, etc., dissolved in dilute sulphuric acid; of resin, albumen,
etc., dissolved in alkalies, were in turn submitted to the electrolytic power
of the voltaic current. In all these cases, secondary results to a greater or
smaller extent were produced at the positive electrode.

In concluding this division of these *Researches,* it cannot but occur
to the mind that the final result of the action of the electric current upon
substances placed between the electrodes, instead of being simple, may
be very complicated. There are two modes by which these substances may
be decomposed, either by the direct force of the electric current or by
the action of bodies which that current may evolve. There are also two
modes by which new compounds may be formed, *i.e.* by combination of
the evolving substances, whilst in their nascent state, directly with the
matter of the electrode; or else their combination with those bodies which,
being contained in, or associated with, the body suffering decomposition,
are necessarily present at the *anode* and *cathode.* The complexity is rendered still greater by the circumstance that two or more of these actions
may occur simultaneously, and also in variable proportions to each other.
But it may in a great measure be resolved by attention to the principles
already laid down.

On the definite nature and extent of Electro-chemical Decomposition

In the first part of these *Researches,* after proving the identity of electricities derived from different sources, I announced a law, derived from experiment, which seemed to me of the utmost importance to the science of electricity in general, and that branch of it denominated electro-chemistry in particular. The law was expressed thus: *The chemical power of a current of electricity is in direct proportion to the absolute quantity of electricity which passes.*

It is now my object to consider this great principle more closely, and to develop some of the consequences to which it leads. That the evidence for it may be the more distinct and applicable, I shall quote cases of decomposition subject to as few interferences from secondary results as possible, effected upon bodies very simple yet very definite in their nature.

In the first place, I consider the law as so fully established with respect to the decomposition of *water,* and under so many circumstances which might be supposed, if anything could, to exert an influence over it, that I may be excused entering into further detail respecting that substance, or even summing up the results here.

In the next place, I also consider the law as established with respect to *muriatic acid* by the experiments and reasoning already advanced, when speaking of that substance, in the subdivision respecting primary and secondary results.

Without speaking with the same confidence, yet from the experiments described, and many others not described, relating to hydro-fluoric, hydro-cyanic, ferro-cyanic, and sulpho-cyanic acids, and from the close analogy which holds between these bodies and the hydracids of chlorine, iodine, bromine, etc., I consider these also as coming under subjection to the law and assisting to prove its truth.

In the preceding cases, except the first, the water is believed to be inactive; but to avoid any ambiguity arising from its presence, I sought for substances from which it should be absent altogether; and I soon found abundance, amongst which *protochloride of tin* was first subjected to decomposition in the following manner. A piece of platina wire had one extremity coiled up into a small knob, and, having been carefully weighed, was sealed hermetically into a piece of bottle-glass tube, so that the knob should be at the bottom of the tube within (Fig. 20). The tube was suspended by a piece of platina wire, so that the heat of a spirit lamp could be applied to it. Recently fused protochloride of tin was introduced in sufficient quantity to occupy, when melted, about one half of the tube; the wire of the tube was connected with a volta-electrometer, which was itself connected with

FIG. 20.

the negative end of a voltaic battery; and a platina wire connected with the positive end of the same battery was dipped into the fused chloride in the tube; being, however, so bent that it could not by any shake of the hand or apparatus touch the negative electrode at the bottom of the vessel. The whole arrangement is delineated in Fig. 21.

Under these circumstances the chloride of tin was decomposed: the chlorine evolved at the positive electrode formed bichloride of tin, which passed away in fumes, and the tin evolved at the negative electrode combined with the platina, forming an alloy, fusible at the temperature to which the tube was subjected, and therefore never occasioning metallic communication through the decomposing chloride. When the experiment had been continued so long as to yield a reasonable quantity of gas in the volta-electrometer, the battery connection was broken, the positive electrode removed, and the tube and remaining chloride allowed to cool. When cold, the tube was broken open, the rest of the chloride and the glass being easily separable from the platina wire and its button of alloy. The latter when washed was then reweighed, and the increase gave the weight of the tin reduced.

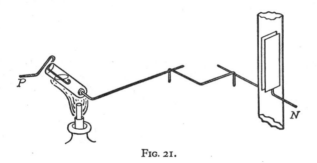

FIG. 21.

I will give the particular results of one experiment, in illustration of the mode adopted in this and others, the results of which I shall have occasion to quote. The negative electrode weighed at first 20 grains; after the experiment, it, with its button of alloy, weighed 23.2 grains. The tin evolved by the electric current at the *cathode* weighed therefore 3.2 grains. The quantity of oxygen and hydrogen collected in the volta-electrometer = 3.85 cubic inches. As 100 cubic inches of oxygen and hydrogen, in the proportions to form water, may be considered as weighing 12.92 grains, the 3.85 cubic inches would weigh 0.49742 of a grain; that being, therefore, the weight of water decomposed by the same electric current as was able to decompose such weight of protochloride of tin as could yield 3.2 grains of metal. Now 0.49742 : 3.2 : : 9 the equivalent of water is to 57.9, which should therefore be the equivalent of tin, if the experiment had been made without error, and if the electro-chemical decomposition *is in this case also definite.* In some chemical works 58 is given as the chemical equivalent of tin, in others 57.9. Both are so near to the result of the experiment, and the experiment itself is so subject to slight causes of variation (as from the absorption of gas in the volta-electrometer), that the numbers leave little doubt of the applicability of the *law of definite action* in this and all similar cases of electro-decomposition.

It is not often I have obtained an accordance in numbers so near as that I have just quoted. Four experiments were made on the protochloride of tin, the quantities of gas evolved in the volta-electrometer being from 2.05 to 10.29 cubic inches. The average of the four experiments gave 58.53 as the electro-chemical equivalent for tin.

The chloride remaining after the experiment was pure protochloride of tin; and no one can doubt for a moment that the equivalent of chlorine had been evolved at the *anode,* and, having formed bichloride of tin as a secondary result, had passed away.

Chloride of lead was experimented upon in a manner exactly similar, except that a change was made in the nature of the positive electrode; for as the chlorine evolved at the *anode* forms no perchloride of lead, but acts directly upon the platina, it produces, if that metal be used, a solution of chloride of platina in the chloride of lead; in consequence of which a portion of platina can pass to the *cathode,* and would then produce a vitiated result. I therefore sought for, and found in plumbago, another substance, which could be used safely as the positive electrode in such bodies as chlorides, iodides, etc. The chlorine or iodine does not act upon it, but is evolved in the free state; and the plumbago has no reaction, under the circumstances, upon the fused chloride or iodide in which it is plunged. Even if a few particles of plumbago should separate by the heat or the mechanical action of the evolved gas, they can do no harm in the chloride.

The mean of three experiments gave the number of 100.85 as the equivalent for lead. The chemical equivalent is 103.5. The deficiency in my experiments I attribute to the solution of part of the gas in the volta-electrometer; but the results leave no doubt on my mind that both the lead and the chlorine are, in this case, evolved in *definite quantities* by the action of a given quantity of electricity.

I endeavoured to experiment upon the *oxide of lead* obtained by fusion and ignition of the nitrate in a platina crucible, but found great difficulty, from the high temperature required for perfect fusion, and the powerful fluxing qualities of the substance. Green-glass tubes repeatedly failed. I at last fused the oxide in a small porcelain crucible, heated fully in a charcoal fire; and, as it was essential that the evolution of the lead at the *cathode* should take place beneath the surface, the negative electrode was guarded by a green-glass tube, fused around it in such a manner as to expose only the knob of platina at the lower end (Fig. 22), so that it could be plunged beneath the surface, and thus exclude contact of air or oxygen with the lead reduced there. A platina wire was employed for the positive electrode, that metal not being subject to any action from the oxygen evolved against it. The arrangement is given in Fig. 23.

In an experiment of this kind the equivalent for the lead came out

93.17, which is very much too small. This, I believe, was because of the small interval between the positive and negative electrodes in the oxide of lead; so that it was not unlikely that some of the froth and bubbles formed by the oxygen at the *anode* should occasionally even touch the lead reduced at the *cathode,* and re-oxidise it. When I endeavoured to correct this by having more litharge, the greater heat required to keep it all fluid caused a quicker action on the crucible, which was soon eaten through, and the experiment stopped.

In one experiment of this kind I used borate of lead. It evolves lead, under the influence of the electric current, at the *anode,* and oxygen at the *cathode;* and as the boracic acid is not either directly or incidentally decomposed during the operation, I expected a result dependent on the oxide of lead. The borate is not so violent a flux as the oxide, but it

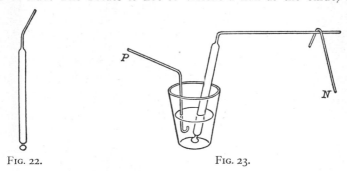

Fig. 22.   Fig. 23.

requires a higher temperature to make it quite liquid; and if not very hot, the bubbles of oxygen cling to the positive electrode and retard the transfer of electricity. The number for lead came out 101.29, which is so near to 103.5 as to show that the action of the current had been definite.

Iodide of potassium was subjected to electrolytic action in a tube. The negative electrode was a globule of lead, and I hoped in this way to retain the potassium, and obtain results that could be weighed and compared with the volta-electrometer indication; but the difficulties dependent upon the high temperature required, the action upon the glass, the fusibility of the platina induced by the presence of the lead, and other circumstances, prevented me from procuring such results. The iodide was decomposed with the evolution of iodine at the *anode,* and of potassium at the *cathode,* as in former cases.

In some of these experiments several substances were placed in succession, and decomposed simultaneously by the same electric current: thus, protochloride of tin, chloride of lead, and water were thus acted on at once. It is needless to say that the results were comparable, the tin, lead, chlorine, oxygen, and hydrogen evolved being *definite in quantity* and electro-chemical equivalents to each other.

Let us turn to another kind of proof of the *definite chemical action of electricity.* If any circumstances could be supposed to exert an influence over the quantity of the matters evolved during electrolytic action, one would expect them to be present when electrodes of different substances, and possessing very different chemical affinities for such matters, were used. Platina has no power in dilute sulphuric acid of combining with the oxygen at the *anode,* though the latter be evolved in the nascent state against it. Copper, on the other hand, immediately unites with the oxygen, as the electric current sets it free from the hydrogen; and zinc is not only able to combine with it, but can, without any help from the electricity, abstract it directly from the water, at the same time setting torrents of hydrogen free. Yet in cases where these three substances were used as the positive electrodes in three similar portions of the same dilute sulphuric acid, specific gravity 1.336, precisely the same quantity of water was decomposed by the electric current, and precisely the same quantity of hydrogen set free at the *cathodes* of the three solutions.

The experiment was made thus. Portions of the dilute sulphuric acid were put into three basins. Three volta-electrometer tubes, of the form Figs. 13, 15, were filled with the same acid, and one inverted in each basin. A zinc plate, connected with the positive end of a voltaic battery, was dipped into the first basin, forming the positive electrode there, the hydrogen, which was abundantly evolved from it by the direct action of the acid, being allowed to escape. A copper plate, which dipped into the acid of the second basin, was connected with the negative electrode of the *first* basin; and a platina plate, which dipped into the acid of the third basin, was connected with the negative electrode of the *second* basin. The negative electrode of the third basin was connected with a volta-electrometer, and that with the negative end of the voltaic battery.

Immediately that the circuit was complete, the *electro-chemical action* commenced in all the vessels. The hydrogen still rose in, apparently, undiminished quantities from the positive zinc electrode in the first basin. No oxygen was evolved at the positive copper electrode in the second basin, but a sulphate of copper was formed there; whilst in the third basin the positive platina electrode evolved pure oxygen gas and was itself unaffected. But in *all* the basins the hydrogen liberated at the *negative* platina electrodes was the *same in quantity,* and the same with the volume of hydrogen evolved in the volta-electrometer, showing that in all the vessels the current had decomposed an equal quantity of water. In this trying case, therefore, the *chemical action of electricity* proved to be *perfectly definite.*

A similar experiment was made with muriatic acid diluted with its bulk of water. The three positive electrodes were zinc, silver, and platina; the first being able to separate and combine with the chlorine *without* the aid of the current; the second combining with the chlorine only after the current had set it free; and the third rejecting almost the whole of it. The three negative electrodes were, as before, platina plates fixed within glass tubes. In this experiment, as in the former, the quantity of hydrogen evolved at the *cathodes* was the same for all, and the same as the hydrogen evolved in the volta-electrometer. I have already given my reasons for believing that in these experiments it is the muriatic acid which is directly decomposed by the electricity; and the results prove that the quantities so decomposed are *perfectly definite* and proportionate to the quantity of electricity which has passed.

Experiments of a similar kind were then made with bodies altogether in a different state, *i.e.* with *fused* chlorides, iodides, etc. I have already described an experiment with fused chloride of silver, in which the electrodes were of metallic silver, the one rendered negative becoming increased and lengthened by the addition of metal, whilst the other was dissolved and eaten away by its abstraction. This experiment was repeated, two weighed pieces of silver wire being used as the electrodes, and a volta-electrometer included in the circuit. Great care was taken to withdraw the negative electrode so regularly and steadily that the crystals of reduced silver should not form a *metallic* communication beneath the surface of the fused chloride. On concluding the experiment the positive electrode was reweighed, and its loss ascertained. The mixture of chloride of silver and metal, withdrawn in successive portions at the negative electrode, was digested in solution of ammonia, to remove the chloride, and the metallic silver remaining also weighed: it was the reduction at the *cathode,* and exactly equalled the solution at the *anode;* and each portion was as nearly as possible the equivalent to the water decomposed in the volta-electrometer.

The infusible condition of the silver at the temperature used and the length and ramifying character of its crystals render the above experiment

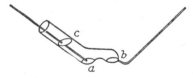

FIG. 24.

difficult to perform and uncertain in its results. I therefore wrought with chloride of lead, using a green-glass tube formed as in Fig. 24. A weighed platina wire was fused into the bottom of a small tube, as before described. The tube was then bent to an angle, at about half an inch distance from the closed end; and the part between the angle and the extremity, being softened, was forced upward, as in the figure, so as to form a bridge, or rather separation, producing two little depressions or basins, *a, b,* within the tube. This arrangement was suspended by a platina wire, as before, so that the heat of a spirit lamp could be applied to it, such inclination being given to it as would allow all air to escape during the fusion of the chloride of lead. A positive electrode was then provided, by bending up the end of a platina wire into a knot, and fusing about twenty grains of metallic lead onto it, in a small closed tube of glass, which was afterwards broken away. Being so furnished, the wire with its lead was weighed, and the weight recorded.

Chloride of lead was now introduced into the tube and carefully fused. The leaded electrode was also introduced; after which the metal, at its extremity, soon melted. In this state of things the tube was filled up to *c* with melted chloride of lead; the end of the electrode to be rendered negative was in the basin *b,* and the electrode of melted lead was retained in the basin *a,* and, by connection with the proper conducting wire of a voltaic battery, was rendered positive. A volta-electrometer was included in the circuit.

Immediately upon the completion of the communication with the voltaic battery, the current passed, and decomposition proceeded. No chlorine was evolved at the positive electrode; but as the fused chloride was transparent, a button of alloy could be observed gradually forming and increasing in size at *b,* whilst the lead at *a* could also be seen gradually to diminish. After a time, the experiment was stopped; the tube allowed to cool, and broken open; the wires, with their buttons, cleaned and weighed; and their change in weight compared with the indication of the volta-electrometer.

In this experiment the positive electrode had lost just as much lead as the negative one had gained, and the loss and gain were very nearly the equivalents of the water decomposed in the volta-electrometer, giving for lead the number 101.5. It is therefore evident, in this instance, that causing *strong affinity,* or *no affinity,* for the substance evolved at the *anode,* to be active during the experiment, produces no variation in the definite action of the electric current.

Then protochloride of tin was subjected to the electric current in the same manner, using, of course, a tin positive electrode. No bichloride of tin was now formed. On examining the two electrodes, the positive had lost precisely as much as the negative had gained; and by comparison with the volta-electrometer, the number for tin came out 59.

All these facts combine into, I think, an irresistible mass of evidence, proving the truth of the important proposition which I at first laid down, namely, *that the chemical power of a current of electricity is in direct proportion to the absolute quantity of electricity which passes.* They prove, too, that this is not merely true with one substance, as water, but generally with all electrolytic bodies; and, further, that the results obtained with any *one substance* do not merely agree amongst themselves, but also with those obtained from *other substances,* the whole combining together into *one series of definite electro-chemical actions.*

The doctrine of *definite electro-chemical action* just laid down, and, I believe, established, leads to some new views of the relations and classifications of bodies associated with or subject to this action. Some of these I shall proceed to consider.

In the first place, compound bodies may be separated into two great classes, namely, those which are decomposable by the electric current and those which are not: of the latter, some are conductors, others non-conductors, of voltaic electricity. The former do not depend for their decomposability upon the nature of their elements only; for, of the same two elements, bodies may be formed of which one shall belong to one class and another to the other class; but probably on the proportions also. I propose to call bodies of this, the decomposable class, *Electrolytes.*

Then, again, the substances into which these divide, under the influence of the electric current, form an exceedingly important general class. They are combining bodies; are directly associated with the fundamental parts of the doctrine of chemical affinity; and have each a definite proportion, in which they are always evolved during electrolytic action. I have proposed to call these bodies generally *ions,* or particularly *anions* and *cations,* according as they appear at the *anode* or *cathode;* and the numbers representing the proportions in which they are evolved, *electro-chemical equivalents.* Thus hydrogen, oxygen, chlorine, iodine, lead, tin are *ions;* the three former are *anions,* the two metals are *cations,* and 1, 8, 36, 125, 104, 58 are their *electro-chemical equivalents* nearly.

A summary of certain points already ascertained respecting *electrolytes, ions,* and *electro-chemical equivalents* may be given in the following general form of propositions, without, I hope, including any serious error.

i. A single *ion, i.e.* one not in combination with another, will have no tendency to pass to either of the electrodes, and will be perfectly indifferent to the passing current, unless it be itself a compound of more elementary *ions,* and so subject to actual decomposition. Upon this fact is founded much of the proof adduced in favour of the new theory of electro-chemical decomposition, which I put forth in a former part of these *Researches.*

ii. If one *ion* be combined in right proportions with another strongly opposed to it in its ordinary chemical relations, *i.e.* if an *anion* be combined with a *cation,* then both will travel, the one to the *anode,* the other to the *cathode,* of the decomposing body.

iii. If, therefore, an *ion* pass towards one of the electrodes, another *ion* must also be passing simultaneously to the other electrode, although, from secondary action, it may not make its appearance.

iv. A body decomposable directly by the electric current, *i.e.* an *electrolyte,* must consist of two *ions,* and must also render them up during the act of decomposition.

v. There is but one *electrolyte* composed of the same two elementary *ions;* at least such appears to be the fact, dependent upon a law, that *only single electro-chemical equivalents of elementary ions can go to the electrodes, and not multiples.*

vi. A body not decomposable when alone, as boracic acid, is not directly decomposable by the electric current when in combination. It may act as an *ion* going wholly to the *anode* or *cathode,* but does not yield up its elements, except occasionally by a secondary action. Perhaps it is superfluous for me to point out that this proposition has *no relation* to such cases as that of water, which, by the presence of other bodies, is rendered a better conductor of electricity, and *therefore* is more freely decomposed.

vii. The nature of the substance of which the electrode is formed, provided it be a conductor, causes no difference in the electro-decomposition, either in kind or degree: but it seriously influences, by secondary action, the state in which the *ions* finally appear. Advantage may be taken of this principle in combining and collecting such *ions* as, if evolved in their free state, would be unmanageable.

viii. A substance which, being used as the electrode, can combine with the *ion* evolved against it is also, I believe, an *ion,* and combines, in such cases, in the quantity represented by its *electro-chemical equivalent.* All the experiments I have made agree with this view; and it seems to me, at present, to result as a necessary consequence. Whether, in the secondary actions that take place, where the *ion* acts not upon the matter of the electrode but on that which is around it in the liquid, the same consequence follows, will require more extended investigation to determine.

ix. Compound *ions* are not necessarily composed of electro-chemical equivalents of simple *ions.* For instance, sulphuric acid, boracic acid, phosphoric acid are *ions,* but not *electrolytes, i.e.* not composed of electro-chemical equivalents of simple *ions.*

x. Electro-chemical equivalents are always consistent; *i.e.* the same number which represents the equivalent of a substance A when it is separating from a substance B will also represent A when separating from a third substance C. Thus, 8 is the electro-chemical equivalent of oxygen, whether separating from hydrogen, or tin, or lead; and 103.5 is the electro-chemical equivalent of lead, whether separating from oxygen, or chlorine, or iodine.

xi. Electro-chemical equivalents coincide, and are the same, with ordinary chemical equivalents.

By means of experiment and the preceding propositions, a knowledge of *ions* and their electro-chemical equivalents may be obtained in various ways.

In the first place, they may be determined directly, as has been done with hydrogen, oxygen, lead, and tin in the numerous experiments already quoted.

In the next place, from propositions ii and iii may be deduced the knowledge of many other *ions,* and also their equivalents. When chloride of lead was decomposed, platina being used for both electrodes, there could remain no more doubt that chlorine was passing to the *anode,* although it combined with the platina there, than when the positive electrode, being of plumbago, allowed its evolution in the free state; neither could there, in either case, remain any doubt that for every 103.5 parts of lead evolved at the *cathode,* 36 parts of chlorine were evolved at the *anode,* for the remaining chloride of lead was unchanged. So also, when in a metallic solution one volume of oxygen, or a secondary compound containing that proportion, appeared at the *anode,* no doubt could arise that hydrogen, equivalent to two volumes, had been determined to the *cathode,* although, by a secondary action, it had been employed in reducing oxides of lead, copper, or other metals to the metallic state. In this manner, then, we learn from the experiments already described in these *Researches* that chlorine, iodine, bromine, fluorine, calcium, potassium, strontium, magnesium, manganese, etc., are *ions,* and that their *electro-chemical equivalents* are the same as their *ordinary chemical equivalents.*

Propositions iv and v extend our means of gaining information. For if a body of known chemical composition is found to be decomposable, and the nature of the substance evolved as a primary or even a secondary result at one of the electrodes be ascertained, the electro-chemical equivalent of that body may be deduced from the known constant composition of the substance evolved. Thus, when fused protiodide of tin is decomposed by the voltaic current the conclusion may be drawn that both the iodine and tin are *ions,* and that the proportions in which they combine in the fused compound express their electro-chemical equivalents. Again, with respect to the fused iodide of potassium, it is an electrolyte; and the chemical equivalents will also be the electro-chemical equivalents.

I think I cannot deceive myself in considering the doctrine of definite electro-chemical action as of the utmost importance. It touches by its facts, more directly and closely than any former fact, or set of facts, has done, upon the beautiful idea that ordinary chemical affinity is a mere consequence of the electrical attractions of the particles of different kinds of matter; and it will probably lead us to the means by which we may enlighten that which is at present so obscure, and either fully demonstrate the truth of the idea or develop that which ought to replace it.

On the absolute quantity of Electricity associated with the particles or atoms of Matter

The theory of definite electrolytical or electro-chemical action appears to me to touch immediately upon the *absolute quantity* of electricity or electric power belonging to different bodies. It is impossible, perhaps, to speak on this point without committing oneself beyond what present facts will sustain; and yet it is equally impossible, and perhaps would be impolitic, not to reason upon the subject. Although we know nothing of what an atom is, yet we cannot resist forming some idea of a small particle, which represents it to the mind; and though we are in equal, if not greater, ignorance of electricity, so as to be unable to say whether it is a particular matter or matters, or mere motion of ordinary matter, or some third kind of power or agent, yet there is an immensity of facts which justify us in believing that the atoms of matter are in some way endowed or associated with electrical powers, to which they owe their most striking qualities, and amongst them their mutual chemical affinity. As soon as we perceive, through the teaching of Dalton, that chemical powers are, however varied the circumstances in which they are exerted, definite for each body, we learn to estimate the relative degree of force which resides in such bodies; and when upon that knowledge comes the fact that the electricity, which we appear to be capable of loosening from its habitation for a while and conveying from place to place, *whilst it retains its chemical force,* can be measured out, and being so measured is found to be *as definite in its action* as any of *those portions* which, remaining associated with the particles of matter, give them their *chemical relation;* we seem to have found the link which connects the proportion of that we have evolved to the proportion of that belonging to the particles in their natural state.

Now it is wonderful to observe how small a quantity of a compound body is decomposed by a certain portion of electricity. Let us, for instance, consider this and a few other points in relation to water. *One grain* of water, acidulated to facilitate conduction, will require an electric current to be continued for three minutes and three quarters of time to effect its decomposition, which current must be powerful enough to retain a platina wire $\frac{1}{104}$th of an inch in thickness, red hot, in the air during the whole time; and if interrupted anywhere by charcoal points, will produce a very brilliant and constant star of light. If attention be paid to the instantaneous discharge of electricity of tension, as illustrated in the beautiful experiments of Mr. Wheatstone, and to what I have said elsewhere on the relation of common and voltaic electricity, it will not be too much to say that this necessary quantity of electricity is equal to a very powerful flash of lightning. Yet we have it under perfect command; can evolve, direct, and employ it at pleasure; and when it has performed its full work of electrolysation, it has only separated the elements of *a single grain of water.*

On the other hand, the relation between the conduction of the electricity and the decomposition of the water is so close that one cannot take place without the other. If the water is altered only in that small degree which consists in its having the solid instead of the fluid state, the conduction is stopped, and the decomposition is stopped with it. Whether the conduction be considered as depending upon the decomposition or not, still the relation of the two functions is equally intimate and inseparable.

Considering this close and twofold relation, namely, that without decomposition transmission of electricity does not occur; and, that for a given definite quantity of electricity passed, an equally definite and constant quantity of water or other matter is decomposed; considering also that the agent, which is electricity, is simply employed in overcoming electrical powers in the body subjected to its action; it seems a probable and almost a natural consequence that the quantity which passes is the *equivalent* of, and therefore equal to, that of the particles separated; *i.e.* that if the electrical power which holds the elements of a grain of water in combination, or which makes a grain of oxygen and hydrogen in the right proportions unite into water when they are made to combine, could be thrown into the condition of *a current,* it would exactly equal the current required for the separation of that grain of water into its elements again.

This view of the subject gives an almost overwhelming idea of the extraordinary quantity or degree of electric power which naturally belongs to the particles of matter; but it is not inconsistent in the slightest degree with the facts which can be brought to bear on this point. To illustrate this I must say a few words on the voltaic pile.

IV. ELECTRICITY OF THE VOLTAIC PILE

THOSE BODIES which, being interposed between the metals of the voltaic pile, render it active *are all of them electrolytes;* and it cannot but press upon the attention of everyone engaged in considering this subject that in those bodies (so essential to the pile) decomposition and the transmission of a current are so intimately connected that one cannot happen without the other. This I have shown abundantly in water, and numerous other cases. If, then, a voltaic trough have its extremities connected by a body capable of being decomposed, as water, we shall have a continuous current through the apparatus; and whilst it remains in this state we may look at the part where the acid is acting upon the plates and that where the current is acting upon the water as the reciprocals of each other. In both parts we have the two conditions *inseparable in such bodies as these,* namely, the passing of a current, and decomposition; and this is as true of the cells in the battery as of the water cell; for no voltaic battery has as yet been constructed in which the chemical action is only that of combination: *decomposition is always included,* and is, I believe, an essential chemical part.

But the difference in the two parts of the connected battery, that is, the decomposition or experimental cell and the acting cells, is simply this. In the former we urge the current through, but it, apparently of necessity, is accompanied by decomposition: in the latter we cause decompositions by ordinary chemical actions (which are, however, themselves electrical), and, as a consequence, have the electrical current; and as the decomposition dependent upon the current is definite in the former case, so is the current associated with the decomposition also definite in the latter.

Let us apply this in support of what I have surmised respecting the enormous electric power of each particle or atom of matter. I showed in a former part of these *Researches* on the relation by measure of common and voltaic electricity that two wires, one of platina and one of zinc, each one eighteenth of an inch in diameter, placed five sixteenths of an inch apart and immersed to the depth of five eighths of an inch in acid, consisting of one drop of oil of vitriol and four ounces of distilled water at a temperature of about 60° Fahr., and connected at the other extremities by a copper wire eighteen feet long and one eighteenth of an inch in thickness, yielded as much electricity in little more than three seconds of time as a Leyden battery charged by thirty turns of a very large and powerful plate electric machine in full action. This quantity, though sufficient if passed at once through the head of a rat or cat to have killed it, as by a flash of lightning, was evolved by the mutual action of so small a portion of the zinc wire and water in contact with it that the loss of weight sustained by either would be inappreciable by our most delicate instruments; and as to the water which could be decomposed by that current, it must have been insensible in quantity, for no trace of hydrogen appeared upon the surface of the platina during those three seconds.

What an enormous quantity of electricity, therefore, is required for the decomposition of a single grain of water! We have already seen that it must be in quantity sufficient to sustain a platina wire $\frac{1}{104}$th of an inch in thickness, red hot, in contact with the air, for three minutes and three quarters, a quantity which is almost infinitely greater than that which could be evolved by the little standard voltaic arrangement to which I have just referred. I have endeavoured to make a comparison by the loss of weight of such a wire in a given time in such an acid, according to a principle and experiment to be almost immediately described; but the proportion is so high that I am almost afraid to mention it. It would appear that 800,000 such charges of the Leyden battery as I have referred to above would be necessary to supply electricity sufficient to decompose a single grain of water; or, if I am right, to equal the quantity of electricity which is naturally associated with the elements of that grain of water, endowing them with their mutual chemical affinity.

In further proof of this high electric condition of the particles of matter, and the *identity as to quantity of that belonging to them with that necessary for their separation,* I will describe an experiment of great simplicity but extreme beauty, when viewed in relation to the evolution of an electric current and its decomposing powers.

A dilute sulphuric acid, made by adding about one part by measure of oil of vitriol to thirty parts of water, will act energetically upon a piece of zinc plate in its ordinary and simple state; but, as Mr. Sturgeon has shown, not at all, or scarcely so, if the surface of the metal has in the first instance been amalgamated; yet the amalgamated zinc will act powerfully with platina as an electromotor, hydrogen being evolved on the surface of the latter metal, as the zinc is oxidised and dissolved. The amalgamation is best effected by sprinkling a few drops of mercury upon the surface of the zinc, the latter being moistened with the dilute acid, and rubbing with the fingers or tow so as to extend the liquid metal over the whole of the surface. Any mercury in excess, forming liquid drops upon the zinc, should be wiped off.

Two plates of zinc thus amalgamated were dried and accurately weighed; one, which we will call A, weighed 163.1 grains; the other, to be called B, weighed 148.3 grains. They were about five inches long and 0.4 of an inch wide. An earthenware pneumatic trough was filled with dilute sulphuric acid, of the strength just described, and a gas jar, also filled with the acid, inverted in it. A plate of platina of nearly the same length, but about three times as wide as the zinc plates, was put up into this jar. The zinc plate A was also introduced into the jar and brought in contact with the platina, and at the same moment the plate B was put into the acid of the trough, but out of contact with other metallic matter.

Strong action immediately occurred in the jar upon the contact of the zinc and platina plates. Hydrogen gas rose from the platina and was collected in the jar, but no hydrogen or other gas rose from *either* zinc plate. In about ten or twelve minutes, sufficient hydrogen having been collected, the experiment was stopped; during its progress a few small bubbles had appeared upon plate B, but none upon plate A. The plates were washed in distilled water, dried, and reweighed. Plate B weighed 148.3 grains, as before, having lost nothing by the direct chemical action of the acid. Plate A weighed 154.65 grains, 8.45 grains of it having been oxidised and dissolved during the experiment.

The hydrogen gas was next transferred to a water trough and measured; it amounted to 12.5 cubic inches, the temperature being 52° and the barometer 29.2 inches. This quantity, corrected for temperature, pressure, and moisture, becomes 12.15453 cubic inches of dry hydrogen at mean temperature and pressure; which, increased by one half for the oxygen that must have gone to the *anode, i.e.* to the zinc, gives 18.232 cubic inches as the quantity of oxygen and hydrogen evolved from the water decomposed by the electric current. According to the estimate of the weight of the mixed gas before adopted, this volume is equal to 2.3535544 grains, which therefore is the weight of water decomposed; and this quantity is to 8.45, the quantity of zinc oxidised, as 9 is to 32.31. Now taking 9 as the equivalent number of water, the number 32.5 is given as the equivalent number of zinc; a coincidence sufficiently near to show, what indeed could not but happen, that for an equivalent of zinc oxidised an equivalent of water must be decomposed.

But let us observe *how* the water is decomposed. It is electrolysed, *i.e.* is decomposed voltaically, and not in the ordinary manner (as to appearance) of chemical decompositions; for the oxygen appears at the *anode* and the hydrogen at the *cathode* of the body under decomposition, and these were in many parts of the experiment above an inch asunder. Again, the ordinary chemical affinity was not enough under the circumstances to effect the decomposition of the water, as was abundantly proved by the inaction on plate B; the voltaic current was essential. And to prevent any idea that the chemical affinity was almost sufficient to decompose the water, and that a smaller current of electricity might, under the circumstances, cause the hydrogen to pass to the *cathode,* I need only refer to the results which I have given to show that the chemical action at the electrodes has not the slightest influence over the *quantities* of water or other substances decomposed between them, but that they are entirely dependent upon the quantity of electricity which passes.

What, then, follows as a necessary consequence of the whole experiment? Why, this: that the chemical action upon 32.31 parts, or one equivalent of zinc, in this simple voltaic circle was able to evolve such quantity of electricity in the form of a current as, passing through water, should decompose 9 parts, or one equivalent of that substance: and considering the definite relations of electricity as developed in the preceding parts of the present paper, the results prove that the quantity of electricity which, being naturally associated with the particles of matter, gives them their combining power is able, when thrown into a current, to separate those particles from their state of combination; or, in other words, that *the electricity which decomposes and that which is evolved by the decomposition of a certain quantity of matter are alike.*

The harmony which this theory of the definite evolution and the equivalent definite action of electricity introduces into the associated theories of definite proportions and electro-chemical affinity is very great. According to it, the equivalent weights of bodies are simply those quantities of them which contain equal quantities of electricity, or have naturally equal electric powers; it being the ELECTRICITY which *determines* the equivalent number, *because* it determines the combining force. Or, if we adopt the atomic theory or phraseology, then the atoms of bodies which are equivalents to each other in their ordinary chemical action have equal quantities of electricity naturally associated with them. But I must confess I am jealous of the term *atom;* for though it is very easy to talk of atoms, it is very difficult to form a clear idea of their nature, especially when compound bodies are under consideration.

But admitting that chemical action is the source of electricity, what an infinitely small fraction of that which is active do we obtain and employ in our voltaic batteries! Zinc and platina wires, one eighteenth of an inch in diameter and about half an inch long, dipped into dilute sulphuric acid so weak that it is not sensibly sour to the tongue, or scarcely to our most delicate test papers, will evolve more electricity in one twentieth of a minute than any man would willingly allow to pass through his body at once. The chemical action of a grain of water upon four grains of zinc can evolve electricity equal in quantity to that of a powerful thunderstorm. Nor is it merely true that the quantity is active; it can be directed and made to perform its full equivalent duty. Is there not, then, great reason to hope and believe that, by a closer *experimental* investigation of the principles which govern the development and action of this subtile agent, we shall be able to increase the power of our batteries or invent new instruments which shall a thousandfold surpass in energy those which we at present possess?

THE PERIODIC LAW

by

DMITRI IVANOVICH MENDELEYEV

CONTENTS

The Periodic Law

DMITRI IVANOVICH MENDELEYEV

1834–1907

DMITRI IVANOVICH MENDELEYEV lived in a Russia not familiar to the Western world. He was himself known, however, in scientific circles all over continental Europe; he visited England several times and the United States once. Westerners remembered his tall and slightly stooped figure, his deep-set, bright blue eyes, his finely modeled, gesturing hands, and his flowing hair—which he allowed a barber to cut only once a year, in the spring. They recalled him as "patriarchal," or as "a grand Russian of the province of Tver." His students at the Technological Institute in St. Petersburg and at the University of St. Petersburg remembered less his personal appearance than his talent for exposition in the lecture room and his more remarkable talent for stirring in students an ambition for knowledge. Several generations of them, including many eminent chemists and teachers, have paid tribute to his abilities. To them he said: "I do not wish to cram you with facts, but I want you to understand chemistry. And you should remember that hypotheses are not theories. By a theory I mean a conclusion drawn from the accumulated facts we now possess which enables us to foresee new facts which we do not yet know."

Mendeleyev's name is inseparably associated with the great generalization known as the periodic system of the elements. When he announced the generalization in 1869, it was, according to his own definition, not a hypothesis, but a theory. Subsequently, his own work and that of other chemists has given to the theory the validity of a law; and the Periodic Law is familiar to every student.

Mendeleyev became a teacher partly by accident. His father taught for many years, notably in the gymnasium at Tobolsk, Siberia, where he met and married Maria Dmitrievna. Soon after the birth of his youngest son, Dmitri, in

1834, he became wholly blind. He and his large family—there were then eight children surviving of the fourteen Maria had borne—had only his small pension to live on. But Maria had, like her famous son, intelligence and energy. As a girl, she had educated herself, in a time and a country where women were not schooled, by repeating the lessons assigned to her elder brother, Basil. With the same kind of directness, she now set about the re-establishment of a glassworks once owned by her family in Tobolsk. This she continued to manage and operate until after the death of her husband in 1847.

By this time young Dmitri had progressed through the classes of the Tobolsk gymnasium. He had also met some of the Decembrists in political exile in Tobolsk. They interested him so much in natural science that he and his mother decided that he should become a scientist. Some years later the dying Maria said to Dmitri, "Refrain from illusions, insist on work, and not on words. Patiently search divine and scientific truth." She had perhaps already phrased for herself these instructions for her scientist son when he graduated from the gymnasium. For then, not overcome by the death of her husband or by the calamity of the fire which destroyed her glassworks, she had gathered her scanty means and, with Dmitri and her daughter Elizabeth, had made the long journey to Moscow. Her design was to enter Dmitri at the university there, to make a scientist of him. Official difficulties blocked her way. After a year of effort, though she did not succeed in entering her son at the University of Moscow, she did procure government aid for his continued training at the Central Pedagogic Institute in St. Petersburg, under the Physico-Mathematical Faculty. The function of this school was to prepare teachers for the imperial schools. Maria lived just long enough to see her son complete his training and to graduate as a teacher.

Young Mendeleyev showed symptoms of lung disorder when he finished his course at the institute and was ordered south. Fortunately he obtained a post as chief science master in Simferopol, in the Crimea, and, during the Crimean War, another teaching post in Odessa. Residence in this southern climate cured his pulmonary trouble. In 1856, on his return to St. Petersburg, he took his master's degree in chemistry and became a *privatdocent* at the university. Three years later he was permitted to go to Paris, and later to Heidelberg for studies which he continued in St. Petersburg until he earned his doctor's degree in 1861. In 1866 he was appointed professor of general chemistry in the university, and retained his post there until a disagreement with the university administration forced his retirement in 1890. Three years later he was appointed Director of the Bureau of Weights and Measures, and was still Director at his death in 1907.

Mendeleyev had a full life outside his profession. He twice married, reared a family of five children, took decided views on matters of education, art, and literature, wrote for journals and newspapers on controversial artistic subjects, and, though not a politician, showed himself a liberal in his political thinking. Yet the bulk of his energy he devoted to chemistry. Of his 262 printed publications, the majority are on chemical subjects and on industrial subjects dependent upon chemistry. His earliest paper dealt with the composition of some specimens of orthite. Presently he began a long examination of the physical properties of liquids and a series of experiments on the thermal expansion of liquids. In 1883 he announced as a result a simple expression for the expansion of liquids between $O°$ C. and the boiling point. By 1889 he had closed an extended series of studies on the densities of various solutions, he had studied the elasticity of gases minutely, he had published papers on the nitriles, on fractional distillation, on contact action, on the heat of combustion of organic substances, and on many other subjects in chemistry. He had also published papers of interest to mineralogists and to chemical geologists, had ascended in a balloon during the solar eclipse of 1887 to make observations of the upper atmosphere, and had so far developed his interest in and theories about petroleum that he had been commissioned by the government to investigate the oil industry at Baku and the naphtha springs in the Caucasus, and to study the operation of the oil fields in Pennsylvania.

Much of the experimental and observational work Mendeleyev accomplished in his career retains now only historical interest. Even his great book, the two-volume *Principles of Chemistry* (1869–71), for two generations the standard Russian textbook in chemistry, and a work several times translated into English, is outmoded in many chapters. It contains in Chapter XV his first full statement of the Periodic Law and his own account of the value and import of the law. This is the chapter here reprinted (from the English edition of 1897).

In his later years Mendeleyev maintained the simplicity of private life which had characterized his earlier days. He spent the greater part of the year in St. Petersburg, occasionally visiting his estates in Tver, where he carried on some agricultural experiments. He dined always at six, usually in the company of his family and friends, and he frequently spent the evening reading James Fenimore Cooper and Jules Verne. When he traveled, he chose to go third class so that he might meet plain people. Had he chosen, he could have lived more elaborately. He had earned large sums by his industrial work, he had been honored by the Czar, he had been awarded the Davy Medal by the Royal Society, the Faraday Lectureship by the Chemical Society, and, in 1905, the Copley Medal. His renown as a teacher had attracted students from all over the world to his classes, and his fame as the discoverer of the Periodic Law had made his name familiar wherever scientific study flourished. By the time of his death his great generalization was acknowledged to be the most important chemical law put forward since the establishment of the atomic theory.

Though skilled and ingenious in experiment, Mendeleyev's perspicacity made him pre-eminent in theoretical work. Others' experiments and discoveries have confirmed his theory; it continues to be a lasting influence in all research in chemistry.

THE PERIODIC LAW

THE GROUPING OF THE ELEMENTS AND THE PERIODIC LAW

THE SUM of the data concerning the chemical transformations proper to the elements (for instance, with respect to the formation of acids, salts, and other compounds having definite properties) is insufficient for accurately determining the relationship of the elements, inasmuch as this may be many-sided. Thus, lithium and barium are in some respects analogous to sodium and potassium, and in others to magnesium and calcium. It is evident, therefore, that for a complete judgment it is necessary to have, not only qualitative, but also quantitative, exact and measurable, data. When a property can be measured it ceases to be vague, and becomes quantitative instead of merely qualitative.

Among these measurable properties of the elements, or of their corresponding compounds, are: (*a*) isomorphism, or the analogy of crystalline forms; and, connected with it, the power to form crystalline mixtures which are isomorphous; (*b*) the relation of the volumes of analogous compounds of the elements; (*c*) the composition of their saline compounds; and (*d*) the relation of the atomic weights of the elements. In this chapter we shall briefly consider these four aspects of the matter, which are exceedingly important for a natural and fruitful grouping of the elements, facilitating, not only a general acquaintance with them, but also their detailed study.

Historically the first, and an important and convincing, method for finding a relationship between the compounds of two different elements is by *isomorphism*. This conception was introduced into chemistry by Mitscherlich (in 1820), who demonstrated that the corresponding salts of arsenic acid, H_3AsO_4, and the phosphoric acid, H_3PO_4, crystallise with an equal quantity of water, show an exceedingly close resemblance in crystalline form (as regards the angles of their faces and axes), and are able to crystallise together from solutions, forming crystals containing a mixture of the isomorphous compounds. Isomorphous substances are those which, with an equal number of atoms in their molecules, present an analogy in their chemical reactions, a close resemblance in their properties, and a similar or very nearly similar crystalline form: they often contain certain elements in common, from which it is to be concluded that the remaining elements (as in the preceding example of As and P) are analogous to each other. And inasmuch as crystalline forms are capable of exact measurement, the external form, or the relation of the molecules which causes their grouping into a crystalline form, is evidently as great a help in judging of the internal forces acting between the atoms as a comparison of reactions, vapour densities, and other like relations. It will be sufficient to call to mind that the compounds of the alkali metals with the halogens RX, in a crystalline form, all belong to the cubic system and crystallise in octahedra or cubes—for example, sodium chloride, potassium chloride, potassium iodide, rubidium chloride, &c. The nitrates of rubidium and cæsium appear in anhydrous crystals of the same form as potassium nitrate. The carbonates of the metals of the alkaline earths are isomorphous with calcium carbonate—that is, they either appear in forms like calc-spar or in the rhombic system in crystals analogous to aragonite. Furthermore, sodium nitrate crystallises in rhombohedra, closely resembling the rhombohedra of calc-spar (calcium carbonate), $CaCO_3$, whilst potassium nitrate appears in the same form as aragonite, $CaCO_3$, and the number of atoms in both kinds of salts is the same. They all contain one atom of a metal (K, Na, Ca), one atom of a non-metal (C, N), and three atoms of oxygen. The analogy of form evidently coincides with an analogy of atomic composition. But there is not any close resemblance in their properties. It is evident that calcium carbonate approaches more nearly to magnesium carbonate than to sodium nitrate, although their crystalline forms are all equally alike. Isomorphous substances which are perfectly analogous to each other are not only characterised by a close resemblance of form (homeomorphism), but also by the faculty of entering into analogous reactions, which is not the case with RNO_3 and RCO_3. The most important and direct method of recognising perfect isomorphism—that is, the absolute analogy of two compounds—is given by that property of analogous compounds of separating from solutions *in homogeneous crystals, containing the most varied proportions* of the analogous substances which enter into their composition. These quantities do not seem to be in dependence on the molecular or atomic weights, and if they are governed by any laws they must be analogous to those which apply to indefinite chemical compounds. This will be clear from the following examples. Potassium chloride and potassium nitrate are not isomorphous with each other, and are in an atomic sense composed in a different manner. If these salts be mixed in a solution and the solution be evaporated, independent crystals of the two salts will separate, each in that crystalline form which is proper to it. The crystals will not contain a mixture of the two salts. But if we mix the solutions of two isomorphous salts together, then, under certain circumstances, crystals will be obtained which contain both these substances. However, this cannot be taken as an absolute rule, for if we take a solution saturated at a high temperature with a mixture of potassium and sodium chlorides, then on evaporation sodium chloride only will separate, and on cooling only potassium chloride. The first will contain very little potassium chloride, and the latter very little sodium chloride. But if we take, for example, a mixture of solutions of magnesium sulphate and zinc sulphate, they cannot be separated from each other by evaporating the mixture, notwithstanding the rather considerable difference in the solubility of these salts. Again, the isomorphous salts, magnesium carbonate, and calcium carbonate are found together—that is, in one crystal—in nature. The angle of the rhombohedron of these magnesia-lime spars is intermediate between the angles proper to the two spars individually (for calcium carbonate, the angle of the rhombohedron is 105° 8′; magnesium carbonate, 107° 30′; CaMg(CO$_3$)$_2$, 106° 10′). Certain of these *isomorphous mixtures* of calc and magnesia spars appear in well-formed crystals, and in this case there not unfrequently exists a simple molecular proportion of strictly definite chemical combination between the component salts—for instance, CaCO$_3$,MgCO$_3$—whilst in other cases, especially in the absence of distinct crystallisation (in dolomites), no such simple molecular proportion is observable: this is also the case in many artificially prepared isomorphous mixtures. The microscopical and crystallo-optical researches of Professor Inostrantzoff and others show that in many cases there is really a mechanical, although microscopically minute, juxta-position in one whole of the heterogeneous crystals of calcium carbonate (double refracting) and of the compound CaMgC$_2$O$_6$. If we suppose the adjacent parts to be microscopically small (on the basis of the researches of Mallard, Weruboff, and others), we obtain an idea of isomorphous mixtures. A formula of the following kind is given to isomorphous mixtures: for instance, for spars, RCO$_3$, where R=Mg, Ca, and where it may be Fe, Mn . . . , &c. This means that the Ca is partially replaced by Mg or another metal. Alums form a common example of the separation of iso-morphous mixtures from solutions. They are double sulphates (or seleni-ates) of alumina (or oxides isomorphous with it) and the alkalis, which crystallise in well-formed crystals. If aluminium sulphate be mixed with potassium sulphate, an alum separates, having the composition KAlS$_2$O$_8$,12H$_2$O. If sodium sulphate or ammonium sulphate, or rubidium (or thallium) sulphate be used, we obtain alums having the composition RAlS$_2$O$_8$,12H$_2$O. Not only do they all crystallise in the cubic system, but they also contain an equal atomic quantity of water or crystallisation (12H$_2$O). Besides which, if we mix solutions of the potassium and ammonium (NH$_4$AlS$_2$O$_8$,12H$_2$O) alums together, then the crystals which separate will contain various proportions of the alkalis taken, and separate crystals of the alums of one or the other kind will not be obtained, but each separate crystal will contain both potassium and ammonium. Nor is this all; if we take a crystal of a potassium alum and immerse it in a solution capable of yielding ammonia alum, the crystal of the potash alum will continue to grow and increase in size in this solution—that is, a layer of the ammonia or other alum will deposit itself upon the planes bounding the crystal of the potash alum. This is very distinctly seen if a colourless crystal of a common alum be immersed in a saturated violet solution of chrome alum, KCrS$_2$O$_8$,12H$_2$O, which then deposits itself in a violet layer over the colourless crystal of the alumina alum, as was observed even before Mitscherlich noticed it. If this crystal be then immersed in a solution of an alumina alum, a layer of this salt will form over the layer of chrome alum, so that one alum is able to incite the growth of the other.

If the deposition proceed simultaneously, the resultant intermixture may be minute and inseparable, but its nature is understood from the preceding experiments; the attractive force of crystallisation of isomorphous substances is so nearly equal that the attractive power of an isomorphous substance induces a crystalline superstructure exactly the same as would be produced by the attractive force of like crystalline particles. From this it is evident that one isomorphous substance may *induce the crystallisation* of another. Such a phenomenon explains, on the one hand, the aggregation of different isomorphous substances in one crystal, whilst, on the other hand, it serves as a most exact indication of the nearness both of the molecular composition of isomorphous substances and of those forces which are proper to the elements which distinguish the isomorphous substances. Thus, for example, ferrous sulphate or green vitriol crystallises in the monoclinic system and contains seven molecules of water, $FeSO_4,7H_2O$, whilst copper vitriol crystallises with five molecules of water in the triclinic system, $CuSO_4,5H_2O$; nevertheless, it may be easily proved that both salts are perfectly isomorphous; that they are able to appear in identically the same forms and with an equal molecular amount of water. For instance, Marignac, by evaporating a mixture of sulphuric acid and ferrous sulphate under the receiver of an air pump, first obtained crystals of the hepta-hydrated salt, and then of the penta-hydrated salt $FeSO_4,5H_2O$, which were perfectly similar to the crystals of copper sulphate. Furthermore, Lecoq de Boisbaudran, by immersing crystals of $FeSO_4,7H_2O$ in a supersaturated solution of copper sulphate, caused the latter to deposit in the same form as ferrous sulphate, in crystals of the monoclinic system, $CuSO_4,7H_2O$.

Hence it is evident that isomorphism—that is, the analogy of forms and the property of inducing crystallisation—may serve as a means for the discovery of analogies in molecular composition. We will take an example in order to render this clear. If, instead of aluminium sulphate, we add magnesium sulphate to potassium sulphate, then, on evaporating the solution, the double salt $K_2MgS_2O_8,6H_2O$ separates instead of an alum, and the ratio of the component parts (in alums one atom of potassium per $2SO_4$, and here two atoms) and the amount of water of crystallisation (in alums 12, and here 6 equivalents per $2SO_4$) are quite different; nor is this double salt in any way isomorphous with the alums, nor capable of forming an isomorphous crystalline mixture with them, nor does the one salt provoke the crystallisation of the other. From this we must conclude that although alumina and magnesia, or aluminium and magnesium, resemble each other, they are not isomorphous, and that although they give partially similar double salts, these salts are not analogous to each other. And this is expressed in their chemical formulæ by the fact that the number of atoms in alumina or aluminium oxide, Al_2O_3, is different from the number in magnesia, MgO. Aluminium is trivalent and magnesium bivalent. Thus, having obtained a double salt from a given metal, it is possible to judge of the analogy of the given metal with aluminium or with magnesium, or of the absence of such an analogy, from the composition and

TABLE I

Distribution of the Elements in Groups and Series

Group	I	II	III	IV	V	VI	VII	VIII
Series 1	H							
" 2	Li	Be	B	C	N	O	F	
" 3	Na	Mg	Al	Si	P	S	Cl	
" 4	K	Ca	Sc	Ti	V	Cr	Mn	Fe · Co · Ni · Cu
" 5	(Cu)	Zn	Ga	Ge	As	Se	Br	
" 6	Rb	Sr	Y	Zr	Nb	Mo	—	Ru · Rh · Pd · Ag
" 7	(Ag)	Cd	In	Sn	Sb	Te	I	
" 8	Cs	Ba	La	Ce	Di?	—	—	—
" 9	—	—	—	—	—	—	—	—
" 10	—	—	Yb	—	Ta	W	—	Os · Ir · Pt · Au
" 11	(Au)	Hg	Tl	Pb	Bi	—	—	—
" 12	—	—	—	Th	—	U	—	
Higher oxides	R_2O	R_2O_2	R_2O_3	R_2O_4	R_2O_5	R_2O_6	R_2O_7	RO_4
	—	RO	—	RO_2	—	RO_8	—	
Hydrogen compounds	—	—	—	RH_4	RH_3	RH_2	RH	

form of this salt. Thus zinc, for example, does not form alums, but forms a double salt with potassium sulphate, which has a composition exactly like that of the corresponding salt of magnesium. It is often possible to distinguish the bivalent metals analogous to magnesium or calcium from the trivalent metals, like aluminium, by such a method. Furthermore, the specific heat and vapour density serve as guides. There are also indirect proofs. Thus iron gives ferrous compounds, FeX_2, which are isomorphous with the compounds of magnesium, and ferric compounds, FeX_3, which are isomorphous with the compounds of aluminium; in this instance the relative composition is directly determined by analysis, because, for a given amount of iron, $FeCl_2$ only contains two thirds of the amount of chlorine which occurs in $FeCl_3$, and the composition of the corresponding oxygen compounds, *i.e.* of ferrous oxide, FeO, and ferric oxide, Fe_2O_3, clearly indicates the analogy of the ferrous oxide with MgO and of the ferric oxide with Al_2O_3.

Thus in the building up of similar molecules in crystalline forms we see one of the numerous means for judging of the internal world of molecules and atoms, and one of the weapons for conquests in the invisible world of molecular mechanics which forms the main object of physicochemical knowledge. This method has more than once been employed for discovering the analogy of elements and of their compounds; and as crystals are measurable, and the capacity to form crystalline mixtures can be experimentally verified, this method is a numerical and measurable one, and in no sense arbitrary.

The regularity and simplicity expressed by the exact laws of crystalline form repeat themselves in the aggregation of the atoms to form molecules. Here, as there, there are but few forms which are essentially different, and their apparent diversity reduces itself to a few fundamental differences of type. There the molecules aggregate themselves into crystalline forms; here, the atoms aggregate themselves into molecular forms or into *the types of compounds*. In both cases the fundamental crystalline or molecular forms are liable to variations, conjunctions, and combinations. If we know that potassium gives compounds of the fundamental type KX, where X is a univalent element (which combines with one atom of hydrogen, and is, according to the law of substitution, able to replace it), then we know the composition of its compounds: K_2O, KHO, KCl, NH_2K, KNO_3, K_2SO_4, $KHSO_4$, $K_2Mg(SO_4)_2,6H_2O$, &c. All the possible derivative crystalline forms are not known. So also all the atomic combinations are not known for every element. Thus in the case of potassium, KCH_3, K_3P, K_2Pt, and other like compounds which exist for hydrogen or chlorine, are unknown.

Only a few fundamental types exist for the building up of atoms into molecules, and the majority of them are already known to us. If X stands for a univalent element, and R for an element combined with it, then eight atomic types may be observed:—

$$RX, \ RX_2, \ RX_3, \ RX_4, \ RX_5, \ RX_6, \ RX_7, \ RX_8.$$

Let X be chlorine or hydrogen. Then as examples of the first type we have: H_2, Cl_2, HCl, KCl, NaCl, &c. The compounds of oxygen or calcium may serve as examples of the type RX_2: OH_2, OCl_2, OHCl, CaO, $Ca(OH)_2$, $CaCl_2$, &c. For the third type RX_3 we know the representative NH_3 and the corresponding compounds N_2O_3, NO(OH), NO(OK), PCl_3, P_2O_3, PH_3, SbH_3, Sb_2O_3, B_2O_3, BCl_3, Al_2O_3, &c. The type RX_4 is known among the hydrogen compounds. Marsh gas, CH_4, and its corresponding saturated hydrocarbons, C_nH_{2n+2}, are the best representatives. Also CH_3Cl, CCl_4, $SiCl_4$, $SnCl_4$, SnO_2, CO_2, SiO_2 and a whole series of other compounds come under this class. The type RX_5 is also already familiar to us, but there are no purely hydrogen compounds among its representatives. Sal-ammoniac, NH_4Cl, and the corresponding $NH_4(OH)$, $NO_2(OH)$, $ClO_2(OK)$, as well as PCl_5, $POCl_3$, &c., are representatives of this type. In the higher types also there are no hydrogen compounds, but in the type RX_6 there is the chlorine compound WCl_6. However, there are many oxygen compounds, and among them SO_3 is the best known representative. To this class also belong $SO_2(OH)_2$, SO_2, Cl_2, $SO_2(OH)Cl$, CrO_3, &c., all of an acid character. Of the higher types there are in general only oxygen and acid representatives. The type RX_7 we know in perchloric acid, $ClO_3(OH)$, and potassium permanganate, $MnO_3(OK)$, is also a member. The type RX_8 in a free state is very rare; osmic anhydride, OsO_4, is the best known representative of it.

The four lower types RX, RX_2, RX_3, and RX_4 are met with in compounds of the elements R with chlorine and oxygen, and also in their compounds with hydrogen, whilst the four higher types only appear for such acid compounds as are formed by chlorine, oxygen, and similar elements.

Among the oxygen compounds the *saline oxides* which are capable of forming salts either through the function of a base or through the function of an acid anhydride attract the greatest interest in every respect. Certain elements, like calcium and magnesium, only give one saline oxide—for example, MgO, corresponding with the type MgX_2. But the majority of the elements appear in several such forms. Thus copper gives CuX and CuX_2, or Cu_2O and CuO. If an element R gives a higher type RX_n, then there often also exist, as if by symmetry, lower types, RX_{n-2}, RX_{n-4}, and in general such types as differ from RX_n by an even number of X. Thus in the case of sulphur the types SX_2, SX_4, and SX_6 are known—for example SH_2, SO_2, and SO_3. The last type is the highest, SX_6. The types SX_5 and SX_3 do not exist. But even and uneven types sometimes appear for one and the same element. Thus the types RX and RX_2 are known for copper and mercury.

Among the *saline* oxides only the *eight types* enumerated below are known to exist. They determine the possible formulæ of the compounds of the elements, if it be taken into consideration that an element which gives a certain type of combination may also give lower types. For this reason the rare type of the *suboxides* or quaternary oxides R_4O (for instance, Ag_4O, Ag_2Cl) is not characteristic; it is always accompanied by

TABLE II

The periodic dependence of the composition of the simplest compounds and properties of the simple bodies upon the atomic weights of the elements

Group headings:
- **Molecular composition of the higher hydrogen and metallo-organic compounds.** F=CH_4, C_2H_6, &c. — columns [1] [2] [3] [4]
- **Atomic weights of the elements** — columns [5] [6]
- **Composition of the saline compounds, X=Cl.** Br, (NO_2), ½O, ½(SO_4) OH, (OM)=Z, where M=K, ½Ca, ⅓Al, &c. — columns [7]–[14]
  - Form / Oxides: [7] RX, R_2O · [8] RX_2, RO · [9] RX_3, R_2O_3 · [10] RX_4, RO_2 · [11] RX_5, R_2O_5 · [12] RX_6, RO_3 · [13] RX_7, R_2O_7 · [14] RX_8, RO_4
- **Peroxides** — column [15]
- **Lower hydrogen compounds** — column [16]
- **Simple bodies** — Sp. gr. [17], Sp. vol. [18], Melting point [19]

[1]	[2]	[3]	[4]	[5]	[6]	[7]	[8]	[9]	[10]	[11]	[12]	[13]	[14]	[15]	[16]	[17]	[18]	[19]
			HH	H	1,005 (mean)	HX or H_2O								H_2O_2	—	*0·05	20	−250°?
				Li	7·02 (Stas)	LiX								—	—	0·59	11·9	180°
				Be	9·1 (Nilson Pettersson)		BeX_2							—	BeH	1·64	5·5	900°?
	BE_3			B	11·0 (Ramsay Ashton)			BX_3						—	—	2·5	4·4	1,300°?
CH_4		C_2H_4	C_2H_2	C	12·00 (Roscoe)		CO		CO_2	COZ_2				C_2O_3*	—	*1·9	6·3	2,600°?
	NH_3	N_2H_4		N	14·04 (Stas)	N_2O	NO	NOZ	NO_2	NO_2Z				N_2O_4*	—	*·06	23	−203°
		OH_2		O	16 (conventional)		OX_2							O_2	—	*·09	18	−230°?
			FH	F	19·0 (Christiansen)	FZ								—	—	*1·0	19	?
			NaE	Na	23·04 (Stas)	NaX								NaO	Na_2H	0·98	23·5	96°
		MgE_2		Mg	24·3 (Burton)		MgX_2							—	MgH	1·74	14	500°
	AlE_3			Al	27·1 (Mallet)			AlX_3						—	—	2·6	11	600°
SiH_4				Si	28·4 (Thorpe Young)				$SiOZ_2$					—	—	2·3	12	1,300°?
	PH_3	P_2H_4		P	31·0 (v. d. Plaats)			PX_3		POZ_3				—	PH	2·2	14	44°
				S	32·06 (Stas)		SX_2		SOZ_2		SO_2Z_2			S_2O_7	—	2·07	15	114°
			ClH	Cl	35·45 (Stas)	ClZ		$ClOZ$		$ClOZ$		$ClOZ$		—	—	*1·3	27	−75°
				K	39·15 (Stas)	KX								KO_2	K_2H	0·87	45	58°
				Ca	40·0 (Dumas)		CaX_2							CaO_2	CaH	1·56	26	800°
				Sc	44·0 (Nilson)			ScX_3						—	—	2·5	?18	1,200°?
				Ti	48·1 (Thorpe)		TiX_2	TiX_3	TiX_4					TiO_3	—	3·6	13	2,500°?
				V	51·2 (Roscoe)		VO	VOX		VOZ_3				—	—	5·5	9	3,000°?
				Cr	52·1 (Rawson)		CrX_2	CrX_3	CrO_2		CrO_2Z_2			Cr_2O_7	—	6·7	7·7	2,000°?
				Mn	55·1 (Marignac)		MnX_2	MnX_3	MnO_2		MnO_2Z			—	—	7·5	7·3	1,500°
				Fe	56·0 (Dumas)		FeX_2	FeX_3			FeO_2Z_2			—	Fe_2H*	7·8	7·2	1,450°
				Co	58·9 (Zimmermann)		CoX_2		CoO_2					—	—	8·6	6·8	1,400°
				Ni	59·4 (Winkler)		NiX_2	NiX_3						—	Ni_2H	8·7	6·8	1,350°
				Cu	63·6 (Richards)	CuX	CuX_2							Cu_2O_3*	CuH	8·8	7·2	1,054°
	ZnE_2			Zn	65·3 (Marignac)		ZnX_2							ZnO_2	—	7·1	9·2	418°
	GaE_3			Ga	69·9 (Boisbaudran)			GaX_3						—	—	5·96	11·7	30°
GeE_4				Ge	72·3 (Winkler)		GeX_2		GeX_4					—	—	5·47	13·2	900°
	AsH_3			As	75·0 (Dumas)		AsS	AsX_3	AsS_2	$AsOZ$				—	As_4H_3*	5·65	13·3	500°

Lower cmpd	Element	At. wt	(Observer)	RX	RX_2	RX_3	RX_4	ROZ	RO_2Z	RO_2Z_2	RO_4	Oxide	Hydride	Sp. gr.	At. vol.	M.P.
SeH_2	Se	79·0†	(Pettersson)	—	—	—	—	$SeOZ$	$SeOZ_2$	SeO_2Z_2	—	—	—	4·8	16	217°
BrH	Br	79·95	(Stas)	BrZ	—	—	—	$BrOZ$	BrO_2Z	BrO_2Z	—	—	—	3·1	26	−7°
	Rb	85·5	(Godeffroy)	RbX	—	—	—	—	—	—	—	RbO	Rb_4H*	1·5	57	39°
	Sr	87·6	(Dumas)	—	SrX_2	—	—	—	—	—	—	SrO_2	SrH	2·5	35	600°?
	Y	89	(Cleve)	—	—	YX_3	—	—	—	—	—	—	—	*3·4	26	1,000°?
	Zr	90·6	(Bailey)	—	—	—	ZrX_4	—	—	—	—	—	Zr_4H_2*	4·1	*22	1,500°?
	Nb	94	(Marignac)	—	—	NbX_3	—	—	NbO_2Z	—	—	—	Nb_4H_2*	7·1	13	1,800°?
	Mo	96·1	(Maas)	—	—	MoX_3	MoX_4	—	—	MoO_2Z_2	MoO_2Z	Mo_2O_7	—	8·6	11	2,200°?
			Unknown metal (eka-manganese, Em=99).	—	—	—	—	—	—	—	EmO_2Z	—	—	—	—	—
	Ru	101·7	(Joly)	—	RuX_2	RuX_3	RuX_4	—	RuO_2Z	RuO_2Z_2	RuO_4	—	Ru_4H*	12·2	8·4	2,000°?
	Rh	102·7	(Seubert)	—	RhX_2	RhX_3	—	—	RhO_2Z	RhO_2Z_2	—	—	Rh_4H*	12·1	8·6	1,900°?
	Pd	106·4	(Keller Smith)	PdX	PdX_2	—	PdX_4	—	—	—	—	—	Pd_2H	11·4	8·3	1,500°
	Ag	107·92	(Stas)	AgX	—	—	—	—	—	—	—	AgO	—	10·5	10·3	950°
CdE_2	Cd	112·1	(Lorimer Smith)	—	CdX_2	—	—	—	—	—	—	CdO_2	—	8·6	13	320°
InE_3	In	113·6	(Winkler)	—	InX_2	InX_3	—	—	—	—	—	—	—	7·4	14	176°
SnE_4	Sn	119·1	(Classen)	—	SnX_2	—	SnX_4	—	—	—	—	SnO_4	—	7·2	16	232°
SbH_3	Sb	120·4	(Schneider)	—	—	SbX_3	—	—	SbO_2Z	—	—	—	—	6·7	18	432°
TeH_2	Te	125·1	(Brauner)	—	—	—	TeZ	—	TeO_2Z	TeO_2Z_2	—	—	—	6·4	20	455°
IH	I	126·85	(Stas)	IZ	—	I_3	—	IOZ	IO_2Z	—	—	—	—	4·9	26	114°
	Cs	132·7	(Godeffroy)	CsX	—	—	—	—	—	—	—	—	Cs_2H*	2·37	56	27°
	Ba	137·4	(Richards)	—	BaX_2	—	—	—	—	—	—	BaO_2	BaH	3·75	36	?
	La	138·2	(Brauner)	—	—	LaX_3	—	—	—	—	—	—	—	6·1	23	?
	Ce	140·2	(Brauner)	—	—	CeX_3	CeX_4	—	—	—	—	—	—	6·6	21	700°?
			Little known Di=142.1 and Yb=173.2, and over 15 unknown elements.													
	Ta	182·7	(Marignac)	—	—	—	—	—	TaO_2Z	—	—	—	Ta_3H*	10·4	18	?
	W	184·0	(Waddel)	—	—	—	WX_4	—	—	WO_2Z_2	WO_2Z	W_2O_7	—	19·1	9·6	2,600°
			Unknown element.													
	Os	191·6	(Seubert)	—	—	OsX_3	OsX_4	—	—	OsO_2Z_2	OsO_4	—	—	22·5	8·5	2,700°?
	Ir	193·3	(Joly)	—	—	IrX_3	IrX_4	—	IrO_2Z	IrO_2Z_2	—	—	Ir_3H*	22·4	8·6	2,000°
	Pt	196·0	(Dittmar McArthur)	—	PtX_2	—	PtX_4	—	—	—	—	—	Pt_3H*	21·4	9·2	1,775°
	Au	197·5	(Mallet)	AuX	—	AuX_3	—	—	—	—	—	—	—	19·3	10	1,045°
HgE_2	Hg	200·5	(Erdmann Mar.)	HgX	HgX_2	—	—	—	—	—	—	—	—	13·6	15	−39°
TlE_3	Tl	204·1	(Crookes)	TlX	—	TlX_3	—	—	—	—	—	—	—	11·8	17	294°
PbE_4	Pb	206·90	(Stas)	—	PbX_2	—	—	—	PbO_2Z	—	—	—	—	11·3	18	328°
BiE_3	Bi	208·9	(Classen)	—	—	BiX_3	—	$BiOZ$	—	—	—	—	—	9·8	21	269°
			Five unknown elements.													
	Th	232·4	(Kruss Nilson)	—	—	—	ThX_4	—	—	—	—	ThO_2	—	11·1	21	?
			Unknown element.													
	U	239·3	(Zimmermann)	—	—	—	—	—	UO_2	UO_2X_2	UO_2X_2	UO_4	—	18·7	13	2,400°?

[See notes on following page.]

†From analogy there is reason for thinking that the atomic weight of selenium is really slightly less than 79·0.

Columns 1, 2, 3, and 4 give the molecular composition of the hydrogen and metallo-organic compounds, exhibiting the most characteristic forms assumed by the elements. The first column contains only those which correspond to the form RX, the second column those of the form RX_2, the third of the form RX_3, and the fourth of the form RX_4, so that the periodicity stands out clearly (see Column 16).

Column 5 contains the symbols of all the more or less well-known elements, placed according to the order of the magnitude of their atomic weights.

Column 6 contains the atomic weights of the elements according to the most trustworthy determinations. The names of the investigators are given in parenthesis. The atomic weight of oxygen, taken as 16, forms the basis upon which these atomic weights were calculated. Some of these have been recalculated by me on the basis of Stas's most trustworthy data.

Columns 7–14 contain the composition of the saline compounds of the elements, placed according to their forms, RX, RX_2 to RX_8 (in the 14th column). If the element R has a metallic character like H, Li, Be, &c., then X represents Cl, NO_3, $\frac{1}{2}SO_4$, &c., haloid radicles, or (OH) if a perfect hydrate is formed (alkali, aqueous base), or $\frac{1}{2}O$, $\frac{1}{2}S$, &c. when an anhydrous oxide, sulphide, &c. is formed. For instance, NaCl, $Mg(NO_3)_2$, $Al_2(SO_4)_3$, correspond to NaX, MgX_2, and AlX_3; so also $Na(OH)$, $Mg(OH)_2$, $Al(OH)_3$, Na_2O, MgO, Al_2O_3, &c. But if the element, like C or N, be of a metalloid or acid character, X must be regarded as (OH) in the formation of hydrates; (OM) in the formation of salts, where M is the equivalent of a metal, $\frac{1}{2}O$ in the formation of an anhydride, and Cl in the formation of a chloranhydride; and in this case (i.e. in the acid compounds) Z is put in the place of X; for example, the formulae COZ_2, NO_2Z, MnO_2Z, FeO_2Z_3, and IZ_3 correspond to $CO(NaO)_2=Na_2CO_3$, $COCl_2$, CO_2, $NO_2(NaO)=NaNO_3$, NO_2Cl, $NO_2(OH)=HNO_3$; $MnO_2(OK)=KMnO_4$, ICl, &c.

The 15th column gives the compositions of the peroxides of the elements, taking them as anhydrous. An asterisk (*) is attached to those of which the composition has not been well established, and a dash (—) shows that for a given element no peroxides have yet been obtained. The peroxides contain more oxygen than the higher saline oxides of the same elements, are powerfully oxidising, and easily give peroxide of hydrogen. This latter circumstance necessitates their being referred to the type of peroxide of hydrogen, if bases and acids are referred to the type of water.

The 16th column gives the composition of the lower hydrogen compounds like N_3H and Na_2H. They may often be regarded as alloys of hydrogen, which is frequently disengaged by them at a comparatively moderate temperature. They differ greatly in their nature from the hydrogen compounds given in columns 1–4.

Column 17 gives the specific gravity of the elements in a solid and a liquid state. An asterisk (*) is placed by those which can either only be assumed from analogy (for example, the sp. gr. of fluorine and hydrogen, which have not been obtained in a liquid state), or which vary very rapidly with a variation of temperature and pressure (like oxygen and nitrogen), or physical state (for instance, carbon in passing from the state of charcoal to graphite and diamond). But as the sp. gr. in general varies with the temperature, mechanical condition, &c., the figures given, although chosen from the most trustworthy sources, can only be regarded as approximate, and not as absolutely true. They clearly show a certain periodicity; for instance, the sp. gr. diminishes from Al on both sides (Al, Mg, Na, with decreasing atomic weight; and Al, Si, P, S, Cl, with increasing atomic weight), it also diminishes on both sides from Cu, Ru, and Os.

The same remarks refer to the figures in the 18th column, which gives the so-called atomic volumes of the simple bodies, or the quotient of their atomic weight and specific gravity. For Na, K, Rb, and Cs the atomic volume is greatest among the neighbouring elements. For Ni, Pd, and Os it is least, and this indicates the periodicity of this property of the simple bodies.

The last (19th) column gives the melting points of the simple bodies. Here also a periodicity is seen, i.e. a maximum and minimum value between which there are intermediate values, as we see, for instance, in the series Cl, K, Ca, Se, and Ti, or in the series Cr, Mn, Fe, Co, Ni, Cu, Zn, Ga, and Ge.

one of the higher grades of oxidation, and the compounds of this type are distinguished by their great chemical instability, and split up into an element and the higher compound (for instance, $Ag_4O=2Ag+Ag_2O$). Many elements, moreover, form transition oxides whose composition is intermediate, which are able, like N_2O_4, to split up into the lower and higher oxides. Thus iron gives magnetic oxide, Fe_3O_4, which is in all respects (by its reactions) a compound of the suboxide FeO with the oxide Fe_2O_3. The independent and more or less stable saline compounds correspond with the following eight types:—

R_2O; salts RX, hydroxides ROH. Generally basic like K_2O, Na_2O, Hg_2O, Ag_2O, Cu_2O; if there are acid oxides of this composition they are very rare, are only formed by distinctly acid elements, and even then have only feeble acid properties; for example, Cl_2O and N_2O.

R_2O_2 or RO; salts RX_2, hydroxides $R(OH)_2$. The most simple basic salts R_2OX_2 or $R(OH)X$; for instance, the chloride Zn_2OCl_2; also an almost exclusively basic type; but the basic properties are more feebly developed than in the preceding type. For example, CaO, MgO, BaO, PbO, FeO, MnO, &c.

R_2O_3; salts RX_3, hydroxides $R(OH)_3$, RO(OH), the most simple basic salts ROX, $R(OH)X_3$. The bases are feeble, like Al_2O_3, Fe_2O_3, Tl_2O_3, Sb_2O_3. The acid properties are also feebly developed; for instance, in B_2O_3; but with the non-metals the properties of acids are already clear; for instance, P_2O_3, $P(OH)_3$.

R_2O_4 or RO_2; salts RX_4 or ROX_2, hydroxides $R(OH)_4$, $RO(OH)_2$. Rarely bases (feeble), like ZrO_2, PtO_2, more often acid oxides; but the acid properties are in general feeble, as in CO_2, SO_2, SnO_2. Many intermediate oxides appear in this and the preceding and following types.

R_2O_5; salts principally of the types ROX_3, RO_2X, $RO(OH)_3$, $RO_2(OH)$, rarely RX_5. The basic character (X, a halogen, simple or complex; for instance, NO_3, Cl, &c.) is feeble, the acid character predominates, as is seen in N_2O_5, P_2O_5, Cl_2O_5, then X=OH, OK, &c., for example, $NO_2(OK)$.

R_2O_6 or RO_3; salts and hydroxides generally of the type RO_2X_2, $RO_2(OH)_2$. Oxides of an acid character, as SO_3, CrO_3, MnO_3. Basic properties rare and feebly developed as in UO_3.

R_2O_7; salts of the form RO_3X, $RO_3(OH)$, acid oxides; for instance, Cl_2O_7, Mn_2O_7. Basic properties as feebly developed as the acid properties in the oxides R_2O.

R_2O_8 or RO_4. A very rare type, and only known in OsO_4 and RuO_4.

It is evident from the circumstance that in all the higher types the *acid hydroxides* (for example, $HClO_4$, H_2SO_4, H_3PO_4) and salts with a single atom of one element contain, like the higher saline type RO_4, *not more than four atoms of oxygen;* that the formation of the saline oxides is governed by a certain common principle which is best looked for in the fundamental properties of oxygen, and in general of the most simple compounds. The hydrate of the oxide RO_2 is of the higher type $RO_2 2H_2O = RH_4O_4 = R(HO)_4$. Such, for example, is the hydrate of silica and the salts (orthosilicates) corresponding with it, $Si(MO)_4$. The oxide R_2O_5 corresponds with the hydrate $R_2O_53H_2O = 2RH_3O_4 = 2RO(OH)_3$. Such is orthophosphoric acid, PH_3O_3. The hydrate of the oxide RO_3 is $RO_3H_2O = RH_2O_4 = RO_2(OH)_2$—for instance, sulphuric acid. The hydrate corresponding to R_2O_7 is evidently $RHO = RO_3(OH)$—for example, perchloric acid. Here, besides containing O_4, it must further be remarked that *the amount of hydrogen in the hydrate is equal to the amount of hydrogen in the hydrogen compound.* Thus silicon gives SiH_4 and SiH_4O_4, phosphorus PH_3 and PH_3O_4, sulphur SH_2 and SH_2O_4, chlorine ClH and $ClHO_4$. This, if it does not explain, at least connects in a harmonious and general system the fact that *the elements are capable of combining with a greater amount of oxygen, the less the amount of hydrogen which they are able to retain.* In this the key to the comprehension of all further deductions must be looked for, and we will therefore formulate this rule in general terms. An element R gives a hydrogen compound RH_n, the hydrate of its higher oxide will be RH_nO_4, and therefore the higher oxide will contain $2RH_nO_4 - nH_2O = R_2O_{8-n}$. For example, chlorine gives ClH, hydrate $ClHO_4$, and the higher oxide Cl_2O_7. Carbon gives CH_4 and CO_2. So also, SiO_2 and SiH_4 are the higher compounds of silicon with hydrogen and oxygen, like CO_2 and CH_4. Here the amounts of oxygen and hydrogen are equivalent. Nitrogen combines with a large amount of oxygen, forming N_2O_5, but, on the other hand, with a small quantity of hydrogen in NH_3. *The sum of the equivalents of hydrogen and oxygen,* occurring in combination with an atom of nitrogen, is, as always in the higher types, equal to *eight.* It is the same with the other elements which combine with hydrogen and oxygen. Thus sulphur gives SO_3; consequently, six equivalents of oxygen fall to an atom of sulphur, and in SH_2 two equivalents of hydrogen. The sum is again equal to eight. The relation between Cl_2O_7 and ClH is the same. This shows that the property of elements of combining with such different elements as oxygen and hydrogen is subject to one common law, which is also formulated in the system of the elements presently to be described.[1]

[1]The hydrogen compounds, R_2H, in equivalency correspond with the type of the suboxides, R_4O. Palladium, sodium, and potassium give such hydrogen compounds, and it is worthy of remark that according to the periodic system these elements stand near to each other, and that in those groups where the hydrogen compounds R_2H appear, the quaternary oxides R_4O are also present.

Not wishing to complicate the explanation, I here only touch on the general features of the relation between the hydrates and oxides and of the oxides among themselves. Thus, for instance, the conception of the ortho-acids and of the normal acids will be considered in speaking of phosphoric and phosphorous acids.

As in the further explanation of the periodic law only those oxides which give salts will be considered, I think it will not be superfluous to mention here the following facts relative to the peroxides. Of the *peroxides* corresponding with hydrogen peroxide, the following are at present known: H_2O_2, Na_2O_2, S_2O_7 (as HSO_4?), K_2O_4, K_2O_2, CaO_2, TiO_3, Cr_2O_7, $CuO_2(?)$, ZnO_2, Rb_2O_2, SrO_2, Ag_2O_2, CdO_2, CsO_2, Cs_2O_2, BaO_2, Mo_2O_7, SnO_3, W_2O_7, UO_4. It is probable that the number of peroxides will increase with further investigation. A periodicity is seen in those now known, for the elements (excepting

In the preceding we see not only the regularity and simplicity which govern the formation and properties of the oxides and of all the compounds of the elements, but also a fresh and exact means for recognising the analogy of elements. Analogous elements give compounds of analogous types, both higher and lower. If CO_2 and SO_2 are two gases which closely resemble each other both in their physical and chemical properties, the reason of this must be looked for not in an analogy of sulphur and carbon, but in that identity of the type of combination, RX_4, which both oxides assume, and in that influence which a large mass of oxygen always exerts on the properties of its compounds. In fact, there is little resemblance between carbon and sulphur, as is seen not only from the fact that CO_2 is the *higher form* of oxidation, whilst SO_2 is able to further oxidise into SO_3, but also from the fact that all the other compounds—for example, SH_2 and CH_4, SCl_2 and CCl_4, &c.—are entirely unlike both in type and in chemical properties. This absence of analogy in carbon and sulphur is especially clearly seen in the fact that the highest saline oxides are of different composition, CO_2 for carbon, and SO_3 for sulphur. Previously we considered the limit to which carbon tends in its compounds, and in a similar manner there is for every element in its compounds a tendency to attain a certain highest limit RX_n. This view was particularly developed in the middle of the present century by Frankland in studying the metallo-organic compounds, *i.e.* those in which X is wholly or partially a hydrocarbon radicle; for instance, $X=CH_3$ or C_2H_5 &c. Thus, for example, antimony, Sb, gives, with chlorine, compounds SbCl and $SbCl_5$ and corresponding oxygen compounds Sb_2O_3 and Sb_2O_5, whilst under the action of CH_3I, C_2H_3I, or in general EI (where E is a hydrocarbon radicle of the paraffin series), upon antimony or its alloy with sodium there are formed SbE_3 (for example, $Sb(CH_3)_3$, boiling at about $81°$), which, corresponding to the lower form of combination SbX_3, are able to combine further with EI, or Cl_2, or O, and to form compounds of the limiting type SbX_5; for example, SbE_4Cl corresponding to NH_4Cl with the substitution of nitrogen by antimony, and of hydrogen by the hydrocarbon radicle. The elements which are most chemically analogous are characterised by the fact of their giving compounds of similar form RX_n. The halogens which are analogous give both higher and lower compounds. So also do

Li) of the first group, which give R_2O, form peroxides, and then the elements of the sixth group seem also to be particularly inclined to form peroxides, R_2O_7; but at present it is too early, in my opinion, to enter upon a generalisation of this subject, not only because it is a new and but little studied matter (not investigated for all the elements), but also, and more especially, because in many instances only the hydrates are known—for instance, $Mo_2H_2O_8$—and they perhaps are only compounds of peroxide of hydrogen—for example, $Mo_2H_2O_8 = 2MoO_3 + H_2O_2$—since Professor Schöne has shown that H_2O_2 and BaO_2 possess the property of combining together and with other oxides. Nevertheless, I have, in the general table expressing the periodic properties of the elements, endeavoured to sum up the data respecting all the known peroxide compounds whose characteristic property is seen in their capability to form peroxide of hydrogen under many circumstances.

the metals of the alkalis and of the alkaline earths. And we saw that this analogy extends to the composition and properties of the nitrogen and hydrogen compounds of these metals, which is best seen in the salts. Many such groups of analogous elements have long been known. Thus there are analogues of oxygen, nitrogen, and carbon, and we shall meet with many such groups. But an acquaintance with them inevitably leads to the questions, what is the cause of analogy and what is the relation of one group to another? If these questions remain unanswered, it is easy to fall into error in the formation of the groups, because the notions of the degree of analogy will always be relative, and will not present any accuracy or distinctness. Thus lithium is analogous in some respects to potassium and in others to magnesium; beryllium is analogous to both aluminium and magnesium. Thallium has much kinship with lead and mercury, but some of its properties appertain to lithium and potassium. Naturally, where it is impossible to make measurements one is reluctantly obliged to limit oneself to approximate comparisons, founded on apparent signs which are not distinct and are wanting in exactitude. But in the elements there is one accurately measurable property, which is subject to no doubt —namely, that property which is expressed in their atomic weights. Its magnitude indicates the relative mass of the atom, or, if we avoid the conception of the atom, its magnitude shows the relation between the masses forming the chemical and independent individuals or elements. And according to the teaching of all exact data about the phenomena of nature, the mass of a substance is that property on which all its remaining properties must be dependent, because they are all determined by similar conditions or by those forces which act in the weight of a substance, and this is directly proportional to its mass. Therefore it is most natural to seek for a dependence between the properties and analogies of the elements on the one hand and their atomic weights on the other.

This is the fundamental idea which leads *to arranging all the elements according to their atomic weights*. A periodic repetition of properties is then immediately observed in the elements. We are already familiar with examples of this:—

$$F = 19, \quad Cl = 35.5, \quad Br = 80, \quad I = 127,$$
$$Na = 23, \quad K = 39, \quad Rb = 85, \quad Cs = 133,$$
$$Mg = 24, \quad Ca = 40, \quad Sr = 87, \quad Ba = 137.$$

The essence of the matter is seen in these groups. The halogens have smaller atomic weights than the alkali metals, and the latter than the metals of the alkaline earths. Therefore, *if all the elements be arranged in the order of their atomic weights, a periodic repetition of properties is obtained.* This is expressed by the *law of periodicity; the properties of the elements, as well as the forms and properties of their compounds, are in periodic dependence or (expressing ourselves algebraically) form a periodic function of the atomic weights of the elements.*[2] Table I of *the*

[2] In laying out the accumulated information respecting the elements, I had occasion to reflect on their mutual relations. At the beginning of 1869 I distributed among many

periodic system of the elements is designed to illustrate this law. It is arranged in conformity with the eight types of oxides described in the preceding pages, and those elements which give the oxides, R_2O and consequently salts RX, form the 1st group; the elements giving R_2O_2 or RO as their highest grade of oxidation belong to the 2nd group, those giving R_2O_3 as their highest oxides form the 3rd group, and so on; whilst the elements of all the groups which are nearest in their atomic weights are arranged in series from 1 to 12. The even and uneven series of the same groups present the same forms and limits, but differ in their properties, and therefore two contiguous series, one even and the other uneven—for instance, the 4th and 5th—form a period. Hence the elements of the 4th, 6th, 8th, 10th, and 12th, or of the 3rd, 5th, 7th, 9th, and 11th,

---

chemists a pamphlet entitled 'An Attempted System of the Elements, based on their Atomic Weights and Chemical Analogies,' and at the March meeting of the Russian Chemical Society, 1869, I communicated a paper 'On the Correlation of the Properties and Atomic Weights of the Elements.' The substance of this paper is embraced in the following conclusions: (1) The elements, if arranged according to their atomic weights, exhibit an evident *periodicity* of properties. (2) Elements which are similar as regards their chemical properties have atomic weights which are either of nearly the same value (platinum, iridium, osmium) or which increase regularly (*e.g.* potassium, rubidium, cæsium). (3) The arrangement of the elements or of groups of elements in the order of their atomic weights corresponds with their so-called *valencies*. (4) The elements, which are the most widely distributed in nature, have *small* atomic weights, and all the elements of small atomic weight are characterised by sharply defined properties. They are therefore typical elements. (5) The *magnitude* of the atomic weight determines the character of an element. (6) The discovery of many yet unknown elements may be expected. For instance, elements analogous to aluminium and silicon, whose atomic weights would be between 65 and 75. (7) The atomic weight of an element may sometimes be corrected by aid of a knowledge of those of the adjacent elements. Thus the combining weight of tellurium must lie between 123 and 126, and cannot be 128. (8) Certain characteristic properties of the elements can be foretold from their atomic weights.

The entire periodic law is included in these lines. In the series of subsequent papers (1870–72, for example, in the *Transactions* of the Russian Chemical Society, of the Moscow Meeting of Naturalists, of the St. Petersburg Academy, and Liebig's *Annalen*) on the same subject we only find applications of the same principles, which were afterwards confirmed by the labours of Roscoe, Carnelley, Thorpe, and others in England; of Rammelsberg (cerium and uranium), L. Meyer (the specific volumes of the elements), Zimmermann (uranium), and more especially of C. Winkler (who discovered germanium, and showed its identity with ekasilicon), and others in Germany; of Lecoq de Boisbaudran in France (the discoverer of gallium = ekaaluminium); of Clève (the atomic weights of the cerium metals), Nilson (discoverer of scandium = ekaboron), and Nilson and Pettersson (determination of the vapour density of beryllium chloride) in Sweden; and of Brauner (who investigated cerium, and determined the combining weight of tellurium = 125) in Austria, and Piccini in Italy.

I consider it necessary to state that, in arranging the periodic system of the elements, I made use of the previous researches of Dumas, Gladstone, Pettenkofer, Kremers, and Lenssen on the atomic weights of related elements, but I was not acquainted with the works preceding mine of De Chancourtois (*vis tellurique,* or the spiral of the elements according to their properties and equivalents) in France, and of J. Newlands

series form analogues, like the halogens, the alkali metals, &c. The conjunction of two series, one even and one contiguous uneven series, thus forms one large *period*. These periods, beginning with the alkali metals, end with the halogens. The elements of the first two series have the lowest atomic weights, and in consequence of this very circumstance, although they bear the general properties of a group, they still show many peculiar and independent properties. Thus fluorine, as we know, differs in many points from the other halogens, and lithium from the other alkali metals, and so on. These lightest elements may be termed *typical elements*. They include—

H.
Li, Be, B, C, N, O, F.
Na, Mg . . . . .

In the annexed table all the remaining elements are arranged, not in groups and series, but *according to periods*. In order to understand the essence of the matter, it must be remembered that here the atomic weight gradually increases along a given line; for instance, in the line commencing with K=39 and ending with Br=80, the intermediate elements have intermediate atomic weights, as is clearly seen in Table II, where the elements stand in the order of their atomic weights.

I	II	III	IV	V	VI	VII				I	II	III	IV	V	VI	VII
		Even Series.									Mg	Al	Si	P	S	Cl
K	Ca	Sc	Ti	V	Cr	Mn	Fe	Co	Ni	Cu	Zn	Ga	Ge	As	Se	Br
Rb	Sr	Y	Zr	Nb	Mo	—	Ru	Rh	Pd	Ag	Cd	In	Sn	Sb	Te	I
Cs	Ba	La	Ce	Di	?	—	—	—	—	—	—	—	—	—	—	—
—	—	Yb	—	Ta	W	—	Os	Ir	Pt	Au	Hg	Tl	Pb	Bi	—	—
—	—	—	Th	—	U								Uneven Series.			

The same degree of analogy that we know to exist between potassim, rubidium, and cæsium; or chlorine, bromine, and iodine; or calcium,

(Law of Octaves—for instance, H, F, Cl, Co, Br, Pd, I, Pt form the first octave, and O, S, Fe, Se, Rh, Te, Au, Th the last) in England, although certain germs of the periodic law are to be seen in these works. With regard to the work of Professor Lothar Meyer respecting the periodic law (Notes 5 and 6), it is evident, judging from the method of investigation, and from his statement (Liebig's *Annalen, Supt. Band* 7, 1870, 354), at the very commencement of which he cites my paper of 1869 above mentioned, that he accepted the periodic law in the form which I proposed.

In concluding this historical statement I consider it well to observe that no law of nature, however general, has been established all at once; its recognition is always preceded by many hints; the establishment of a law, however, does not take place when its significance is recognised, but only when it has been confirmed by experiment, which the man of science must consider as the only proof of the correctness of his conjecture and opinions. I therefore, for my part, look upon Roscoe, De Boisbaudran, Nilson, Winkler, Brauner, Carnelley, Thorpe, and others who verified the adaptability of the periodic law to chemical facts, as the true founders of the periodic law, the further development of which still awaits fresh workers.

strontium, and barium, also exists between the elements of the other vertical columns. Thus, for example, zinc, cadmium, and mercury present a very close analogy with magnesium. For a true comprehension of the matter[3] it is very important to see that all the aspects of the distribution

[3]Besides arranging the elements (*a*) in a successive order according to their atomic weights, with indication of their analogies by showing some of the properties—for instance, their power of giving one or another form of combination—both of the *elements* and of their compounds (as is done in Table II), (*b*) according to periods (as in Table I), and (*c*) according to groups and series or small periods (as in the same tables), I am acquainted with the following methods of expressing the periodic relations of the elements: (1) By a curve drawn through points obtained in the following manner: The elements are arranged along the horizontal axis as abscissæ at distances from zero proportional to their atomic weights, whilst the values for all the elements of some property—for example, the specific volumes or the melting points, are expressed by the ordinates. This method, although graphic, has the theoretical disadvantage that it does not in any way indicate the existence of a limited and definite number of elements in each period. There is nothing, for instance, in this method of expressing the law of periodicity to show that between magnesium and aluminium there can be no other element with an atomic weight of, say, 25, atomic volume 13, and in general having properties intermediate between those of these two elements. The actual periodic law does not correspond with a continuous change of properties, with a continuous variation of atomic weight—in a word, it does not express an uninterrupted function—and as the law is purely chemical, starting from the conception of atoms and molecules which combine in multiple proportions, with intervals (not continuously), it *above all* depends on there being but few types of compounds, which are arithmetically simple, *repeat themselves,* and offer no uninterrupted transitions, so that each period can only contain a definite number of members. For this reason there can be no other elements between magnesium, which gives the chloride $MgCl_2$, and aluminium, which forms AlX_5; there is a break in the continuity, according to the law of multiple proportions. The periodic law ought not, therefore, to be expressed by geometrical figures in which continuity is always understood. Owing to these considerations I never have and never will express the periodic relations of the elements by any geometrical figures. (2) *By a plane spiral.* Radii are traced from a centre, proportional to the atomic weights; analogous elements lie along one radius, and the points of intersection are arranged in a spiral. This method, adopted by De Chancourtois, Baumgauer, E. Huth, and others, has many of the imperfections of the preceding, although it removes the indefiniteness as to the number of elements in a period. It is merely an attempt to reduce the complex relations to a simple graphic representation, since the equation to the spiral and the number of radii are not dependent upon anything. (3) *By the lines of atomicity,* either parallel, as in Reynolds's and the Rev. S. Haughton's method, or as in Crookes's method, arranged to the right and left of an axis, along which the magnitudes of the atomic weights are counted, and the position of the elements marked off, on the one side the members of the even series (paramagnetic, like oxygen, potassium, iron), and on the other side the members of the uneven series (diamagnetic, like sulphur, chlorine, zinc, and mercury). On joining up these points a periodic curve is obtained, compared by Crookes to the oscillations of a pendulum, and, according to Haughton, representing a cubical curve. This method would be very graphic did it not require, for instance, that sulphur should be considered as bivalent and manganese as univalent, although neither of these elements gives stable derivatives of these natures, and although the one is taken on the basis of the lowest possible compound SX_2, and the other of the highest, because manganese can be referred to the univalent elements only by the analogy of $KMnO_4$ to

of the elements according to their atomic weights essentially express one and the same fundamental *dependence—periodic properties.*[4] The following points then must be remarked in it.

$KClO_4$. Furthermore, Reynolds and Crookes place hydrogen, iron, nickel, cobalt, and others outside the axis of atomicity, and consider uranium as bivalent without the least foundation. (4) Rantsheff endeavoured to classify the elements in their periodic relations by a system dependent on solid geometry. He communicated this mode of expression to the Russian Chemical Society, but his communication, which is apparently not void of interest, has not yet appeared in print. (5) *By algebraic formulæ:* for example, E. J. Mills (1886) endeavours to express all the atomic weights by the logarithmic function $A=15$ $(n—0.9375t)$, in which the variables n and t are whole numbers. For instance, for oxygen $n=2$, $t=1$; hence $A=15.94$; for antimony $n=9$, $t=0$; whence $A=120$, and so on, n varies from 1 to 16 and t from 0 to 59. The analogues are hardly distinguishable by this method: thus for chlorine the magnitudes of n and t are 3 and 7; for bromine 6 and 6; for iodine 9 and 9; for potassium 3 and 14; for rubidium 6 and 18; for cæsium 9 and 20; but a certain regularity seems to be shown. (6) A more natural method of expressing the dependence of the properties of elements on their atomic weights is obtained by *trigonometrical functions,* because this dependence is periodic like the functions of trigonometrical lines, and therefore Ridberg in Sweden (Lund, 1885) and F. Flavitzky in Russia (Kazan, 1887) have adopted a similar method of expression, which must be considered as worthy of being worked out, although it does not express the absence of intermediate elements—for instance, between magnesium and aluminium, which is essentially the most important part of the matter. (7) The investigations of B. N. Tchitchérin (1888, *Journal of the Russian Physical and Chemical Society*) form the first effort in the latter direction. He carefully studied the alkali metals, and discovered the following simple relation between their atomic volumes: they can all be expressed by $A(2—0.0428\ An)$, where A is the atomic weight and $n=1$ for lithium and sodium, $\frac{4}{8}$ for potassium, $\frac{3}{8}$ for rubidium, and $\frac{2}{8}$ for cæsium. If n always $= 1$, then the volume of the atom would become zero at $A=46\frac{2}{3}$, and would reach its maximum when $A=23\frac{1}{3}$, and the density increases with the growth of A. In order to explain the variation of n, and the relation of the atomic weights of the alkali metals to those of the other elements, as also the atomicity itself, Tchitchérin supposes all atoms to be built up of a primary matter; he considers the relation of the central to the peripheric mass, and, guided by mechanical principles, deduces many of the properties of the atoms from the reaction of the internal and peripheric parts of each atom. This endeavour offers many interesting points, but it admits the hypothesis of the building up of all the elements from one primary matter, and at the present time such an hypothesis has not the least support either in theory or in fact.

[4]Many natural phenomena exhibit a dependence of a periodic character. Thus the phenomena of day and night and of the seasons of the year, and vibrations of all kinds, exhibit variations of a periodic character in dependence on time and space. But in ordinary periodic functions one variable varies continuously, whilst the other increases to a limit, then a period of decrease begins, and having in turn reached its limit a period of increase again begins. It is otherwise in the periodic function of the elements. Here the mass of the elements does not increase continuously, but abruptly, by steps, as from magnesium to aluminium. So also the valency or atomicity leaps directly from 1 to 2 to 3, &c., without intermediate quantities, and in my opinion it is these properties which are the most important, and it is their periodicity which forms the substance of the periodic law. It expresses *the properties of the real elements,* and not of what may be termed their manifestations visually known to us. The external properties of

1. The composition of the higher oxygen compounds is determined by the groups: the first group gives R_2O, the second R_2O_2 or RO, the third R_2O_3, &c. There are eight type of oxides and therefore eight groups. Two series give a period, and the same type of oxide is met with twice in a period. For example, in the period beginning with potassium, oxides of the composition RO are formed by calcium and zinc, and of the composition RO_3 by molybdenum and tellurium. The oxides of the even series, of the same type, have stronger basic properties than the oxides of the uneven series, and the latter as a rule are endowed with an acid character. Therefore the elements which exclusively give bases, like the alkali metals, will be found at the commencement of the period, whilst such purely acid elements as the halogens will be at the end of the period. The interval will be occupied by intermediate elements. It must be observed that the acid character is chiefly proper to the elements with small atomic weights in the uneven series, whilst the basic character is exhibited by the heavier elements in the even series. Hence elements which give acids chiefly predominate among the lightest (typical) elements, especially in the last groups; whilst the heaviest elements, even in the last groups (for instance, thallium, uranium), have a basic character. Thus the basic and acid characters of the higher oxides are determined (*a*) by the type of oxide, (*b*) by the even or uneven series, and (*c*) by the atomic weight. The groups are indicated by Roman numerals from I to VIII.

2. *The hydrogen compounds* being volatile or gaseous substances which are prone to reaction—such as HCl, H_2O, H_3N, and H_4C—are only formed by the elements of the uneven series and higher groups giving oxides of the forms R_2O_n, RO_3, R_2O_5, and RO_2.

3. If an element gives a hydrogen compound, RX_m, it forms an *organo-metallic compound* of the same composition, where $X = C_nH_{2n+1}$; that is, X is the radicle of a saturated hydrocarbon. The elements of the uneven series, which are incapable of giving hydrogen compounds, and give oxides of the forms RX, RX_2, RX_3, also give organo-metallic compounds of this form proper to the higher oxides. Thus zinc forms the oxide ZnO, salts ZnX_2, and zinc ethyl $Zn (C_2H_5)_2$. The elements of the even series do not seem to form organo-metallic compounds at all; at

---

elements and compounds are in periodic dependence on the atomic weight of the elements only because these external properties are themselves the result of the properties of the real elements which unite to form the "free" elements and the compounds. To explain and express the periodic law is to explain and express the cause of the law of multiple proportions, of the difference of the elements, and the variation of their atomicity, and at the same time to understand what mass and gravitation are. In my opinion this is still premature. But just as without knowing the cause of gravitation, it is possible to make use of the law of gravity, so for the aims of chemistry it is possible to take advantage of the laws discovered by chemistry without being able to explain their causes. The above-mentioned peculiarity of the laws of chemistry respecting definite compounds and the atomic weights leads one to think that the time has not yet come for their full explanation, and I do not think that it will come before the explanation of such a primary law of nature as the law of gravity.

least all efforts for their preparation have as yet been fruitless—for instance, in the case of titanium, zirconium, or iron.

4. The atomic weights of elements belonging to contiguous periods differ approximately by 45; for example, K<Rb, Cr<Mo, Br<I. But the elements of the typical series show much smaller differences. Thus the difference between the atomic weights of Li, Na, and K, between Ca, Mg, and Be, between Si and C, between S and O, and between Cl and F, is 16. As a rule, there is a greater difference between the atomic weights of two elements of one group and belonging to two neighboring series (Ti—Si =V—P=Cr—S=Mn—Cl=Nb—As, &c.=20); and this difference attains a maximum with the heaviest elements (for example, Th—Pb=26, Bi—Ta =26, Ba—Cd=25, &c.). Furthermore, the difference between the atomic weights of the elements of even and uneven series also increases. In fact, the differences between Na and K, Mg and Ca, Si and Ti, are less abrupt than those between Pb and Th, Ta and Bi, Cd and Ba, &c. Thus even in the magnitude of the differences of the atomic weights of analogous elements there is observable a certain connection with the gradation of their properties.[5]

5. According to the periodic system every element occupies a certain position, determined by the group (indicated in Roman numerals) and series (Arabic numerals) in which it occurs. These indicate the atomic weight, the analogues, properties, and type of the higher oxide, and of the hydrogen and other compounds—in a word, all the chief quantitative and qualitative features of an element, although there yet remains a whole series of further details and peculiarities whose cause should perhaps be looked for in small differences of the atomic weights. If in a certain group there occur elements, R, R_2, R_3, and if in that series which contains one of these elements, for instance R_2, an element Q_2 precedes it and an element T_2 succeeds it, then the properties of R_2 are determined by the properties of R_1, R_3, Q_2, and T_2. Thus, for instance, the atomic weight of $R_2 = \frac{1}{4}(R_1+R_3+Q_2+T_2)$. For example, selenium occurs in the same group as sulphur, S = 32, and tellurium, Te = 125, and, in the

---

[5] The relation between the atomic weights, and especially the difference=16, was observed in the sixth and seventh decades of this century by Dumas, Pettenkofer, L. Meyer, and others. Thus Lothar Meyer in 1864, following Dumas and others, grouped together the tetravalent elements carbon and silicon; the trivalent elements nitrogen, phosphorus, arsenic, antimony, and bismuth; the bivalent oxygen, sulphur, selenium, and tellurium; the univalent fluorine, chlorine, bromine, and iodine; the univalent metals lithium, sodium, potassium, rubidium, cæsium, and thallium; and the bivalent metals beryllium, magnesium, strontium and barium—observing that in the first the difference is, in general=16, in the second about=46, and the last about=87–90. The first germs of the periodic law are visible in such observations as these. Since its establishment this subject has been most fully worked out by Ridberg (Note 3), who observed a periodicity in the variation of the differences between the atomic weights of two contiguous elements, and its relation to their atomicity. A. Bazaroff (1887) investigated the same subject, taking, not the arithmetical differences of contiguous and analogous elements, but the ratio of their atomic weights; and he also observed that this ratio alternately rises and falls with the rise of the atomic weights.

7th series As $= 75$ stands before it and Br $= 80$ after it. Hence the atomic weight of selenium should be $\frac{1}{4}(32+125+75+80) = 78$, which is near to the truth. Other properties of selenium may also be determined in this manner. For example, arsenic forms H_3As, bromine gives HBr, and it is evident that selenium, which stands between them, should form H_2Se, with properties intermediate between those of H_3As and HBr. Even the physical properties of selenium and its compounds, not to speak of their composition, being determined by the group in which it occurs, may be foreseen with a close approach to reality from the properties of sulphur, tellurium, arsenic, and bromine. *In this manner it is possible to foretell the properties of still unknown elements.* For instance, in the position IV, 5—that is, in the IVth group and 5th series —an element is still wanting. These unknown elements may be named after the preceding known element of the same group by adding to the first syllable the prefix *eka-*, which means *one* in Sanskrit. The element IV, 5, follows after IV, 3, and this latter position being occupied by silicon, we call the unknown element ekasilicon and its symbol Es. The following are the properties which this element should have on the basis of the known properties of silicon, tin, zinc, and arsenic. Its atomic weight is nearly 72, higher oxide EsO_2, lower oxide EsO, compounds of the general form EsX_4, and chemically unstable lower compounds of the form EsX_2. Es gives volatile organo-metallic compounds—for instance, $Es(CH_3)_4$, Es $(CH_3)_3$ Cl, and $Es(C_2H_5)_4$, which boil at about $160°$, &c.; also a volatile and liquid chloride, $EsCl_4$, boiling at about $90°$ and of specific gravity about $1·9$. EsO_2 will be the anhydride of a feeble colloidal acid, metallic Es will be rather easily obtainable from the oxides and from K_2EsF_6 by reduction, EsS_2 will resemble SnS_2 and SiS_2, and will probably be soluble in ammonium sulphide; the specific gravity of Es will be about $5·5$, EsO_2 will have a density of about $4·7$, &c. Such a prediction of the properties of ekasilicon was made by me in 1871, on the basis of the properties of the elements analogous to it: IV, 3, $=$ Si, IV, 7 $=$ Sn, and also II, 5 $=$ Zn and V, 5 $=$ As. And now that this element has been discovered by C. Winkler, of Freiberg, it has been found that its actual properties entirely correspond with those which were foretold.[6] In this we see a most impor-

[6]The laws of nature admit of no exceptions, and in this they clearly differ from such rules and maxims as are found in grammar, and other inventions, methods, and relations of man's creation. The confirmation of a law is only possible by deducing consequences from it, such as could not possibly be foreseen without it, and by verifying those consequences by experiment and further proofs. Therefore, when I conceived the periodic law, I (1869–1871) deduced such logical consequences from it as could serve to show whether it were true or not. Among them was the prediction of the properties of undiscovered elements and the correction of the atomic weights of many, and at that time little known, elements. Thus uranium was considered as trivalent, U$=$120; but as such it did not correspond with the periodic law. I therefore proposed to double its atomic weight—U$=$240, and the researches of Roscoe, Zimmermann, and others justified this alteration. It was the same with cerium, whose atomic weight it was necessary to change according to the periodic law. I therefore determined its specific heat, and the result I obtained was verified by the new determinations of

tant confirmation of the truth of the periodic law. This element is now called germanium, Ge. It is not the only one that has been predicted by the periodic law.[7] Properties were foretold of an element ekaaluminium, III, 5, El = 68, and were afterwards verified when the metal termed "gallium" was discovered by De Boisbaudran. So also the properties of scandium corresponded with those predicted for ekaboron, according to Nilson.

6. As a true law of nature is one to which there are no exceptions, the periodic dependence of the properties on the atomic weights of the elements gives a *new means for determining by the equivalent the atomic weight* or atomicity of imperfectly investigated but known elements, for which no other means could as yet be applied for determining the true atomic weight. At the time (1869) when the periodic law was first proposed there were several such elements. It thus became possible to learn their true atomic weights, and these were verified by later researches. Among the elements thus concerned were indium, uranium, cerium, yttrium, and others.[8]

Hillebrand. I then corrected certain formulæ of the cerium compounds, and the researches of Rammelsberg, Brauner, Cleve, and others verified the proposed alteration. It was necessary to do one or the other—either to consider the periodic law as completely true, and as forming a new instrument in chemical research, or to refute it. Acknowledging the method of experiment to be the only true one, I myself verified what I could, and gave everyone the possibility of proving or confirming the law, and did not think, like L. Meyer (Liebig's *Annalen, Supt. Band* 7, 1870, 364), when writing about the periodic law that "it would be rash to change the accepted atomic weights on the basis of so uncertain a starting point." In my opinion, the basis offered by the periodic law had to be verified or refuted, and experiment in every case verified it. The starting point then became general. No law of nature can be established without such a method of testing it. Neither De Chancourtois, to whom the French ascribe the discovery of the periodic law, nor Newlands, who is put forward by the English, nor L. Meyer, who is now cited by many as its founder, ventured to foretell the *properties* of undiscovered elements, or to alter the "accepted atomic weights," or, in general, to regard the periodic law as a new, strictly established law of nature, as I did from the very beginning (1869).

[7]When in 1871 I wrote a paper on the application of the periodic law to the determination of the properties of hitherto undiscovered elements, I did not think I should live to see the verification of this consequence of the law, but such was to be the case. Three elements were described—ekaboron, ekaaluminium, and ekasilicon—and now, after the lapse of twenty years, I have had the great pleasure of seeing them discovered and named Gallium, Scandium, and Germanium, after those three countries where the rare minerals containing them are found, and where they were discovered. For my part I regard L. de Boisbaudran, Nilson, and Winkler, who discovered these elements, as the true corroborators of the periodic law. Without them it would not have been accepted to the extent it now is.

[8]Taking indium, which occurs together with zinc, as our example, we will show the principle of the method employed. The equivalent of indium to hydrogen in its oxide is 37.7—that is, if we suppose its composition to be like that of water; then $In = 37.7$, and the oxide of indium is In_2O. The atomic weight of indium was taken as double the equivalent—that is, indium was considered to be a bivalent element—and

7. The periodic variability of the properties of the elements in dependence on their masses presents a distinction from other kinds of periodic dependence (as, for example, the sines of angles vary periodically and successively with the growth of the angles, or the temperature of the atmosphere with the course of time), in that the weights of the atoms do not increase gradually, but by leaps, that is, according to Dalton's law of multiple proportions, there not only are not, but there cannot be, any transitive or intermediate elements between two neighbouring ones (for example, between $K = 39$ and $Ca = 40$, or $Al = 27$ and $Si = 28$, or $C = 12$ and $N = 14$, &c.). As in a molecule of a hydrogen compound there may be either one, as in HF, or two, as in H_2O, or three, as in NH_3, &c., atoms of hydrogen; but as there cannot be molecules containing $2\frac{1}{2}$ atoms of hydrogen to one atom of another element, so there cannot be any element intermediate between N and O, with an atomic weight greater than 14 or less than 16, or between K and Ca. Hence the periodic dependence of the elements cannot be expressed by any algebraical continuous function in the same way that it is possible, for instance, to express the variation of the temperature during the course of a day or year.

8. The essence of the notions giving rise to the periodic law consists in a general physico-mechanical principle which recognises the correla-

---

$In = 2 \times 37.7 = 75.4$. If indium only formed an oxide, RO, it should be placed in group II. But in this case it appears that there would be no place for indium in the system of the elements, because the positions II, $5 = Zn = 65$ and II, $6 = Sr = 87$ were already occupied by known elements, and according to the periodic law an element with an atomic weight 75 could not be bivalent. As neither the vapour density nor the specific heat, nor even the isomorphism (the salts of indium crystallise with great difficulty), of the compounds of indium were known, there was no reason for considering it to be a bivalent metal, and therefore it might be regarded as trivalent, quadrivalent, &c. If it be trivalent, then $In = 3 \times 37.7 = 113$, and the composition of the oxide is In_2O_3, and of its salts InX_3. In this case it at once falls into its place in the system, namely, in group III and 7th series, between $Cd = 112$ and $Sn = 118$, as an analogue of aluminium or dvialuminium (dvi $= 2$ in Sanskrit). All the properties observed in indium correspond with this position; for example, the density, cadmium $= 8.6$, indium $= 7.4$; tin $= 7.2$; the basic properties of the oxides CdO, In_2O_3, SnO_2, successively vary, so that the properties of In_2O_3 are intermediate between those of CdO and SnO_2 or Cd_2O_2 and Sn_2O_4. That indium belongs to group III has been confirmed by the determination of its specific heat, (0.057 according to Bunsen, and 0.055 according to me) and also by the fact that indium forms alums like aluminium, and therefore belongs to the same group.

The same kind of considerations necessitated taking the atomic weight of titanium as nearly 48, and not as 52, the figure derived from many analyses. And both these corrections, made on the basis of the law, have now been confirmed, for Thorpe found, by a series of careful experiments, the atomic weight of titanium to be that foreseen by the periodic law. Notwithstanding that previous analyses gave $Os = 199.7$, $Ir = 198$, and $Pt = 187$, the periodic law shows, as I remarked in 1871, that the atomic weights should rise from osmium to platinum and gold, and not fall. Many recent researches, and especially those of Seubert, have fully verified this statement, based on the law. Thus a true law of nature anticipates facts, foretells magnitudes, gives a hold on nature, and leads to improvements in the methods of research, &c.

tion, transmutability, and equivalence of the forces of nature. Gravitation, attraction at small distances, and many other phenomena are in direct dependence on the mass of matter. It might therefore have been expected that chemical forces would also depend on mass. A dependence is in fact shown, the properties of elements and compounds being determined by the masses of the atoms of which they are formed. The weight of a molecule, or its mass, determines many of its properties independently of its composition. Thus carbonic oxide, CO, and nitrogen, N_2, are two gases having the same molecular weight, and many of their properties (density, liquefaction, specific heat, &c.) are similar or nearly similar. The differences dependent on the nature of a substance play another part, and form magnitudes of another order. But the properties of atoms are mainly determined by their mass or weight, and are in dependence upon it. Only in this case there is a peculiarity in the dependence of the properties on the mass, for this *dependence is determined by a periodic law.* As the mass increases the properties vary, at first successively and regularly, and then return to their original magnitude and recommence a fresh period of variation like the first. Nevertheless here as in other cases a small variation of the mass of the atom generally leads to a small variation of properties, and determines differences of a second order. The atomic weights of cobalt and nickel, of rhodium, ruthenium, and palladium, and of osmium, iridium, and platinum, are very close to each other, and their properties are also very much alike—the differences are not very perceptible. And if the properties of atoms are a function of their weight, many ideas which have more or less rooted themselves in chemistry must suffer change and be developed and worked out in the sense of this deduction. Although at first sight it appears that the chemical elements are perfectly independent and individual, instead of this idea of the nature of the elements, the notion of the dependence of their properties upon *their mass* must now be established; that is to say, the subjection of the individuality of the elements to a common higher principle which evinces itself in gravity and in all physico-chemical phenomena. Many chemical deductions then acquire a new sense and significance, and a regularity is observed where it would otherwise escape attention. This is more particularly apparent in the physical properties, to the consideration of which we shall afterwards turn, and we will now point out that Gustavson first, and subsequently Potilitzin, demonstrated the direct dependence of the reactive power on the atomic weight and that fundamental property which is expressed in the forms of their compounds, whilst in a number of other cases the purely chemical relations of elements proved to be in connection with their periodic properties. As a case in point, it may be mentioned that Carnelley remarked a dependence of the decomposability of the hydrates on the position of the elements in the periodic system; whilst L. Meyer, Willgerodt, and others established a connection between the atomic weight or the position of the elements in the periodic system and their property of serving as media in the transference of the halogens to the hydrocarbons. Bailey pointed out a periodicity in the stability (under the action of heat) of the oxides, namely: (*a*) in the even series (for instance, CrO_3, MoO_3, WO_3, and UO_3) the higher oxides of a given group decompose with greater ease the smaller the atomic weight, while in the uneven series (for example, CO_2, GeO_2, SnO_2, and PbO_2) the contrary is the case; and (*b*) the stability of the higher saline oxides in the even series (as in the fourth series from K_2O to Mn_2O_7) decreases in passing from the lower to the higher groups, while in the uneven series it increases from the Ist to the IVth group, and then falls from the IVth to VIIth; for instance, in the series Ag_2O, CdO, In_2O_3, SnO_2, and then SnO_2, Sb_2O_5, TeO_3, I_2O_7. K. Winkler looked for and actually found (1890) a dependence between the reducibility of the metals by magnesium and their position in the periodic system of the elements. The greater the attention paid to this field the more often is a distinct connection found between the variation of purely chemical properties of analogous substances and the variation of the atomic weights of the constituent elements and their position in the periodic system. Besides, since the periodic system has become more firmly established, many facts have been gathered, showing that there are many similarities between Sn and Pb, B and Al, Cd and Hg, &c., which had not been previously observed, although foreseen in some cases, and a consequence of the periodic law. Keeping our attention in the same direction, we see that the most widely distributed elements in nature are those with small atomic weights, whilst in organisms the lightest elements exclusively predominate (hydrogen, carbon, nitrogen, oxygen), whose small mass facilitates those transformations which are proper to organisms. Poluta (of Kharkoff), C. C. Botkin, Blake, Brenton, and others even discovered a correlation between the physiological action of salts and other reagents on organisms and the positions occupied in the periodic system by the metals contained in them.

As, from the necessity of the case, the physical properties must be in dependence on the composition of a substance, *i.e.* on the quality and quantity of the elements forming it, so for them also a dependence on the atomic weight of the component elements must be expected, and consequently also on their periodic distribution. We will content ourselves with citing the discovery by Carnelley in 1879 of the dependence of the magnetic properties of the elements on the position occupied by them in the periodic system. Carnelley showed that all the elements of the *even series* (beginning with lithium, potassium, rubidium, cæsium) belong to the number of magnetic (paramagnetic) substances; for example, according to Faraday and others, C, N, O, K, Ti, Cr, Mn, Fe, Co, Ni, Ce, are magnetic; and the elements of the *uneven series are diamagnetic,* H, Na, Si, P, S, Cl, Cu, Zn, As, Se, Br, Ag, Cd, Sn, Sb, I, Au, Hg, Tl, Pb, Bi.

Carnelley also showed that the *melting point* of elements varies periodically, as is seen by the figures in Table II (nineteenth column), where all the most trustworthy data are collected, and predominance is given to those having maximum and minimum values.

There is no doubt that many other physical properties will, when further studied, also prove to be in periodic dependence on the atomic weights, but at present only a few are known with any completeness, and we will only refer to the one which is the most easily and frequently determined—namely, the *specific gravity* in a solid and liquid state, the more especially as its connection with the chemical properties and relations of substances is shown at every step. Thus, for instance, of all the metals those of the alkalis, and of all the non-metals the halogens, are the most energetic in their reactions, and they have the lowest specific gravity among the adjacent elements, as is seen in Table II, column 17. Such are sodium, potassium, rubidium, cæsium among the metals, and chlorine, bromine, and iodine among the non-metals; and as such less energetic metals as iridium, platinum, and gold (and even charcoal or the diamond) have the highest specific gravity among the elements near to them in atomic weight; therefore the degree of the condensation of matter evidently influences the course of the transformations proper to a substance, and furthermore this dependence on the atomic weight, although very complex, is of a clearly periodic character. In order to account for this to some extent, it may be imagined that the lightest elements are porous, and, like a sponge, are easily penetrated by other substances, whilst the heavier elements are more compressed, and give way with difficulty to the insertion of other elements. These relations are best understood when, instead of the specific gravities referring to a unit of volume, the *atomic volumes of the elements*—that is, the quotient A/d of the atomic weight A by the specific gravity d—are taken for comparison. As, according to the entire sense of the atomic theory, the actual matter of a substance does not fill up its whole cubical contents, but is surrounded by a medium (ethereal, as is generally imagined), like the stars and planets which travel in the space of the heavens and fill it, with greater or less intervals, so the quotient A/d only expresses the *mean* volume corresponding to the sphere of the atoms, and therefore $\sqrt[3]{A/d}$ is *the mean distance between the centres of the atoms.* For compounds whose molecules weigh $M,$ the mean magnitude of the atomic volume is obtained by dividing the mean molecular volume M/d by the number of atoms n in the molecule. The above relations may easily be expressed from this point of view by comparing the atomic volumes. Those comparatively light elements which easily and frequently enter into reaction have the greatest atomic volumes: sodium 23, potassium 45, rubidium 57, cæsium 71, and the halogens about 27; whilst with those elements which enter into reaction with difficulty, the mean atomic volume is small; for carbon in the form of a diamond it is less than 4, as charcoal about 6, for nickel and cobalt less than 7, for iridium and platinum about 9. The remaining elements having atomic weights and properties intermediate between those elements mentioned above have also intermediate atomic volumes. Therefore *the specific gravities and specific volumes of solids and liquids stand in periodic dependence on the atomic weights,* as is seen in Table II, where both A (the atomic weight) and d (the specific gravity), and A/d (specific volumes of the atoms) are given (column 18).

Thus we find that in the large periods beginning with lithium, sodium, potassium, rubidium, cæsium, and ending with fluorine, chlorine, bromine, iodine, the extreme members (energetic elements) have a small density and large volume, whilst the intermediate substances gradually increase in density and decrease in volume—that is, as the atomic weight increases the density rises and falls, again rises and falls, and so on. Furthermore, the energy decreases as the density rises, and the greatest density is proper to the atomically heaviest and least energetic elements; for example, Os, Ir, Pt, Au, U.

In order to explain the relation between the volumes of the elements and of their compounds, the densities (column S) and volumes (column M/s) of some of the higher saline oxides arranged in the same order as in the case of the elements are given on p. 566. For convenience of comparison the volumes of the oxides are all calculated per two atoms of an element combined with oxygen. For example, the density of $Al_2O_3=4\cdot0$, weight $Al_2O_3=102$, volume $Al_2O_3=25\cdot5$. Whence, knowing the volume of aluminium to be 11, it is at once seen that in the formation of aluminium oxide, 22 volumes of it give 25·5 volumes of oxide. A distinct periodicity may also be observed with respect to the specific gravities and volumes of the higher saline oxides. Thus in each period, beginning with the alkali metals, the specific gravity of the oxides first rises, reaches a maximum, and then falls on passing to the acid oxides, and again becomes a minimum about the halogens. But it is especially important to call attention to the fact that the volume of the alkali oxides is less than that of the metal contained in them, which is also expressed in the last column, giving this difference for each atom of oxygen. Thus 2 atoms of sodium, or 46 volumes, give 24 volumes of Na_2O, and about 37 volumes of $2NaHO$—that is, the oxygen and hydrogen in distributing themselves in the medium of sodium have not only not increased the distance between its atoms, but have brought them nearer together, have drawn them together by the force of their great affinity, by reason, it may be presumed, of the small mutual attraction of the atoms of sodium. Such metals as aluminium and zinc, in combining with oxygen and forming oxides of feeble salt-forming capacity, hardly vary in volume, but the common metals and non-metals, and especially those forming acid oxides, always give an increased volume when oxidised—that is, the atoms are set further apart in order to make room for the oxygen. The oxygen in them does not compress the molecule as in the alkalis; it is therefore comparatively easily disengaged.

As the volumes of the chlorides, organo-metallic and all other corresponding compounds, also vary in a like periodic succession with a change of elements, it is evidently possible to indicate the properties of substances yet uninvestigated by experimental means, and even those of yet undiscovered elements. It was possible by following this method to foretell, on the basis of the periodic law, many of the properties of scandium, gallium, and germanium, which were verified with great accuracy after

	S	M/s	Volume of Oxygen
H_2O	1·0	18	? — 22
Li_2O	2·0	15	— 9
Be_2O_2	3·06	16	+ 2·6
B_2O_3	1·8	39	+ 10·0
C_2O_4	1·6	55	+ 10·6
N_2O_5	1·64	66	? + 4
Na_2O	2·6	24	— 22
Mg_2O_2	3·5	23	— 4·5
Al_2O_3	4·0	26	+ 1·3
Si_2O_4	2·65	45	+ 5·2
P_2O_5	2·39	59	+ 6·2
S_2O_6	1·96	82	+ 8·7
Cl_2O_7	?1·92	95	+ 6
K_2O	2·7	35	— 35
Ca_2O_2	3·25	34	— 8
Sc_2O_3	3·86	35	? 0
Ti_2O_4	4·2	38	+ 3
V_2O_5	3·49	52	+ 6·7
Cr_2O_6	2·74	73	+ 9·5
Cu_2O	5·9	24	+ 9·6
Zn_2O_2	5·7	23	+ 4·8
Ga_2O_3	?5·1	36	+ 4
Ge_2O_4	4·7	44	+ 4·5
As_2O_5	4·1	56	+ 6·0
Sr_2O_2	4·7	44	— 13
Y_2O_3	5·0	45	? — 2
Zr_2O_4	5·5	44	0
Nb_2O_5	4·7	57	+ 6
MoO_6	4·4	65	+ 6·8
Ag_2O	7·5	31	+ 11
Cd_2O_3	8·0	32	+ 3
In_2O_3	7·18	38	+ 2·7
Sn_2O_4	7·0	43	+ 2·7
Sb_2O_5	6·5	49	+ 2·6
TeO_6	5·1	68	+ 4·7
Ba_2O_2	5·7	52	— 10
La_2O_3	6·5	50	+ 1
Ce_2O_4	6·74	50	+ 2
Ta_2O_5	7·5	59	+ 4·6
W_2O_6	6·8	68	+ 8·2
Hg_2O_2	11·1	39	+ 4·5
Pb_2O_4	8·9	53	+ 4·2
Th_2O_4	9·86	54	+ 2

these metals had been discovered. The periodic law, therefore, has not only embraced the mutual relations of the elements and expressed their analogy, but has also to a certain extent subjected to law the doctrine of the types of the compounds formed by the elements: it has enabled us to see a regularity in the variation of all chemical and physical properties of elements and compounds, and has rendered it possible to foretell the properties of elements and compounds yet uninvestigated by experimental means; thus it has prepared the ground for the building up of atomic and molecular mechanics.

RADIOACTIVITY

by

MARIE CURIE

CONTENTS

Radioactivity

MARIE CURIE

1867-1934

MARIE CURIE was born Marie Sklodovska in Warsaw, in 1867, the youngest child of a poorly paid Polish teacher in the Russian-controlled schools of Warsaw. At three she had learned by herself to read; from an early age she displayed an infallible memory, quick comprehension, unbelievable powers of concentration. This precocity her parents, particularly her father, after his wife's death when Marie was scarcely more than an infant, tried to curb. But the four other children in the family also had great gifts, and the atmosphere of the household encouraged intellectual striving. At sixteen Marie had finished the course at the gymnasium and had there won the gold medal—the third to be carried off by the Sklodovski children. And after a year of visiting her relatives in rural Poland, she began earning her living as a private teacher in Warsaw.

Like the other young people of her set, she devoted herself to Comte, read Darwin and Pasteur, made an effort—patriotic in origin—to educate the illiterate poor, and joined secret classes for the study of science. The local university being open only to men, she and her favorite sister, Bronya, yearned to go to Paris to study. Finally she persuaded Bronya to take their slender resources and to proceed to the Sorbonne. Their plan was that once Bronya had qualified for her degree, she would aid Marie. Meantime, Marie would contribute what she could earn to Bronya's support.

There followed several years of service as a governess, now in Warsaw, now in a country village miles from a town. In the intervals of her exacting duties Marie found time to organize secret Polish classes for the children of the poor, to study mathematics, and to teach herself such chemistry and physics as she could dig out of textbooks without the aid of either teacher or laboratory. The dream of getting to Paris faded. Then Bronya finished her medical course, married a fellow Pole in Paris, and began to practice. Suddenly Marie was summoned to her opportunity.

In 1889, almost without financial resources, Marie was living in Paris with her sister and was entered at the Sorbonne. Presently she felt that the gaiety of her sister's Polish friends—even the occasional concert and the occasional theater—interfered with her work. She moved to a lodging in the Latin Quarter. In that neighborhood, in one poor, unheated, almost barren room or another, she lived her student days. There, unable to cook, too poor to buy food and fuel, she studied early and late until she almost succumbed to overwork and malnutrition. In 1893, at the top of her class, she took her master's degree in physics; in 1894, her master's degree in mathematics.

About this time Marie undertook her first commission: to study the magnetic properties of steels. In the course of this work she met Pierre Curie. He was a man of thirty-five, already a highly esteemed physicist. Like Marie, he came of a most cultivated, middle-class family; like her, he was devoted to his science to the exclusion of people. The two were quickly in sympathy, and shortly they were close friends. Two years later they married.

The Curies now began an amazing collaborative work at the School of Physics and Chemistry of the City of Paris, where Pierre was chief of laboratory. Marie, searching for a subject for a doctoral dissertation, had become interested in Becquerel rays and their sources. As she systematically examined all known elements and minerals, she began to suspect that in the pitchblende (uranium ore) she had studied there was a hitherto-unidentified element capable of radiation far stronger than that from uranium. Pierre at once abandoned his work with crystals to join in the study of the Becquerel rays. In 1898 they together announced the probable existence of polonium; a few months later they announced radium.

From 1898 to 1902 they devoted themselves to the long, arduous task of preparing a sample of pure radium from the masses of pitchblende they were, with difficulty, able to obtain. Together they studied the physical and chemical properties of the new element. Finally, in 1902, Marie isolated pure radium salt and determined its atomic weight, 225.

Meantime, Pierre had become a teacher at the P.C.N., an annex of the Sorbonne, and Marie had become a lecturer in physics at the girls' normal school at Sèvres. Though these teaching duties constantly drained their energies, though their earnings scarcely paid their modest bills, though Pierre's health failed, they never halted in their research. By 1904 they had published twenty-nine papers on radioactivity, most of them so completely joint products that the work of one is indistinguishable from that of the other.

For her work on radium Marie won her doctoral degree in 1903; in the same year the Curies began to receive the honors which, until Marie's death in 1934, never stopped coming. They visited London to present the results of their studies to the Royal Society, and Marie attended the meeting —the first woman ever admitted; they were jointly awarded the Davy Medal in 1903, and a few months later, together with Becquerel, the Nobel Prize for Physics. Even this triumph scarcely persuaded them to pause in their labors long enough to visit Stockholm for the presentation of the prize money. They scarcely paused to celebrate Pierre's election to the Academy of Science, or his elevation to a professorship at the Sorbonne. Suddenly, in 1906, after an idyllic Easter holiday in the country, Pierre died, the victim of a street accident. The great collaboration was ended.

The tremendous official and the genuine friendly sympathy which rose round Marie meant nothing to her. She was sustained only by that devotion to science which had persuaded her and Pierre several years before to refuse to patent their process for refining radium: by that devotion, and by her ingrained habit of work. Within a few months the Sorbonne entrusted her with Pierre's course, as his successor. She labored upon her lectures, and in November she delivered the first of them, beginning exactly where Pierre had left off. The first woman ever to lecture at the Sorbonne, she soon began to give the first—and for long the only—course in the world on radioactivity.

From 1906 to 1914, as the fame of Marie Curie grew, she never stopped working—hardly even for an occasional visit to Warsaw, such as that in 1913 to inaugurate a laboratory for the study of radioactivity, or for a quick trip to a foreign university to receive an honorary degree, or for a summer walking tour in the Engadine, or for a second excursion to Stockholm to receive in 1911 the Nobel Prize for Chemistry. She studied polonium exhaustively; she administered the fellowships for the study of radioactivity established by Carnegie; she prepared the first and only sample of pure metallic radium and redetermined its atomic weight; when the University of Paris and the Pasteur Institute jointly undertook the construction of an Institute for Radium, she supervised the execution of the scheme.

This building was just ready for occupancy when World War I broke out in 1914. For the next five years Mme. Curie was occupied constantly with the war work she made peculiarly hers. She observed at once that the army hospitals were not equipped to use radiology. Almost unaided, and frequently in the face of official lethargy, by the end of the war she had equipped two hundred radiological rooms, most of them in field hospitals, and twenty radiological cars. She herself performed prodigies in the field as an X-ray technician; she trained one hundred and fifty X-ray technicians, and she organized and operated the radium emanation service. Her patriotic fervor blazed: not only her services—and those of all the scientists she could commandeer—but her prize winnings and her whole fortune, she put at the disposal of the government. But immediately the war ended, she resumed her investigative studies.

Though the hard work never ended, nor her eagerness for it, Mme. Curie's life for the next fifteen years had a brighter tone than before. She had wonderful summer holidays at Larcouest, a quiet spot in Brittany, with a group of congenial academic people from the Sorbonne. She watched the progress of her daughter and her son-in-law, the Joliot-Curies, who were rising to eminence in the world of science. She even occasionally accepted the world's homage; for she came to believe that whatever was offered her was in reality a tribute to science. Thus in 1921 she made a trip to America, an almost royal progress, to receive from the women of America the gift of a gram of radium, and repeated the same tour for the same reason in 1929. (The first gift she immediately transferred to the Paris Radium Institute, and the second to the Warsaw Institute, founded in 1925.) Thus she journeyed to Rio de Janeiro, to Italy, to Holland, to England, to Czechoslovakia, to Spain. The learned societies of the world elected her to membership; the universities of the world conferred their honorary degrees upon her. She accepted everything with complete self-effacement. It even seemed to her that these expeditions, pleasurable as they sometimes were, cost overmuch in their interruptions of her work. Even when her health declined and her sight dimmed, her energy did not. Almost until the day of her death she was busy writing her last, her greatest, book. It was just finished when she died.

Mme. Curie's story has been so colorfully told by her daughter Eve—and so vividly presented on the movie screen—that everyone knows of her, and thinks of her, probably, as a fairy-tale heroine of science. Yet her genius was not romantic. It was a genius for hard work. She had a passionate devotion to accuracy, to truth, to science—a devotion which made her all but selfless. Even when she must credit herself with her own achievements, as in the pages here translated from her last book, *Radioactivity,* she speaks of herself in the third person. For she cared nothing for personal glory, everything for labor and knowledge.

RADIOACTIVITY

THE DISCOVERY OF RADIOACTIVITY AND OF THE RADIOELEMENTS

THE STUDY of radioactivity includes the study of the chemistry of the radioelements, the study of the rays emitted by these elements, and the conclusions to be drawn from such studies relative to the structure of the atom. The radioelements can be defined as particular elements from which there emanate, spontaneously and atomically, rays designated as *alpha, beta,* and *gamma*—positive corpuscular rays, negative corpuscular rays (electrons in motion), and electromagnetic radiations. The emission is accompanied by an atomic transformation. Arranged according to their respective abilities to penetrate matter, the *alpha* rays are the weakest: they are stopped by a sheet of paper or by a leaf of aluminum 0.1 mm. in thickness; they travel through air a few centimeters. The *beta* rays travel farther in air and can penetrate several millimeters of aluminum. The *gamma* rays can penetrate several centimeters of relatively opaque material such as lead.

The Rays of Uranium. The Rays of Thorium.

Henri Becquerel discovered radioactivity in 1896.

After the discovery of Roentgen rays, Becquerel began his researches upon the photographic effects of phosphorescent and fluorescent substances.

The first tubes which produced Roentgen rays had no metallic anticathode. The source of the rays was the glass wall of the tube, rendered fluorescent by the action of the cathode rays. It was natural to inquire whether the emission of Roentgen rays did not necessarily accompany the production of fluorescence, whatever might be the cause of the latter. Henri Poincaré suggested that it did, and various attempts were made to obtain photographic impressions on plates shielded in black paper, using zinc sulphide and calcium sulphide previously exposed to light; the results were finally negative.

H. Becquerel made similar experiments with the salts of uranium, some of which are fluorescent. He obtained impressions on photographic plates wrapped in black paper with the double sulphate of uranyl and potassium. Subsequent experiment showed that the phenomenon observed was not linked to that of fluorescence. The salt used need not be activated by sunlight; further, uranium and all of its compounds, whether fluorescent or not, act on the photographic plate in the same way, and metallic uranium is the most active of all. Becquerel eventually discovered that compounds of uranium, placed in complete darkness, continued for a period of years to make impressions on photographic plates wrapped in black paper. He then affirmed that uranium and its compounds emit special rays: uranium rays. These rays can penetrate thin metallic screens; as they pass through gases, they ionize them and render them conductors of electricity. The radiation from uranium is spontaneous and constant; it is independent of external conditions of light and temperature.

The electrical conductivity caused in the air or other gases by the uranium rays is the same as that caused by Roentgen rays. The ions produced in both cases have the same mobility and the same coefficient of diffusion. Measurement of the current for saturation provides a convenient means of measuring the intensity of radiation under given conditions.

The Thorium Rays. Researches made simultaneously by G. Schmidt and Marie Curie have shown that the compounds of thorium emit rays like the uranium rays. Such rays are usually called *Becquerel rays.* The substances which emit Becquerel rays are called radioactive, and the new property of matter revealed by that emission has been named by Marie Curie radioactivity. The elements which so radiate are called radioelements.

Radioactivity an Atomic Property. New Method of Chemical Analysis Based on Radioactivity. Discovery of Radium and Polonium.

From Becquerel's researches, it was clear that the radiation from uranium is more intense than that from its compounds. Marie Curie made a systematic study of all known metallic elements and their compounds to investigate the radioactivity of various materials. She pulverized the various substances and spread them in uniform layers on plates of the same diameter which could be inserted into an ionization chamber. Using the piezo-electric quartz method, she measured the saturation current produced in the chamber between the plates A and B (see p. 228). With plates 3 cm. in diameter, placed three centimeters apart, an even layer of uranium oxide gives a current of about 2×10^{-11} amperes, which scarcely increases as the thickness of the layer increases after it exceeds a fraction of a millimeter; the emanations are almost all alpha rays of uranium, easily absorbed. Measurements made upon the compounds of uranium have certified that the intensity of radiation increases with the uranium content. The same thing is true for the thorium compounds. The radioactivity of these elements is therefore an atomic property.

On the contrary, a substance such as phosphorus cannot be considered radioactive because to produce ionization it must be in the state of white phosphorus; in the red state, or in a compound such as sodium phosphate, it does not produce ionization. Similarly, quinine sulphate, which produces ionization only while it is being heated or cooled, is not radioactive, for the emission of ions is produced here by the variation in temperature and is not an indication of radioactivity of any one of the constituent elements. It is, indeed, a fundamental characteristic of radioactivity that it is a spontaneous phenomenon and an atomic property. These considerations played an important part in the discovery of radium.

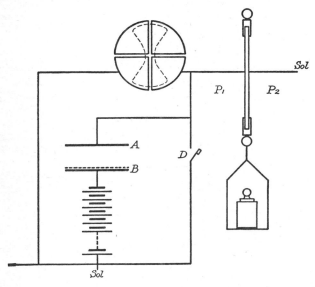

Marie Curie carried on her measurements, using both the widely distributed elements and the rare elements, and as many of their compounds as possible. In addition to pure substances, she also examined a great many samples of various rocks and ores. For simple substances and their compounds, she demonstrated that none except thorium showed an activity equal to 1% of that of uranium.

Among the ores examined, several were radioactive: pitchblende, chalcolite, autunite, thorite, and some others. Since all of these contain either uranium or thorium, it was natural to find them active; but the intensity of the phenomenon with certain minerals was unexpected. Thus some pitchblendes (oxide of uranium) were four times as active as metallic uranium. Chalcolite (copper phosphate and crystalline uranium) was twice as active as uranium. These facts did not agree with the results from the study of simple substances and their compounds, according to which none of these minerals should have shown more activity than uranium or thorium. Furthermore, double phosphate of copper and uranium, of the same formula as chalcolite, prepared from uranium salts and pure copper, showed an activity quite normal (less than half that of uranium). Marie Curie formed the hypothesis that pitchblende, chalcolite, and autunite each contain a very small quantity of a very strongly active material, different from uranium, from thorium, and from already known elements. She undertook to extract that substance from the ore by the ordinary processes of chemical analysis. The analysis of these ores, previously made in general to an accuracy of nearly 1% or 2%, did not destroy the possibility that there might occur in them, in a proportion of that order, a hitherto unknown element. Experiment verified the prophecy relative to the existence of new, powerfully radioactive radioelements; but their quantity turned out to be much smaller than had been supposed. Several years were required to extract one of them in a state of purity.

The research upon the radioelement hypothesized was made first by Pierre Curie and Marie Curie together, using pitchblende.

The research method had to be based upon radioactivity, for no other property of the hypothesized substance was known.

Radioactivity is used in a research of this kind in the following way: the activity of a product is measured; it is then subjected to chemical separation; the radioactivity of each resulting product is measured, and it is observed whether the radioactive substance now remains integrally in one of the products or is divided among them, and if so, in what proportion. The first chemical operations carried out showed that an enrichment in active material was possible. The activity of the solid products— well-dried and spread in a powdered state on plates—was measured under comparable conditions. As more and more active products are obtained, it is necessary to modify the technique of measurements. Some methods of quantitative analysis for radioactive materials will be described later on in this work.

The method of analysis just described is comparable to spectrum analysis from low to high frequencies. It not only discovers a radioactive material, but also distinguishes between the various radioactive elements. For they differ from one another in the quality of their radiations and in their length of life.

The pitchblende from St. Joachimstahl which was used in the first experiments is an ore of uranium oxide. Its greatest bulk is uranium oxide, but it contains also a considerable quantity of flint, of lime, of magnesia, of iron, and of lead, and smaller quantities of some other elements: copper, bismuth, antimony, the rare earth elements, barium, silver, and so on. Analysis made by using the new method showed a concentration of the radioactive property in the bismuth and in the barium extracted from the pitchblende. Yet the bismuth and the barium in commercial use, which are extracted from non-radioactive ores, are not themselves active. In agreement with the original hypothesis, Pierre and Marie Curie concluded that there were in the pitchblende two new radioactive elements: polonium and radium. The first of these they took to be analogous in its chemical properties to bismuth, and the second to barium.

They announced these conclusions in 1898. At the same time, they indicated that polonium could be separated from the bismuth by such chemical treatments as the fractional precipitation of the sulphides or the nitrites, and that radium could be separated from barium by the fractional crystallization of the chlorides in water, or their fractional precipitation by alcohol. Theoretically, they claimed, such processes should lead to the isolation of the new radioelements.

A specimen of radium-bearing barium chloride, sixty times as active as the oxide of uranium, was submitted to spectral analysis by Demarçay. He found, accompanying the spectrum of barium, a new line of 3815 Ångstrom units. Later, examining a specimen nine hundred times as active as the oxide of uranium, he found the line of 3815 Å. much strengthened, and two other new lines. Examination of polonium-bearing bismuth, though the specimen was very active, revealed no new lines.

It had become clear that the new elements occurred in the ore in very small proportions, and that they could be isolated only by treating hundreds or even thousands of kilograms of the ore. To accomplish this labor, it was necessary to have recourse to industrial operations, and to treat the concentrated products thus obtained. After several years, Marie Curie succeeded in obtaining several decigrams of a pure radium salt, in determining the atomic weight of that element, and in assigning to it a place in the periodic table hitherto vacant. Still later, Marie Curie and A. Debierne isolated radium in the metal state. Thus the chemical individuality of radium was established in the most complete and rigorous way.

The application of the new method of investigation later led to the discovery of other new radioelements: first, actinium (discovered by A. Debierne), then ionium (by Boltwood), then mesothorium and radiothorium (by O. Hahn), then protoactinium (by O. Hahn and L. Meitner), etc. There have also been identified radioactive gases called emanations.

Among all these substances, radium is the most widely known and most widely used. Practically unvarying because of the slowness of its transformation, it is now industrially prepared, especially because of the medical applications of the gamma radiations to which it apparently gives rise, and which are, in reality, only indirectly attributable to it. Radium produces, apparently continuously, a radioactive gas named radon, and this gas gives birth to a series of substances: radium A, radium B, radium C. The last of these emits particularly penetrating gamma rays. Radium and the derivatives which usually accompany it furnish intense sources of alpha, beta, and gamma radiations. These have been and are the principal ones used in researches upon such radiations. From the point of view of chemistry, the studies of radium have confirmed the atomic theory of radioactivity and have provided a solid foundation for a theory of radioactive transformation.

Spectrum and Atomic Weight of Radium. Metallic Radium.

Since radium is an alkaline-earth metal, it is extracted from its ores simultaneously with the barium also found there, or combined with it. The mixture of radium and barium is submitted to a series of operations of which the result is the separation of the radium from the barium in the form of a pure salt.

As the products of these operations are successively enriched in radium, their radioactivity increases, the intensity of the spectral lines for radium increases—as compared with the barium lines—and the mean atomic weight increases. When the radium salt is wholly pure, the photographed spark spectrum shows only the lines characteristic of radium; the strong 4554.4 Å line of barium, of such sensitivity that it is extremely hard to eliminate, is now scarcely discernible.

A radium salt introduced into a flame gives it a carmine-red color, and produces a visible spectrum composed of the characteristic radium lines (Giesel).

In general, the appearance of the radium spectrum resembles that of the alkaline-earth metals. It includes bright, narrow lines and also cloudy bands. The principal lines of the spark spectrum and of the flame spectrum follow:

Spark Spectrum	Flame Spectrum
4821.1 faint	6653
4682.3 very bright	6700–6530 band
4533.3 faint	6329
4340.8 bright	6330–6130 band
3814.6 very bright	4826
3649.7 bright	
2814.0 bright	
2708.6 bright	

The spark spectrum shows two bright, nebulous bands, with maximum intensity at 4627.5 and 4455.2 Å respectively.

The spectral reaction of radium is very sensitive. It makes possible the identification of radium present in a substance in the proportion of 10^{-5}. But the radioactive reaction is still more sensitive; it makes possible the identification of the radium when its concentration is no more than 10^{-12}.

The atomic weight of radium, or the mean atomic weight of a mixture of radium and barium, can be determined, as for barium, with precision. Although the radioactivity of the mixture is not less than 1000 times that of uranium, its atomic weight differs only negligibly from that of barium.

The method used to make this determination is as follows: chloride of radium, the purity of which had been certified by spectral analysis, was deprived of its water of crystallization at a temperature of about 150° C. and was carefully weighed in the state of an anhydrous salt. From a clear solution of this salt, the chlorine was precipitated as silver chloride, and the silver chloride was weighed. From the relation of that second weight to the first, supposing that the formula for anhydrous chloride of radium is $RaCl_2$—by analogy with the formula $BaCl_2$, accepted for barium chloride—and using the accepted atomic weights of chlorine and silver, the atomic weight of radium could be calculated.

The details of this technique have been explained in special reports (Marie Curie, E. Hoenigschmid). The quantities of the chloride of radium used have varied from 0.1 gm. to 1.0 gm., and the various determinations have resulted uniformly. Taking the atomic weight of silver as 107.88 and that of chlorine as 35.457, the atomic weight of radium is 226 (Hoenigschmid).

To isolate radium in its metallic state, the amalgam of radium was prepared by electrolyzing, with a cathode of mercury, a solution containing 0.1 gm. of pure radium chloride. The resulting liquid amalgam decomposes water and is modified by air. It was dried, placed in a vessel of pure iron, and distilled in an atmosphere of pure hydrogen obtained by osmosis through incandescent platinum. The amalgam solidified at about 400° C. The metal, cleared of mercury, melts at 700° C. and begins to volatilize. Radium is a white, shining metal which rapidly alters in air, and which decomposes water energetically.

In accord with its atomic weight, radium has been placed in the periodic table of the elements as a higher homologue of barium, in the last line of the table; its atomic number is 88; its spectrum and its chemical properties accord with its position; similarly with its high-frequency spectra (values of L_1 and L_2 levels) (Maurice de Broglie).

Here is a résumé of the chemical properties of the radium salts: the sulphate is insoluble in water and the common acids (solubility in water at 20° C. is 1.4×10^{-3} gm. per liter); the carbonate is insoluble in water and in solutions of alkaline carbonates; the chloride is soluble in water (at 20° C., 245 gm. of $RaCl_2$ per liter), insoluble in concentrated hydrochloric acid and in pure alcohol; the bromide behaves similarly (at 20° C., 706 gm. of $RaBr_2$ per liter); the hydrate and the sulphide are soluble. The separation of radium from barium by fractional crystallization depends upon the fact that the chloride and the bromide of radium are less soluble than the corresponding salts of barium (at 20° C., 357 gm. of $BaCl_2$ and 1041 gm. of $BaBr_2$ per liter of water).

The Radioelements

Each radioelement undergoes a transformation consisting of the successive destruction of all its atoms, in accord with a law that half the number existing at a given moment are transformed in a time T which is characteristic of the radioelement under consideration, and which is called its *period*. Measured by the magnitude of the period, radioelements have a life which is more or less long. Some, like uranium and thorium, which have survived several geological epochs in the ores which contain them, have a very long life. Others, such as radium, actinium, polonium, mesothorium, radiothorium, and so on, would have disappeared wholly from the ores if their decay had not been compensated for by their production from uranium and thorium. These two primary elements form, therefore, the heads of series or families to which belong all the other radioelements —derivatives of the two, bound to one another by lines of descent. The quantities of the derived elements which exist in untreated ores are proportional to the quantities of the primary elements there, and to the periods of the derivatives. Each derived element with a life sufficiently long can be extracted from uranium and thorium ores, just as the primary elements are; but sometimes it can be obtained by the decay of a more or less distantly related element which has already been extracted from the ore. For the radioelements of short life, only the latter method is available. In this chapter are given descriptions of the radioelements in the order which they occupy in the several families.

The chemical properties of uranium and of thorium have been described in treatises on chemistry, and will be omitted here. There exist at least two isotopes of uranium, U_I (period of the order of 10^9 years) and U_{II}, a derivative with a very short life, existing in small proportion along with U_I. There is probably also a third isotope, AcU.

The Derivatives of Uranium

A. THE RADIUM BRANCH

Uranium X. The compounds of uranium emit alpha, beta, and gamma rays; always, the alpha rays come from the uranium itself (U_I and U_{II}); the penetrating beta and gamma rays are emitted by a group of derivatives which together form Uranium X, discovered by Crookes. Experiments show that the alpha-radiating material cannot be separated from the uranium; but by various reactions, the material which emits the beta and gamma radiations can be separated from the uranium. The methods of operation most employed are the following: fractional crystallization of uranium nitrate, extraction of the uranium from solution by the addition of ammonium carbonate in excess, and the treatment with ether of a highly concentrated solution of uranium nitrate. In the first process, uranium X is concentrated in the more soluble portions. In the second, uranium passes into solution, and the uranium X remains, with insoluble impurities such as iron, in the alkaline solution. In the third, two layers of the liquid form; the one richer in ether contains a solution of uranium without uranium X; the one richer in water contains uranium X in excess. The active material thus separated has a period of twenty-four days.

Uranium X is not simple, but is composed of several radioelements.

The substance with a period of twenty-four days, preparation of which has just been described, is an isotope of thorium (atomic number, 90), and is called uranium X_1; it is produced by U_I, and it emits a group of beta rays only mildly penetrative.

Uranium X_1 gives rise to a derivative of very short life, uranium X_2 or brevium (Fajans and Goehring). Its period is 1.13 minutes; it is a higher homologue of tantalum (atomic number, 91); it emits a group of pene-trating beta rays. Finally, there are found in uranium X, in very small proportions, two other radioelements: uranium Y (Antonoff), an isotope of thorium (atomic number, 90; period, 25 hours); and uranium Z (Hahn) (atomic number, 91; period, 6.7 hours).

Ionium. Ionium, discovered by Boltwood, is the derivative of uranium which is transformed directly into radium. Its period is 83,000 years. Its chemical properties are exactly those of thorium, the two elements being isotopes (atomic number, 90). In the treatment of ores, ionium is found in the same portions as the thorium, and it is separated at the same time as that rare earth element. From the uranium ore, what is actually extracted is, therefore, a mixture of thorium-ionium; and though the pro-portion of ionium is generally smaller than that of thorium, it may be com-parable to it.

The spectrum of a thorium-ionium mixture containing 30% of ionium is identical with that of thorium. This fact has been taken as an argument that the spectra of isotopes are identical. Later researches into the isotopes of lead have shown, however, that the identity is not com-plete; there are very minute differences.

Though ionium occurs in relatively important quantities in the ura-nium ores (perhaps 20 gm. per ton of uranium), it cannot be extracted as a pure salt because of its close association with thorium.

The radiation of ionium is simple; it is composed principally of alpha rays accompanied by a weak gamma ray of little penetrative power.

Radium and its first derivatives. The chemical individuality of radium has already been given in earlier sections. Its period is 1600 years. By radioactive transformations, radium produces a series of short-lived radio-elements by which it is generally accompanied. These are a radioactive gas, or emanation from radium, called radon, and the components A,B,C,C′,C″ of the active deposit. The radiation of this group is complex, and is composed of alpha, beta, and gamma rays.

Radium D. Radium E. Radium D is an isotope of lead (atomic number, 82; period, 22 years). It emits a beta radiation of which the ionizing power is very small; its presence is revealed by the formation of deriva-tives. Of these derivatives, the first, radium E (isotope of bismuth; atomic number, 83; period, 5 days), has a beta radiation; the second, radium F, identical with polonium, has an alpha radiation. Radium D can be ex-tracted from uranium ores at the same time as the lead which they contain, and cannot be separated from this lead. This radioactive lead—or radiolead—can be used as the primary material for the preparation of polonium. Radium D can also be obtained from radium, from which it derives through the intermediary steps of radon and the materials of its active deposit.

Polonium. Polonium is the first radioactive element discovered by the new method of chemical analysis based on radioactivity. It is a derivative of uranium through the intermediary stage of radium. It is characterized by an alpha radiation, and by the absence of penetrating rays. Its presence was recognized in the sulphides precipitated in an acid solution of pitchblende, and, in the analysis of these sulphides, it particularly clung to the bismuth. By means of the fractional precipitation of the bismuth salts from water, the polonium can be concentrated in the less soluble portions. Later research has shown that this element occurs in the ores in a much smaller proportion than radium, and that it decays, with a period of 140 days. Marckwald has demonstrated that in certain of its chemical properties, polonium is analogous to tellurium. It is characterized also by the ease with which certain metals (iron, copper, silver) displace it from acid solutions. It can be prepared either from ores or from radiolead or from radium.

The largest quantity of polonium hitherto prepared (Marie Curie and A. Debierne) consists of about 0.1 mg. mixed with several milligrams of foreign metals easily reducible. The radiation of that sample was comparable to that of 0.5 gm. of radium. Among the lines in the spark spectrum, there was one (4170.5 Å) which seems to belong to polonium. More recently, there has been announced the existence of a line of 2450 Å (A. Czapek).

To polonium, in the periodic table, has been assigned a place, hitherto vacant, beside bismuth (atomic number, 84), as a higher analogue of tellurium.

The analogy which polonium presents in part with tellurium, in part with bismuth, is explainable, apparently, on considerations of valency. For the compounds in which polonium is trivalent (sulphide), the analogy with bismuth is valid; for those in which it is tetravalent (chloride, hydroxide), the analogy with tellurium is valid (M. Guillot). Polonium is soluble in acid solutions and also in concentrated soda solutions. It can behave, then, like a metal, or it can enter, like tellurium, into an acid radical. In solutions almost neutral, its compounds undergo hydrolysis and the radioactive material is deposited on the walls of the container; this process is hastened by centrifugation. Polonium appears to be susceptible to linkage in certain complexes such as chloropoloniate of ammonia, an isomorph of the corresponding salts of iron, lead, strontium, platinum; or the diethylthiosulfocarbonate of polonium, an isomorph of the salt of cobalt having the same formula. Experiment in electrolysis points to ions of complex form.

Polonium can be volatilized, and the distilled material can be caught by a gas current. The purest preparation so far obtained upon a small surface corresponds, according to numerical evaluations, to more than fifty molecular layers, superimposed; the color is gray or black, attributable to polonium or to one of its oxides. Some polonium compounds, such as the hydride and the polonium carbonyl have been reported to be particularly volatile.

B. THE ACTINIUM BRANCH

The elements of the actinium family are, in all probability, derivatives of uranium; but they are not of the same linked series as radium and its derivatives. It is supposed that the isotopes of uranium give rise to two lines of derivatives, of which the radium family forms one and the actinium family the other. The first certainly known member of the latter family is protoactinium. The connection between protoactinium and uranium is probably through the intermediary UY.

Protoactinium (Hahn and Meitner, Soddy and Cranston). Protoactinium was discovered in the residue remaining from the treatment of pitchblende from St. Joachimsthal. It is the immediate parent of actinium. It emits alpha and beta rays, and it has a period of 30,000 years. In certain of its chemical properties it is analogous to tantalum, of which it is the higher homologue (atomic number, 91). But according to the experiments of Grosse, its oxide, instead of having the properties of an acid, behaves rather like a weak base. Grosse has perfected a method of fractional crystallization of the chlorides of zirconium and of protoactinium, the latter concentrating in the solution, and has obtained several centigrams of the radioelement in a pure state. Protoactinium occurs in the ores of uranium in a proportion comparable to that of radium, and can be extracted in sufficient quantity to determine its atomic weight.

Like tantalum, protoactinium can easily be dissolved as an oxide or hydrate in hydrofluoric acid. The oxide (probable formula, Pa_2O_5) is a white powder with a high fusion point; calcined, it is insoluble in hydrochloric, nitric, sulphuric acids. By fusion with $NaSO_4$ and recovery by water and sulphuric acid, it can be dissolved and separated from tantalum. After fusion with K_3CO_3 and recovery by water, protoactinium remains in the insoluble residue, whereas the tantalum dissolves. In a hydrochloric, nitric, or sulphuric solution, the protoactinium can be precipitated entirely by an excess of phosphoric acid.

Actinium. Actinium (A. Debierne) belongs, according to its chemical properties, among the rare earth elements. Extracted from ore at the same time as the elements of this group, it can be separated only by laborious fractionations. Its presence is revealed by the radiation of its successive derivatives. These are formed so slowly that the activity of actinium freshly prepared increases for several months. The period of actinium being about ten years, it forms with its derivatives a relatively stable group (actinium family) with a complex alpha, beta, gamma radiation.

Like polonium and radium, actinium was first found in pitchblende. This generally contains, in a small proportion, rare earths, principally of the cerium group: cerium, lanthanum, neodymium, praseodymium, samarium; there are also always small quantities of thorium. In this mixture of substances with neighboring properties, thorium is the element most weakly basic, and lanthanum the one most strongly basic. Actinium is especially close to lanthanum and is even more strongly basic.

Actinium is precipitated with thorium and with the rare earth elements in the state of hydrates, fluorides, or oxalates (the precipitation being relatively less complete than for lanthanum). It remains with the other rare earths when thorium and cerium are separated from them by the usual methods. The rare earths can be separated from one another by the methodical fractionation of their double ammoniacal nitrates in a nitric solution. The actinium comes out at the same time as the lanthanum, in the least soluble fractions. To enrich the actinium-bearing lanthanum in actinium, there has been used successfully the fractional precipitation of the oxalate in a nitric solution; the actinium concentrates in the solution (Marie Curie and collaborators). By applying this method to the actinium-bearing lanthanum extracted from uranium ore from Haut Katanga, several grams of the oxide, containing 1 to 2 milligrams of actinium, have recently been obtained; this quantity corresponds in the ore to about ten tons of uranium.

The isomorphism of the salts of actinium and lanthanum being demonstrated by the regularity of the fractional crystallizations, it can be supposed that the chemical formulas of the actinium compounds are of the same type as the corresponding formulas for lanthanum.

In the periodic table, there has been assigned to actinium a place, hitherto vacant, in the column of the trivalent elements, in the last line of the table (atomic number, 89).

Radioactinium. Actinium X. These substances are the first derivatives of actinium and are obtained by beginning with it. Radioactinium (Hahn) is an isotope of thorium (atomic number, 90), with a period of 18.9 days; it emits an alpha radiation and also weak beta and gamma radiations. It can be separated from actinium by the same methods used to separate thorium from lanthanum. It gives rise to the formation of actinium X (Giesel, Godlewski), which has a period of 11.2 days and a radiation like that of radioactinium. Actinium X is an isotope of radium (atomic number, 88). From a solution containing actinium, radioactinium, and actinium X, the first two can be separated by precipitating them with ammonia; the actinium X remains in solution. Actinium X gives birth to *actinon* (a radioactive gas), which produces an *active deposit* from actinium composed of a number of constituents.

The Derivatives of Thorium

Mesothorium 1. This substance, discovered by O. Hahn, accompanies the radium extracted from ores which contain uranium and thorium (thorianite, monazite). The beta and gamma radiations which it appears to give really come from a short-lived derivative of it, mesothorium 2. The latter can be separated from the former by precipitation by ammonia, and it immediately re-forms. Mesothorium 1 gives off no measurable radiation. It has not been separated from radium, of which it is an isotope (atomic number, 88); its period is 6.7 years. Its use in medicine is analogous to that of radium, and it has been industrially extracted as a by-product of the preparation of thorium in the incandescent-mantle industry.

Mesothorium 2 is an isotope of actinium (atomic number, 89), and though its period is only 6.2 hours, it has nevertheless been possible to study its chemical properties (Yovanovitch). Thence has been learned much about the chemical properties of actinium, the study of which, as has been observed, involves great delays. This is an example of the method of radioactive indicators.

To separate mesothorium 2 from mesothorium 1, the method is currently used of crystallization in a strongly acid hydrochloric solution in the presence of barium. This operation leaves mesothorium 2 in solution while the chloride of mesothorium 1 crystallizes with the barium-chloride.

Mesothorium is a source of radiothorium. After the solution has been for some time undisturbed, that substance accumulates, and can be separated by NH_3 after the addition of several milligrams of another reagent. In the crystallization hitherto described, radiothorium accumulates in the solution with mesothorium 1; but if the operation is repeated several times at intervals of a day, finally mesothorium 2 quite free of radiothorium collects, the speed of formation of these two being different.

Radiothorium. Thorium X. Radiothorium was found by O. Hahn in thorianite from Ceylon of which some hundreds of kilos had been submitted to treatment for the extraction of radium. This ore is composed chiefly of thorium oxide, but contains also some uranium oxide, and, consequently, some radium. When the chloride of radium-bearing barium coming from this mineral was submitted to fractional crystallization, it was remarked that at the same time that the radium concentrated in the less soluble portions, another radioactive substance concentrated in the more soluble portions. This material had the radioactive properties of thorium, but in a heightened degree; in particular, it gave off in great quantities the radioactive gas which is obtained from thorium compounds and which is called *thoron,* or *thorium emanation.* The new radioelement responsible for this release of gas has been called radiothorium. It is now known that it is present in the compounds of thorium as a derivative. Radiothorium has also been discovered in the deposits of some hot springs in Savoy

(Blanc). Radiothorium is an isotope of thorium (atomic number, 90); its period is 1.9 years. Its radiation is made up chiefly of alpha rays, but it also feebly gives off beta rays. It produces a short-lived derivative, thorium X (Rutherford, Soddy) (isotope of radium, period of 3.64 days, alpha and weak beta radiation), which is used in medicine. It can be separated from a solution of radiothorium by precipitating the latter with ammonia or with oxygenated water; thorium X remains in solution. Thorium X is the direct parent of thoron, from which come other derivatives forming its active deposit.

THE RADIOACTIVE ORES AND THE EXTRACTION OF THE RADIOELEMENTS

The Radioactive Ores

THESE ORES, of which a large number are known, are all ores of uranium and thorium, containing these two elements in varying proportions, in association with inactive elements. Sought for more actively since the discovery of radium, they have been found in different parts of the globe. The radioelements, derivatives of uranium or of thorium, occur in the ores in quantities proportional to those of the primary substances, respectively. Among the exploitable ores of uranium, some are almost free of thorium and contain only the series of derivatives which begin with uranium; the radium which is extracted from them is free of mesothorium. On the contrary, the commercial ores of thorium contain an appreciable quantity of uranium; with the descendants of thorium there are also present those of uranium. The mesothorium obtained in industry is therefore always accompanied by radium. For equivalent radiation, such a mixture is less valuable than radium, for mesothorium decays in accord with its period of 6.7 years, whereas radium is practically constant, its period being 1600 years.

The radioactive ores occur sometimes in a concentrated form, but more frequently in a dispersed form. In the first case, they form crystals of considerable volume, or compact masses which are found as threads or beads embedded in massive rock. In the second case, they are intimately mixed through rock or soil which they impregnate wholly, or through which they are disseminated in the form of extremely tiny crystals. Industrially, not only the rich ores—containing 50 milligrams or more of radium per ton—but also the poorer ores—containing only a few milligrams of radium per ton—have been successfully used. In the ores, the relation between the quantity of radium and that of uranium has a constant value of 3.4×10^{-7}. Consequently, no ore can possibly contain more than 340 milligrams of radium per ton of uranium.

To recognize that an ore is radioactive, two simple processes are available: 1. A piece of the ore is placed on a photographic plate which is kept entirely in darkness for a day before it is developed. In the image obtained, the dark portions correspond to the active portions of the specimen, and the light portions to the inactive parts. 2. A piece of the ore may be pulverized, the powder so obtained placed upon a plate, and the ionization produced by the specimen measured in an electrical apparatus. Both processes are used in prospecting, and for that purpose there is available a portable electroscope. The primary, compact ores of uranium, composed of uranium oxide more or less pure, are black and dense; those in which the uranium is accompanied by acids—tantalic, niobic, titanic (samarskite, betafite, etc.)—are similarly black or dark brown. But there are also uranium ores of more recent origin, the result of the alteration of primary ores (autunite, chalcolite, curite, etc.) which are vividly colored. The thorium ores are generally of a more or less dark brown (thorite, orangite, thorianite, monazite, etc.).

Below is given a table showing a certain number of the ores, and later are recited the principal points in the treatment of first the uranium ores and then the uranium and thorium ores.

A. Ores of the oxides of uranium or of uranium and thorium:
   Pitchblende (uraninite), possibly containing 30% to 80% of uranium in the form of the oxides UO_2 and UO_3, with little or almost no thorium, but with a great number of other materials in small quantities: SiO_2, Fe, Ca, Ba, Sb, Cu, Pb, Bi, etc. Compact or cryptocrystalline structure (St. Joachimstahl, England, United States, Belgian Congo, Canada).
   Broggerite, cleveite, etc. Ores of crystallized uranium oxide, possibly containing thorium oxide, ThO_2, in varying proportions (Norway, United States).
   Thorianite, an ore of the crystalline oxide of uranium and thorium with a great predominance of thorium (e.g., Th, 65%, U, 10%) (Ceylon).
B. Ores of hydrated deterioration:
   Becquerelite (UO_3 $2H_2O$), 72% U (Belgian Congo).
   Curite ($2PbO$ $5UO_3$ $4H_2O$), lead uranate, 55% uranium (Belgian Congo).
   Kasolite ($3PbO$ $3UO_3$ $3SiO_2$ $4H_2O$), 40% uranium, silicouranate of lead (Belgian Congo).
C. Hydrated silicates:
   Soddite ($12UO_2$ $5SiO_2$ $14H_2O$), 72% uranium (Belgian Congo).
   Orangite, 66% thorium, 1% uranium (Norway).
   Thorite, 45%–65% thorium, 9% uranium (Norway).
D. Phosphates:
   Autunite (Ca $2UO_4$ $2PO_4$ $8H_2O$), phosphate of calcium and uranyl, about 50% uranium, in green crystalline spangles (Portugal, Tonkin).
   Chalcolite, torbernite (Cu $2UO_2$ $2PO_4$ $8H_2O$), phosphate of copper and uranyl, about 50% uranium, in green crystals (Cornwall, England; Portugal).
   Monazite, phosphate of rare earths, principally ceric ($CePO_4$), containing thorium (of the order of 10%) and a little uranium (of the order of 1%) (Brazil, United States, India).
E. Vanadates:
   Carnotite, vanadate of UO_2 and hydrated K, about 50% uranium, in yellow crystalline powder (United States).
   Ferghanite, Tuyamunite, composed of UO_3 and V_2O_5, about 50% uranium (Turkestan).

F. Niobates, tantalates, titanates:

Samarskite, niobate and tantalate of rare earths (especially the yttrium group), 3% to 15% uranium, 4% thorium (Russia, United States, India, Madagascar).

Euxenite, niobate and titanate of rare earths (yttrium), 3% to 15% uranium, 6% thorium (Norway, United States, Madagascar).

Betafite, titanoniobate and tantalate of uranium, crystallized, 25% uranium, 1% thorium (Madagascar).

Uranium Ores Containing a little Thorium. Treatment of Pitchblende

The principal ores which the radium industry has used are pitchblende, autunite, carnotite, betafite. Some of these contain so little thorium that the Th/U ratio is of the order of 10^{-5} (pitchblendes from St. Joachimstahl and from Haut Katanga). In betafite, the ratio is higher, 1 to 4%. The St. Joachimstahl pitchblende is the ore in which were discovered polonium and radium; exploited first for uranium, it was later exploited for radium. It occurs in association with dolomite and quartz in veins located at great depths (500 meters and more) in the granite mass of the region. Its composition is complex and variable; here is an example:

U_3O_8	76.82
F_2O_3	4.0
PbO	4.63
Bi_2O_3	.67
As_2O_5	.82
ZnO	.22
MnO	.04
SiO_2	5.07
CaO	2.45
MgO	.19
K_2O	.28
Na_2O	1.19
Rare earths	.52
H_2O	3.25
S	1.15
Thorium	traces

The pitchblende from the Belgian Congo (Haut Katanga) occurs in nuggets within sedimentary rocks; it is accompanied by ores resulting from the alteration of pitchblende under the action of various physical and chemical agents: chalcolite, kasolite, etc. These ores are treated in the Oolen plant in Belgium and actually provide the chief source of radium. In Canada, pitchblende has been found in lengthy veins, in ancient sedimentary rock near the Arctic Circle.

The principal phases in the extraction of radium are the following: 1. Reduction of the ore to which has been added previously a proper amount of barium to serve as a radium capturer. 2. Separation of the crude sulphates containing the radium-bearing barium. 3. Purification of the crude sulphates and transformation of the radium-bearing barium into a chloride. 4. Fractional crystallization of the chloride to obtain a salt enriched in radium. 5. Purification of the enriched chloride and final fractional crystallization of the chlorides or bromides.

These operations are represented in the accompanying table with an indication of the products of the treatment in which certain radioelements are concentrated. It must be observed that this treatment is adapted to its principal objective—the extraction of radium and of uranium. The other radioelements, of which less accurate account is given, are dispersed in the course of the operations. (See Table I.)

TABLE I

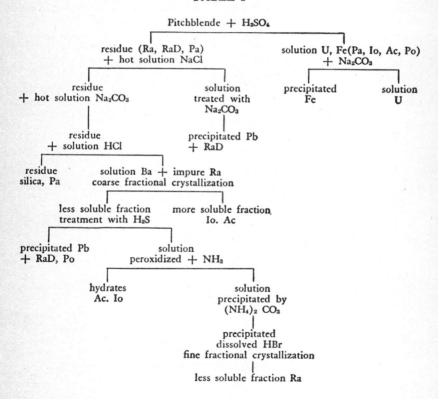

Pitchblende is generally reduced by the use of weak sulphuric acid; but that operation must sometimes be preceded by a preliminary treatment such as the roasting of the ore finely ground and mixed with carbonate of soda.

The fractional crystallization of the chlorides (the method originated by Marie Curie) is a fundamental step in the treatment. It is accomplished at first in an aqueous solution. As the extraction of the radium salt advances, it is desirable to crystallize it in a solution of increasing acidity, partly to decrease its solubility, partly to aid in the elimination of various impurities (iron, calcium, rare earth elements). Generally, the fractional crystallization is not continued until a pure radium salt is obtained, but is stopped when a concentration fixed by the use to which the product is to be put (50% to 90%) has been reached. To enrich the concentrated products, fractional crystallization of bromides replaces that of chlorides (Giesel).

The method of treating pitchblende in order to obtain polonium, used in some attempts in that direction, is given in an accompanying table. The separation of polonium with lead, bismuth, and other easily reducible metals is accomplished by making use of the chemical and electrochemical properties of polonium described earlier. (See Table II.)

TABLE II

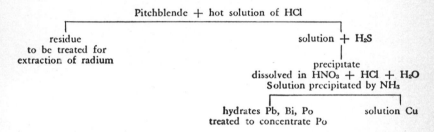

From Table I, it is clear that radiolead (lead + RaD) is a by-product in the preparation of radium; its separation from the ore is generally sufficiently complete, and the concentration in Radium D is greater as the ore contains less inactive lead. This radiolead may be conserved for the preparation of polonium. The method of concentration involves the following steps: 1. The precipitation of lead in a nitric solution by concentrated hydrochloric acid, leaving the polonium in solution; 2. The deposit of polonium by electrochemical means upon copper or silver leaves plunged into the solution of radiolead; 3. The capture of polonium with a precipitate of colloidal ferric hydrate.

Among the other by-products in the preparation of radium, protoactinium occurs either with the final residue of the reduction—composed principally of silica—or in the sulphuric solution of uranium. Ionium and actinium also occur—in part in that same solution, in part in the insoluble sulphates. The accompanying table records the method used to extract that material, on one hand the mixture thorium-ionium, on the other, actinium associated with lanthanum. In this treatment, hydrofluoric acid may be substituted for the oxalic acid. (See Table III.)

TABLE III

More soluble fraction of solution
resulting from the coarse fractional crystallization
of radium (Ba, Io, Ac)
treated by H₂S

sulphides   peroxidized solution
                                              + NH₃

                    hydrates dissolved in   solution Ba
                    HCl + oxalic acid

                  oxalates   solution Fe
              + hot solution NaOH

            hydrates dissolved in HCl, treatment
                     with Na₂CO₃

solution Th. Io   precipitates Ac + La, Nd, Pr, Ce, etc.
                                        separation of Ce
                                   then fractional precipitation of
                                   the oxalates in a nitric solution

Only a few indications of the treatment used for other ores which have been exploited industrially are given here. The principal phases of the treatment are the same as for pitchblende, but the processes employed for the reduction of the ore and the obtaining of the crude sulphates may vary from one ore to another.

Carnotite—a vanadate of uranium found principally in the United States—and autunite—a phosphate of uranium and lime which has been mined principally in Portugal—can both, in certain cases, be treated with weak, hot hydrochloric acid; from that solution, the crude sulphates are precipitated. In other cases there is an advantage in treating the ore with carbonate of soda prior to dissolving it in acid.

Betafite—an ore from Madagascar which contains uranium with niobic, titanic, and tantalic acids—is reduced by fusion with soda and carbonate of soda in order to cause the rare acids to pass into solution. The reduction can also be accomplished with bisulphate of soda and reclamation with water; the sulphate of radium-bearing barium then remains in the residue with the rare acids. These latter can be separated by treatment with soda or with weak hydrofluoric acid.

Ores of Thorium and Uranium

Some ores of thorium are poor in uranium, and consequently have a scientific interest from the fact that they contain almost solely the derivatives of thorium; this is the situation with certain thorites. But in the ores which have been exploited (thorianite, monazite) the proportion of uranium to thorium is sufficiently large for the derivatives of these two elements to be represented by comparable radiations.

Thorianite is an ore rich in thorium, found in the island of Ceylon in the form of small crystal cubes. By the treatment of several hundred kilograms of that ore, mesothorium and radiothorium were discovered. The proportion of thorium in this ore runs as high as 60 to 80%; that of uranium, 10 to 20%. Monazite, though it is less rich in thorium, is nevertheless regularly exploited for the incandescent-mantle industry, because it is found in great quantities in the so-called monazite sands of the United States and of Brazil.

Monazite is a rare-earth phosphate, crystallized, containing generally 6 to 12% of thorium. It is reduced with hot sulphuric acid, and all the soluble sulphates are extracted; in the insoluble sulphates, along with barium, radium and mesothorium 1 occur. The latter treatment of these crude sulphates does not differ in principle from that already described. The fractional crystallization is undertaken to separate in the less soluble portions the radium and the mesothorium 1 and, in the more soluble portions, the radiothorium—a disintegration product of mesothorium. The fractional crystallization can be continued until there is obtained a chloride or a bromide of radium quite free of barium and containing a negligible amount of mesothorium. After that, continued fractional crystallization does not alter the product thus obtained. The effect of the mesothorium is, however, so important that in certain products a month old it is estimated that about 75% of the most penetrating gamma rays are due to the mesothorium (through its derivative MThII) and about 25% of the most penetrating gamma rays to the radium (through its derivative RaC). The gamma radiation increases constantly for about three years because of the formation of radiothorium and its later derivatives. Having passed a maximum, it lessens because of the destruction of the mesothorium 1; after about fifty years, the radiation is due almost solely to radium, with a diminution of about 2% of the original quantity of radiation.

Catalog

If you are interested in a list of fine Paperback
books, covering a wide range of subjects
and interests, send your name and address,
requesting your free catalog, to:

McGraw-Hill Paperbacks
1221 Avenue of Americas
New York, N.Y. 10020